vademecum

T0133823

Aortic Surgery

Jeffrey L. Ballard, M.D.
Loma Linda University Medical Center
Loma Linda, California, U.S.A.

LANDES
BIOSCIENCE
GEORGETOWN, TEXAS
U.S.A.

Aortic Surgery

VADEMECUM
LANDES BIOSCIENCE
Georgetown, Texas U.S.A.

Copyright ©2000 Landes Bioscience
All rights reserved.
No part of this book may be reproduced or transmitted in any form or by any means, electronic or mechanical, including photocopy, recording, or any information storage and retrieval system, without permission in writing from the publisher.
Printed in the U.S.A.

Please address all inquiries to the Publisher:
Landes Bioscience, 810 S. Church Street, Georgetown, Texas, U.S.A. 78626
Phone: 512/ 863 7762; FAX: 512/ 863 0081

ISBN: 1-57059-628-X

Library of Congress Cataloging-in-Publication Data

Aortic surgery / [edited by] Jeffrey L. Ballard.
    p. ; cm. -- (Vademecum)
  Includes bibliographical references and index.
  ISBN 1-57059-628-X (spiral)
    1. Aortic--Surgery--Handbooks, manuals, etc. 2. Heart--Surgery--Handbooks, manuals, etc. I. Ballard, Jeffrey L., 1960- II. Series.
    [DNLM: 1. Aorta--surgery. 2. Aortic Diseases--surgery. WG 410 A63877 2000]
RD598 .A6223 2000
617.4'13--dc21   00-030206

Dedication

To the pioneers of aortic surgery who laid the groundwork for continued progress. To Tami, Lauren & Katelyn for their support and inspiration, and to Naomi Wilden & family for their vision.

Contents

Editor

Jeffrey L. Ballard, M.D.
Professor of Surgery
Loma Linda University Medical Center
Division of Vascular Surgery
Loma Linda, California, U.S.A.
Chapters 8, 10, 13, 22

Contributors

Paul S. van Bemmelen
Department of Surgery
SUNY at Stony Brook
Stony Brook, New York, U.S.A.
Chapter 25

Kiran Bhirangi
Division of Vascular Surgery
University of Utah Medical Center
Salt Lake City, Utah, U.S.A.
Chapter 2

David C. Brewster
Division of Vascular Surgery
Massachusetts General Hospital
Boston, Massachusetts, U.S.A.
Chapter 11

Keith D. Calligaro
Section of Vascular Surgery
Pennsylvania Hospital
Philadelphia, Pennsylvania, U.S.A.
Chapter 27

Richard P. Cambria
Division of Vascular Surgery
Massachusetts General Hospital
Boston, Massachusetts, U.S.A.
Chapter 6

Joseph S. Coselli
Department of Surgery
Baylor College of Medicine
The Methodist Hospital
Houston, Texas, U.S.A.
Chapter 29

Frank J. Criado
Division of Vascular Surgery
Center for Vascular Intervention
The Union Memorial Hospital/
    MedStar Health
Baltimore, Maryland, U.S.A.
Chapter 23

Michael D. Dake
Cardiovascular-Interventional Radiology
Palo Alto Veterans Administration
    Medical Center
Stanford University School of Medicine
Stanford, California, U.S.A.
Chapter 30

Ronald L. Dalman
Division of Vascular Surgery
Stanford University School of Medicine
Stanford, California, U.S.A.
Chapter 12

Matthew J. Dougherty
Section of Vascular Surgery
Pennsylvania Hospital
Philadelphia, Pennsylvania, U.S.A.
Chapter 27

Robert A. Duensing
Department of Surgery
University of California
    Irvine College of Medicine
Orange, California, U.S.A.
Chapter 9

Robert J. Falconer
Division of Vascular Surgery
Center for Vascular Intervention
The Union Memorial Hospital/
    MedStar Health
Baltimore, Maryland, U.S.A.
Chapter 23

James I. Fann
Department of Cardiovascular
    and Thoracic Surgery
Stanford University School of Medicine
Stanford, California, U.S.A.
Chapters 4, 28

Brian L. Ferris
Division of Vascular Surgery
Oregon Health Sciences University
Portland, Oregon, U.S.A.
Chapter 5

Peter Gloviczki
Division of Vascular Surgery
Mayo Clinic
Rochester, Minnesota, U.S.A.
Chapter 15

David Han
Division of Vascular Surgery
Mayo Clinic
Rochester, Minnesota, U.S.A.
Chapter 15

Kimberley J. Hansen
Department of General Surgery
Wake Forest University School of
    Medicine
Winston-Salem, North Carolina, U.S.A.
Chapter 18

E. John Harris, Jr.
Division of Vascular Surgery
Stanford University School of Medicine
Stanford, California, U.S.A.
Chapter 14

Glenn C. Hunter
Department of Surgery
The University of Texas Medical Branch
Galveston, Texas, U.S.A.
Chapter 16

Kaj Johansen
University of Washington
    School of Medicine
Seattle, Washington, U.S.A.
Chapter 17

John Karwowski
Division of Vascular Surgery
Stanford University School of Medicine
Stanford, California, U.S.A.
Chapter 12

Cüneyt Köksoy
Department of Surgery
Baylor College of Medicine
The Methodist Hospital
Houston, Texas, U.S.A.
Chapter 29

Samer Koussayer
Baylor College of Medicine
    and the Methodist Hospital
Houston, Texas, U.S.A.
Chapter 21

William C. Krupski
Vascular Surgery
University of Colorado
    Health Sciences Center
Denver, Colorado, U.S.A.
Chapter 3

Peter F. Lawrence
Department of Surgery
University of California
    Irvine College of Medicine
Orange, California, U.S.A.
Chapter 2

Scott A. LeMaire
Department of Surgery
Baylor College of Medicine
The Methodist Hospital
Houston, Texas, U.S.A.
Chapter 29

Charles C. Miller III
Baylor College of Medicine
    and the Methodist Hospital
Houston, Texas, U.S.A.
Chapter 21

D. Craig Miller
Section of Cardiothoracic Surgery
VA Palo Alto Health Care System
Palo Alto, California, U.S.A.
Chapter 4

R. Scott Mitchell
Department of Cardiovascular
   and Thoracic Surgery
Stanford University School of Medicine
Stanford, California, U.S.A.
Chapter 28

Gregory L. Moneta
Division of Vascular Surgery
Oregon Health Sciences University
Portland, Oregon, U.S.A.
Chapter 5

Mark D. Morasch
Division of Vascular Surgery
Northwestern University Medical School
Chicago, Illinois, U.S.A.
Chapter 7

Mark R. Nehler
Department of Surgery
University of Colorado
   Health Sciences Center
Denver, Colorado, U.S.A.
Chapter 3

Gustavo S.C. Oderich
Department of Surgery
Mayo Graduate School of Medicine
Rochester, Minnesota, U.S.A.
Chapter 2

William H. Pearce
Division of Vascular Surgery
Northwestern University Medical School
Chicago, Illinois, U.S.A.
Chapter 7

William J. Quiñones-Baldrich
Division of Vascular Surgery
UCLA School of Medicine
Los Angeles, California, U.S.A.
Chapter 20

Thomas F. Rehring
Division of Vascular Surgery
Massachusetts General Hospital
Boston, Massachusetts, U.S.A.
Chapter 11

John J. Ricotta
Department of Surgery
SUNY at Stony Brook
Stony Brook, New York, U.S.A.
Chapter 25

Hazim J. Safi
Baylor College of Medicine
   and the Methodist Hospital
Houston, Texas, U.S.A.
Chapter 21

Aravind B. Sankar
Department of Surgery
The University of Texas Medical Branch
Galveston, Texas, U.S.A.
Chapter 16

Rajabrata Sarkar
Division of Vascular Surgery
University of California
   School of Medicine
San Francisco, California, U.S.A.
Chapter 19

Nancy Schindler
Section of Vascular Surgery
Pennsylvania Hospital
Philadelphia, Pennsylvania, U.S.A.
Chapter 27

Zachary C. Schmittling
Department of Surgery
Baylor College of Medicine
The Methodist Hospital
Houston, Texas, U.S.A.
Chapter 29

Charles P. Semba
Cardiovascular-Interventional Radiology
Palo Alto Veterans Administration
   Medical Center
Stanford University School of Medicine
Stanford, California, U.S.A.
Chapter 30

Suzanne M. Slonim
Cardiovascular-Interventional Radiology
Palo Alto Veterans Administration
    Medical Center
Stanford University School of Medicine
Stanford, California, U.S.A.
Chapter 30

Ronald J. Stoney
Division of Vascular Surgery
University of California
    School of Medicine
San Francisco, California, U.S.A.
Chapter 19

Aileen M. Takahashi
Department of Surgery
University of Southern California
    School of Medicine
Los Angeles, California, U.S.A.
Chapter 26

Frank C. Taylor
Division of Vascular Surgery
Loma Linda University Medical Center
Loma Linda, California, U.S.A.
Chapter 13

Frank J. Veith
Division of Vascular Surgery
Weiler Hospital and
Montefiore Medical Center
    of the Albert Einstein College
    of Medicine
New York, New York, U.S.A.
Chapter 24

Reese A. Wain
Division of Vascular Surgery
Weiler Hospital and
Montefiore Medical Center
    of the Albert Einstein College
    of Medicine
New York, New York, U.S.A.
Chapter 24

Fred A. Weaver
Department of Surgery
University of Southern California
    School of Medicine
Los Angeles, California, U.S.A.
Chapter 26

Samuel E. Wilson
Department of Surgery
University of California
    Irvine College of Medicine
Orange, California, U.S.A.
Chapter 9

Douglas J. Wirthlin
Division of Vascular Surgery
Massachusetts General Hospital
Boston, Massachusetts, U.S.A.
Chapter 6

James M. Wong
Department of General Surgery
Wake Forest University School of Medicine
Winston-Salem, North Carolina, U.S.A.
Chapter 18

Chengpei Xu
Department of Surgery
Stanford University School of Medicine
Stanford, California, U.S.A.
Chapter 1

Christopher K. Zarins
Department of Surgery
Stanford University School of Medicine
Stanford, California, U.S.A.
Chapter 1

Preface

Aortic Surgery was conceived and edited by Jeffrey L. Ballard, M.D., who, together with a group of experienced aortic surgeons, authored the 30 chapters which comprise this work.

Modern surgical treatment of aortic disease began approximately 50 years ago when endarterectomy and homografts were used to treat occlusive and aneurysmal disease respectively. As the diagnosis of aortic diseases improved, technical proficiency matched the demands of surgical repair of complex aortic lesions, and comprehensive perioperative care increased the patients' chances for recovery. Technological advances, a cornerstone in the evolution of aortic repair has revolutionized the treatment of aortic disease in the last decade by the introduction of catheter based endoluminal strategies. These techniques have crossed traditional treatment boundaries and are unarguably visionary methods, which deliver treatment through the arterial tree rather than creating traditional invasive surgical exposure. They are effective, selectively applicable and only their long-term durability remains uncertain.

In reviewing the table of contents, the reader will find that the first quarter of the chapter topics consider pathogenesis, epidemiology, screening for heart and stroke risk, and diagnostic imaging prior to aortic surgery. The next half of the chapters focus on the approach and specific treatment strategies for routine and complex aortic pathology, utilizing standard and highly innovative surgical repair. Also, less invasive extraanatomic procedures and endoluminal dilation, stenting, and grafting are well described, illustrated and referenced. The final quarter of the chapters will acquaint the reader with complications during aortic repair secondary to other disease, complications following aortic grafting, and the surgical and endovascular management of aortic dissection and its peripheral manifestations.

The reader can expect *Aortic Surgery* to be user-friendly! It can be a handy reference for the trainee and offer critical insight into the complexities of aortic diseases through the knowledge and know-how of acknowledged experts in the treatment of aortic disease. References with a brief review accompany each chapter and can expand the knowledge base on any chapter topic for the reader.

Ronald J. Stoney, M.D.
Professor of Surgery Emeritus, UCSF
March 9, 2000

Pathogenesis of Aortic Aneurysmal Disease

Christopher K. Zarins and Chengpei Xu

Aortic aneurysm is the most prominent pathologic manifestation of the human aorta and often leads to fatal rupture of the arterial wall. The prevalence of aortic aneurysmal disease is increasing and it is the 13th most common cause of death in the United States. Pathogenesis is complex and not well defined. A number of theories have been proposed, but no single theory of pathogenesis has been universally accepted. Aortic wall degeneration induced by atherosclerosis, proteolytic enzyme activation, and inflammation is the current leading hypothesis; other theories include infectious processes, genetic predisposition and hemodynamic influences. However, it is likely that aneurysm formation is a consequence of an interaction of multiple factors rather than a single process. An increased understanding of the mechanism of aortic aneurysm formation will facilitate improvements in treatment and, most importantly, may lead to strategies that prevent aortic aneurysm formation, enlargement and rupture.

Atherosclerosis and Aortic Aneurysms

The association of aortic aneurysm with aortic atherosclerosis has long been recognized. Most patients with an abdominal aortic aneurysm have evidence of atherosclerosis in the coronary, carotid, and/or peripheral arteries. This has led to the theory that aortic aneurysmal disease is a variant of atherosclerosis that occurs at weakened sites in the aortic wall. Aortic aneurysms, therefore, are commonly referred to as atherosclerotic aortic aneurysms. Although it has been suggested that there is no etiologic relationship between atherosclerosis and aneurysm formation, evidence has accumulated that the atherosclerotic process has effects on the artery wall that can result in aneurysm formation (Fig 1.1).

Property of Adaptive Enlargement of Arteries

A characteristic feature of atherosclerosis is plaque deposition in the intima of the arterial wall. The pathogenesis of atherosclerosis is a complex and dynamic process involving cellular proliferation and migration, intimal lipid deposition, inflammation, fibrosis and necrosis with dystrophic calcification. These processes constantly induce artery wall remodeling, which act to counter the deleterious effects of intimal plaque deposition. The most prominent response of the artery to atherosclerotic plaque deposition is arterial enlargement, and this response appears to be a general characteristic of atherosclerotic arteries. This enlargement has been demonstrated in the carotid, coronary and superficial femoral arteries, as well as in the human abdominal aorta. Arterial enlargement can prevent or postpone the development of lumen

Aortic Surgery, edited by Jeffrey L. Ballard. ©2000 Landes Bioscience.

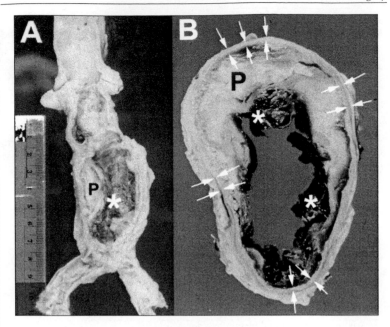

Fig. 1.1. Panel A, a gross specimen of an abdominal aortic aneurysm. The aneurysm is located in the infrarenal segment of the aorta. The longitudinal opening view shows a large atherosclerotic plaque (P) and mural thrombi (*). There are also numerous atherosclerotic lesions spreading over the aorta. Panel B, a cross section of an abdominal aortic aneurysm showing large atherosclerotic plaque (P), the reduced media thickness (arrows) beneath the plaque, and large amount of mural thrombi (*).

stenosis. For example, in the human coronary arteries, enlargement can maintain a normal or near-normal luminal caliber when the cross-sectional area of intimal plaque does not exceed approximately 40% of the area encompassed by the internal elastic lamina (Fig 1.2).

The human aorta enlarges with increasing age and also with increasing atherosclerotic plaque. While both the thoracic and abdominal aortas enlarge with age, abdominal aortic enlargement is more prominently influenced by the amount of atherosclerotic plaque. Since the abdominal aorta is much more prone to atherosclerosis than the thoracic aorta, this may explain the particular propensity for aneurysms to develop in the infrarenal aorta. The human superficial femoral artery also enlarges with increasing atherosclerotic plaque. However, the enlargement response may be restricted and aneurysm formation is much less common than in the abdominal aorta. It is not uncommon to have a twofold enlargement of atherosclerotic arteries as a result of large intimal plaques, with little or no alteration in lumen cross-sectional area. Failure of adequate arterial dilatation, of course, will lead to lumen stenosis. Thus, atherosclerosis characteristically causes enlargement of

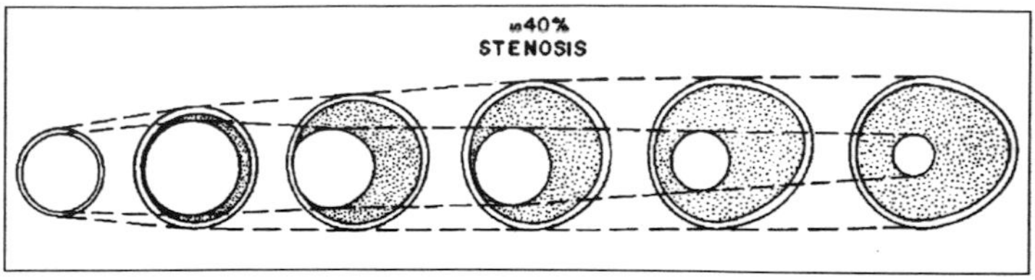

Fig. 1.2. Enlargement of arteries with increasing atherosclerotic plaque. Enlargement can maintain normal or near-normal luminal caliber; when plaque does not exceed 40% of the area encompassed by the internal elastic lamina. Reprinted with permission from Glagov et al. N Engl Med 1987; 316:137.

arteries even though a common end result is constriction of the lumen. The time-dependent enlargement of the human aorta both in response to age and to atherosclerotic influences is an important consideration in therapies such as endovascular stent grafting, which depend on long term radial tension and friction for fixation of stent graft devices. Enlargement of the aorta over time may result in migration of the stent graft or refill of the aneurysm.

Aortic Wall Weakening

Atherosclerotic intimal plaques cause thinning of the adjacent media to it. This may eventually lead to weakening of the arterial wall. The media is the major structural unit of the aorta and is composed of layers of musculoelastic fascicles, or lamellar units. Each group of smooth muscle cells of the media is surrounded by a common collagenous basal lamina interlaced by a basketwork of type III collagen fibrils surrounded by layers of elastic fibers. Thick bundles of type I collagen fibers weave between adjacent fibromuscular layers and provide much of the tensile strength of the media. The elastic fibers distribute mural tensile stresses and provide recoil during the cardiac cycle, while the collagen network prevents over-distention, disruption and enlargement.

During atherosclerotic plaque development the media frequently becomes thin or disappears when the plaques are very large. This can greatly reduce the strength of the arterial wall. It is unclear whether this thinning is the result of atherosclerotic arterial enlargement or is caused by erosive effects of the plaque components on the artery wall. Cavitary excavations of the media are often seen in lipid-rich areas of the plaque and may be associated with regions of macrophage invasion and inflammation. Collagen and fibrous tissue in the adventitia and calcification within the plaque and media may compensate for loss of the media and provide structural support to the aortic wall.

For aortic enlargement to occur in atherosclerosis, the aortic wall matrix fibers of collagen and elastin must be degraded and/or resynthesized in new proportions. Mechanical distention of the aorta by pressure or stretch alone will not result in enlargement in excess of diastolic dimensions without rupture. Thus, during the process of atherosclerotic artery adaptive enlargement, proteolytic enzymes must be activated for this enlargement to take place. During active and rapid enlargement, which may occur during the development of aneurysms, much larger and perhaps less controlled proteolytic activities are likely to take place. Indeed, increased amounts of collagenase, elastase and metalloproteinases have been demonstrated in aortic aneurysms, with maximal concentrations occurring in rapidly enlarging and ruptured aneurysms. Experimental enzymatic destruction of the medial matrix architecture results in dilatation and rupture of the aorta, and experimental mechanical injury, which destroys the medial lamellar architecture, can result in aneurysm formation. These observations support the importance of the media in maintenance of aortic wall integrity.

Human atherosclerotic aneurysms, particularly those of the abdominal aorta, are characterized by extensive atrophy of the media. The normal lamellar architecture is almost totally effaced, and the aortic wall is replaced by a narrow fibrous band. Atrophic changes are also evident in the overlying atherosclerotic lesion to such an extent that plaques may be relatively thinned and contain little residual lipid. Fibrosis and calcification may predominate, depending on the region that is available for histologic study. It is rare to find human abdominal aortic aneurysms without evidence of atherosclerosis. Atherosclerotic plaques remain prominent in the neck of the aneurysm and in the iliac arteries. These are frequently seen posteriorly along the lumbar ostia.

The Process of Aneurysmal Dilation

Atherosclerotic degeneration may result in aneurysmal dilation of the diseased artery. With intimal plaque deposition the structural and functional lamella units of the media are gradually degraded, resulting in thinning of the media and compensatory arterial enlargement. The enlarged atherosclerotic aorta may still receive structural support from the stable, fibrotic, or calcified atherosclerotic plaque, particularly in association with adventitial fibrogenesis, which is characteristic of atherosclerosis.

In advanced atherosclerosis when the aorta is dilated, plaque senescence may occur. This results in reduction in plaque volume and alteration in composition, ulceration or regression, leading to lumen enlargement. There will be reduced tensile support with an atrophic, degenerated media, and progressive aneurysmal enlargement will follow. In addition, metabolic alteration in plaque lipid composition may induce inflammatory cell infiltration with macrophages and lymphocytes. It has been suggested that destruction and weakening of the aortic media may occur as a result of release of inflammatory mediators in response to the atherosclerotic process. The balance between plaque formation, artery wall adaptation and matrix protein synthesis and degradation likely plays a major role in aneurysm pathogenesis. Aneurysms appear to be a relatively late phase of plaque evolution when plaque and media atrophy predominate. This is in contrast to an earlier phase of atherosclerosis when cell proliferation, fibrogenesis and sequestered lipid accumulation are predominant. The observation that patients undergoing surgery for an abdominal aortic aneurysm are generally 10 or more years older than patients undergoing surgery for occlusive disease is explained by this plaque evolution.

Proteolytic Enzymes and Their Inhibitors

Destruction of the structural components of the aortic wall is necessary for aneurysmal enlargement to occur. Both collagenase and elastase activity have been shown to be elevated in aortic aneurysms, with the greatest increase occurring in rapidly enlarging or ruptured aneurysms. While significant destruction of collagen and elastin occurs, there is also synthesis and accumulation of new collagen and elastin in the expanding aorta. This accounts for the thickening of the aortic wall observed clinically in aortic aneurysms and the maintenance of normal collagen content levels. However, the newly synthesized collagen may lack the functional configuration necessary to maintain normal tensile strength. The architecture of the aortic wall is altered by alternation of the media and by accumulation of collagen in the adventitia and neointima. The elastin network is lost from the media, but unstructured elastin accumulates in the adventitia.

Both collagenolytic and elastolytic enzymes have been found in aneurysms and macrophages and inflammatory cells have been implicated as major sources of these proteolytic enzymes. Macrophages are consistently found in the adventitial layer of aneurysms as well as in association with atherosclerotic plaques. Many proteinases are released by macrophages, including a number of important matrix metalloproteinases (MMPs). These include the interstitial collagenase (MMP-1), stromelysin (MMP-3), a 72 kDa gelatinase/type IV collagenase (MMP-2), and a 92 kDa gelatinase/type IV collagenase (MMP-9). All these MMPs have the capacity to degrade all the major connective tissue components of the aortic wall, including collagen, elastin, proteoglycans, fibronectin and laminin. These proteinases are inhibited by tissue inhibitor of metalloproteinase (TIMP), which is also produced by macrophages. In addition, aortic smooth muscle cells, mesenchymal cells, monocytes and capillary endothelial cells are sources of MMPs and/or cytokine mediators. It is likely that all these cells interact during the process of aneurysm formation. However, it is not known which cells have primary roles.

Ongoing investigations will lead to a better understanding of the biochemical balance and control mechanisms regulating aortic matrix synthesis and degradation. This may lead to therapeutic interventions to modulate the excessive proteolytic activity associated with aneurysmal disease. Experimental trial has shown that flow-mediated arterial enlargement is limited by competitive MMP inhibition in a dose-dependent fashion. However, the definitive proof-of-principle for the therapeutic efficacy of anti-MMP or other antiproteinase strategies to prevent the growth of small aortic aneurysms awaits the results of human clinical trials.

Inflammatory Aneurysms

Inflammatory aneurysms account for approximately 5% of abdominal aortic aneurysms. Their characteristic feature is chronic inflammatory infiltrate of varying degree in the outer layers of the media and adventitia. This is not present in the normal aorta, although similar inflammatory cells are seen in association with atherosclerotic plaques. Inflammatory cells are also seen in nonatherosclerotic aortic aneurysms such as those caused by various types of aortitis, including giant cell arteritis, rheumatoid arthritis, systemic lupus erythematosus, polyarteritis nodosa, syphilis, and Takayasu's, Behcet's and Kawasaki's diseases. This suggests the possibility that inflammatory cells, through the release of proteolytic enzymes, may play a primary role in either the causation or exacerbation of aneurysmal dilation.

Macrophages, along with T and B lymphocytes, are the major cellular components of chronic inflammation. Close interdependence exists among these cells during both the initial recognition of antigen and the subsequent perpetuation of inflammation. The cytokine network may play a prominent role in the bidirectional communication among inflammatory cells. Although the exact nature of the relationship between these potent polypeptides and aneurysmal disease is unclear, higher interleukin-1 release has been noted in aortic aneurysms compared to normal aorta. It is clear that inflammatory cells play an important role in aneurysmal enlargement. Whether this role is primary or secondary remains to be determined.

In association with inflammation, infection has been also reported to be related to aneurysmal formation. For example, syphilitic aneurysms and mycotic aneurysms have been reported. In Europe, a series of investigations have demonstrated a close correlation of chlamydia pneumoniae and aneurysmal formation. Whether these specific infections are the direct cause of aortic aneurysmal formation or a coincidence remains to be investigated.

Genetic Predisposition

It is well recognized that a positive family history in a first degree relative is a risk factor for aortic aneurysm. A number of investigators have reported familial clustering of aneurysms and have suggested a genetic basis for the pathogenesis of aneurysms. Several specific genetic abnormalities have been identified in "nonatherosclerotic" aneurysm groups, such as fibrillin gene abnormalities in patients with Marfan's syndrome and procollagen type III defects in patients with vascular type Ehlers-Danlos syndrome.

The search for a genetic defect in abdominal aortic aneurysm formation has centered on abnormalities of matrix proteins, particularly collagenases, elastases, metalloproteinases and their inhibitors. Patients with familial aneurysms have been reported to have less type III collagen in the aortic media, with polymorphisms on the gene for the pro-α1(III) chain of type III collagen. A genetically determined risk has been suggested by the finding of high levels of Lp(a) in the serum of aneurysm patients with a deficiency of α-1-lantitrypsin.

The study of genetic abnormalities in aneurysms is complicated by the fact that aneurysms occur only late in life. Most tests of statistical association using pedigree analysis are based on analysis of first-degree relatives and sibling pairs. Solid information in parents is scarce, and many years will pass before substantial data on the children of probands will be available.

Because 85% of patients with aortic aneurysms have no known family history of aneurysmal disease, a single primary genetic etiology is unlikely to be identified for most patients with arterial aortic atherosclerosis. Although most patients with atherosclerosis do not develop aneurysms, patients with aneurysms invariably have atherosclerotic involvement. The late onset of aneurysmal disease in affected individuals makes it highly probable that genetic factors create, at best, a predisposition and that the subsequent development of aneurysmal disease depends on environmental factors such as smoking and atherosclerotic plaque formation. Genetic factors play an important role in the development of atherosclerosis, and certain genetic predispositions may determine whether some individuals respond to atherogenic stimuli with proliferation and stenosis, while others respond primarily with dilation and aneurysmal enlargement

Hemodynamics and Aneurysm Formation

Hemodynamic and wall mechanical alterations can induce arterial dilation and aneurysm formation. For example, poststenotic aneurysms begin as poststenotic dilations. These become true aneurysms when diameter criterion is met and when ectasia becomes permanent and fixed. Coarctation of the aorta is a classic example. The hemodynamic changes in the poststenotic site are complex, including elevated lateral wall pressure, flow turbulence, abnormal shear stress and vibratory forces. Flow induced arterial enlargement can be observed in patients with arteriovenous fistulas. Long standing fistulas lead to aneurysmal degeneration of the vessels exposed to this high flow state. An experimental abdominal aortic aneurysm model induced by an arteriovenous fistula has been successfully created in rats.

Experimental Observations

Experimental observations support all of these proposed theories of aneurysm pathogenesis. Genetic animal models of aneurysm formation exist, and aneurysms can be induced by exogenous cholesterol feeding in nongenetically susceptible primates. Aneurysm formation in diet-induced atherosclerosis is enhanced by regression of the atherosclerotic plaque, supporting the concept that the interaction between the plaque and the artery wall in atherosclerosis is an important pathogenic mechanism. Hemodynamic models of arteriovenous fistula formation have documented enlargement in response to increased blood flow and wall shear stress, and animal models utilizing proteolytic enzymes in the aorta result in focal aneurysmal dilation.

Enlargement of atherosclerotic arteries can be induced in hypercholesterolemic experimental animals, and such enlargement is associated with destruction of the architecture of the media. This pathologic feature is particularly prominent in those primate species that are susceptible to aneurysm formation. Experimental destruction of aortic medial architecture by mechanical methods alone, or by mechanical injury along with hyperlipidemia, has also been shown to produce aneurysms. Thus, experimental models have supported all of the hypotheses proposed in the pathogenesis of aneurysms.

Conclusion

Pathogenesis of aortic aneurysmal disease is a multifactorial process involving genetic predisposition and atherosclerotic artery wall degeneration. Atherosclerotic plaque deposition, along with artery enlargement and thinning of the media, are important pathogenic processes. Inflammatory cellular and connective tissue responses and proteolytic enzyme activation are important components of the processes leading to weakening of the aortic wall and aneurysmal enlargement. Further understanding of the cellular control mechanisms and biochemical and mechanical responses of the aortic wall are needed to fully comprehend the pathogenesis of aortic aneurysms.

Selected Readings

1.   Zarins CK, Glagov S. Artery wall pathology in atherosclerosis. In: Rutherford RB ed. Vascular Surgery. 5th edition, Vol. 1. Philadelphia: WB Saunders 2000:313-333.
     This chapter discusses the problem of atherosclerosis as it relates to functional biomechanical properties of the artery wall. Both normal and pathologic responses of the artery wall are considered, as well as differences in the evolution of atherosclerotic lesions. Local differences that may account for the propensity of certain areas to form extensive and complex plaques or aneurysms are discussed in detail.

2.   Beckman JA, O'Gara PT. Diseases of the aorta. Adv Intern Med 1999; 44:267-91.
     This article supplies the reader with up-to-date knowledge of diseases of the aorta with an emphasis on aortic aneurysms. Etiology, pathogenesis and diagnosis are thoroughly reviewed.

3.   Rehm JP, Grange JJ, Baxter BT. The formation of aneurysms. Semin Vasc Surg 1998; 3:193-202.
     These authors summarize advanced understanding of the dynamic interactions within a diseased vessel in the fields of immunology, biochemistry, cell biology and genetics. The role of the local inflammatory infiltrates and destructive proteolytic enzymes they produce and regulate is explored. New therapeutic measures are expected to be directed at controlling critical matrix changes, and thus the formation of aortic aneurysms.

4.   Vorp DA, Trachtenberg JD, Webster MW. Arterial hemodynamics and wall mechanics. Semin Vasc Surg 1998; 3:169-80.
     In this article, the authors summarize basic concepts of arterial hemodynamics and wall mechanics as they relate to the development of arterial pathology. The use of computer models for the estimation of wall stresses in individual abdominal aortic aneurysms is also reviewed.

5.   Thompson RW, Parks WC. Role of matrix metalloproteinases in abdominal aortic aneurysms. Ann N Y Acad Sci. 1996; 800:157-74.
     The role of matrix metalloproteinases (MMPs) in aneurysm disease is reviewed. The possibility that these enzymes might serve as rational targets for pharmacotherapy is suggested.

6.   Juvonen J, Juvonen T, Laurila A et al. Demonstration of chlamydia pneumoniae in the walls of abdominal aortic aneurysms. J Vasc Surg 1997; 3:499-505.
     This study and related reports demonstrate that chlamydia pneumoniae is frequently found in the vessel wall of abdominal aortic aneurysms. The potential etiopathogenetic role of chlamydia pneumoniae in the development of these aneurysms is discussed.

CHAPTER 2

Epidemiology of Aortic Aneurysmal Disease

Peter F. Lawrence, Gustavo S.C. Oderich, Kiran Bhirangi

Aneurysm of the aorta is a common disease, representing 83% of all noncerebral aneurysms diagnosed in the United States.[1] Although necropsy studies indicated a predominance of thoracic aortic aneurysms in the beginning of the century, this figure has dramatically changed since then. This is probably due to the loss of syphilis as an etiologic factor and an increase in degenerative atherosclerotic aneurysms of the abdominal aorta. In 1994, 88% of the aortic aneurysms surgically repaired in the United States were located in the abdominal aorta, whereas thoracic and thoracoabdominal aneurysms accounted for 5-12% of the total.[1] Abdominal aortic aneurysms (AAA) are responsible for 0.8% of all deaths in the United States, ranking 10th as cause of death in older males.

Due to the frequency of abdominal aneurysm deaths in the general population, and noninvasive access to the aorta by ultrasound, several large screening programs have been undertaken to diagnose and ultimately treat asymptomatic aneurysms. The detailed epidemiological information from the *United Kingdom (UK) Small Aneurysm Trial* published recently and the ongoing *Aneurysm Detection and Management (ADAM) Study* were designed to answer the question whether a policy of early diagnosis and elective repair of small abdominal aneurysms is preferable to ultrasonographic surveillance.[2,3] The UK trial demonstrated no benefit for early elective surgery over ultrasonographic surveillance of small aneurysms (< 5.5 cm). However, this may be attributed to a higher than expected operative mortality rate (5.8%) in this study. Had this trial achieved an elective surgical mortality rate of 2-3%, it is likely that early surgery would have shown significant benefit. We reported an even higher mortality rate (8.4%) when analyzing the results of all abdominal aneurysms electively repaired in the United States, which may reflect discrepancies between high-volume vascular centers and less specialized hospitals.[1] The ADAM study is continuing and will further elucidate the correct management of patients with asymptomatic small aneurysms.

Knowledge of the prevalence, incidence, risk factors, associated diseases and survival in patients with aneurysms is of paramount importance when planning future screening and treatment programs.

Prevalence

The prevalence of AAA detected through screening programs varies between 1.4-11.9%, depending on the definition of aneurysm and on the population studied.[2]

The Ad Hoc Committee on reporting standards of the Society for Vascular Surgery (SVS) and the International Society for Cardiovascular Surgery (ISCVS) (North American chapter) defined aneurysm as a permanent localized dilatation of an artery to a diameter greater than 50% (1.5 times) of its normal size. Normal diameter for an infra-renal aorta is estimated to be 21.4 ± 3.6 mm (maximum 25 mm) in males and 18.7 ± 3.3 mm (maximum 22 mm) in females. The ADAM study, which is the largest population-based screening study published to date, reported a prevalence of AAA greater than 4.0 cm in 1.4% of the 73,451 veterans who were 50-79 years of age. If the size definition is decreased to 3.0 cm, the prevalence increases to 4.6%. Bengtsson et al also reported a prevalence of 3.3% using the 4.0 cm criteria and a significantly higher prevalence (8.5%) when the 3.0 cm criteria was adopted.

The prevalence of aortic aneurysms increases steadily with age (Fig. 2.1).[2] In the ADAM trial, prevalence was on average 3 times higher among smokers, when compared to nonsmokers of the same age.[2] This increased steadily, reaching a 9-fold peak prevalence within the 29-year interval. The prevalence was 0.3% among smokers with ages between 50 and 54, and 2.7% for those older than 75. This was also confirmed by Morris et al. In this study, prevalence was 2.3% in individuals 50-64 years of age, increasing to 8.8 and 11.9% in individuals 65-79 or more than 80 years of age, respectively. These authors used the 3.0 cm diameter criteria to define aneurysm.

Another method of obtaining an estimate of the prevalence of aortic aneurysms is through "epidemiological necropsy" studies. This method has been developed to counteract the influence of selection bias, such as an overrepresentation of patients with sudden and unexpected deaths, which more frequently are attributed to ruptured aneurysms. The "epidemiological necropsy" approach excludes patients with a suspected aneurysm. Prevalence estimates obtained by this technique are similar to those from screening surveys, ranging from 0.6-3.2% in the 3 largest series published to date.[4] Bengtsson et al studied age- and sex-specific prevalence of AAA, and found that total aneurysm frequency was twice as high in men than in women.[4] In men, the frequency increases rapidly after age of 55, reaching a peak prevalence of 5.9% at 85 years of age, whereas in women, there is a continuous increase after 70 years of age, reaching a 4.5% peak after the age of 90.[6]

Estimates for thoracic and thoracoabdominal aneurysms are not as precise as those for abdominal aneurysms. A Danish study of 6480 autopsies (not using an epidemiological method) reported a prevalence of thoracic aneurysms of 1.2 per million population per year, as compared to a 3.6 per million for abdominal aneurysms.

Incidence

Almost all studies have demonstrated an increasing incidence for both ruptured and nonruptured AAA since the 1950s. The SVS / ISCVS reported that the number of aneurysmorrhaphies more than doubled from 1979-1992 (19 vs. 46/100,000 population). In a report from Rochester, Minnesota, the average increase in incidence was 11% per year, higher than the 4% per year reported in the Western Australia study. This study showed an incidence of 117.2 and 33.9 per 100,000 person-years

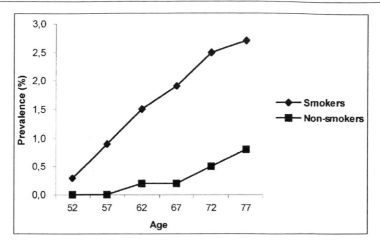

Fig. 2.1. Age-specific prevalence rates in smokers and nonsmokers males: results from the ADAM study.

for males and females, respectively Melton at al demonstrated an incidence of 36.5 per 100,000 person-years, without stratifying for sex. As incidence estimates can only be obtained by screening a defined population for a second time, accurate data for asymptomatic AAA are sparse and unreliable. In addition, comparison between studies is difficult due to variances in sex, age and risk factor distribution.

The incidence of ruptured abdominal aortic aneurysms was 3 per 100,000 person-years in the Western Australia study. This was slightly higher than the incidence of 1 per 100,000 person-years reported in the Göteburg study, which also demonstrated a seven-fold increase in incidence rates over a 36-year period. Bengtsson et al showed an increase in the incidence of ruptured AAA with age. Rupture was extremely rare before age 50 in men, increasing rapidly after age of 55. Women have a more delayed (15-20 years) increase in the incidence of ruptured AAA (Fig. 2.2).

Risk Factors

Several risk factors for abdominal aneurysms have been described (Table 2.1). Male sex and cigarette smoking are the strongest factors in multivariate analysis.[2] Other factors associated with higher prevalence rates of AAA include age, white race, family history, hypertension, peripheral arterial occlusive disease (PAOD) and hypercholesterolemia.[2]

Male Sex

Male sex is associated with a relative risk for abdominal aneurysm of 6.5 (95% confidence interval: 5.9-7.2). The male:female ratio varies from 6:1 to 2:1 in population-based screening studies and necropsy surveys. We reported a 2.3:1 ratio for abdominal aneurysms diagnosed in the United States in 1994.[1] The corresponding figure for thoracic aneurysms is 1:1. Female sex was negatively associated with AAA

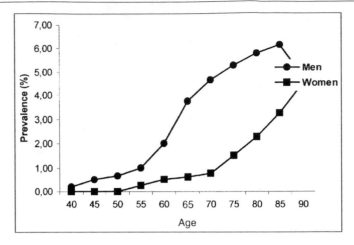

Fig. 2.2. Sex-specific percentage by age in an epidemiological necropsy study. Adapted with permission from Bengtsson et al (5).

Table 2.I. Results adapted from the ADAM study: Risk factors associated with an increased prevalence of AAA in decreasing order of importance

Risk Factor	Odds Ratio	(95% Confidence Interval)
Positive association		
Male sex	6.50	(5.90-7.20)*
Cigarette smoking	5.57	(4.24-7.31)
Family history	1.95	(1.56-2.43)
Age (per 7-year interval)	1.65	(1.53-1.78)
Coronary artery disease	1.62	(1.41-1.84)
Hypercholesterolemia	1.54	(1.31-1.80)
Hypertension	1.16	(1.01-1.32)
Conflicting association		
COPD	1.28	(1.09-1.50)†
PAOD	0.96	(0.74-1.25)‡
Negative Association		
Female sex	0.22	(0.07-0.68)
Black race (compared to white)	0.49	(0.35-0.69)
Diabetes mellitus	0.54	(0.44-0.65)
No association		
Other race (compared to white)	0.91	(0.63-1.33)
Cerebral vascular disease	1.19	(0.99-1.42)
Deep venous thrombosis	0.67	(0.50-0.88)
Cancer	0.90	(0.74-1.09)

*Rotterdam study and Simoni et al
†No association found after adjustment for the number of years of smoking
‡When a diameter higher than 3.0 cm was considered diagnostic of AAA there was a positive association (OR 1.39 and 95% CI 1.20-1.62)

in the ADAM study.[2] In addition, aneurysm repair seems to be performed less frequently in women than in men. Women had a 1.4 higher mortality rate for elective aneurysm repair in the series of Katz et al. While the number of diagnoses increased for both men and women in the years of 1990-1994, 40% of all men and 20% of all women diagnosed with an abdominal aneurysm underwent surgery during the same period (p < .001).[1] One possible explanation for this finding is that the size of the aneurysm in women may not be as great as those in men. This would be expected to result in lower rupture rates in women. However, we recently reported that the percentage of women diagnosed with ruptured AAA was 9.4%, while in men rupture rate was 7.4%.[1] It is possible that women could be better treated using sex-adjusted standards to compensate for their normally smaller aortas. This would increase the number of elective procedures and reduce the number of emergency repairs.

Advancing Age

Advancing age is also positively associated with aneurysm and with higher mortality rates due to rupture. The average age for diagnosis of an asymptomatic AAA was 66.2 ± 7.1 in the ADAM and 69.2 ± 4.4 in the UK Small Aneurysm trial.[2-3] It is estimated that age contributes to a sevenfold increase in death rates due to ruptured AAA over a 15-year period. In the ADAM study, a 7-year interval was associated with a 1.65 (1.53-1.78) increase in the risk of abdominal aneurysm.[2] For nonruptured thoracic aneurysms the average age was 67.6 for men and 74.6 for women in a national survey; ruptured thoracic aneurysms presented on average 10 years later in men (78 years of age).[1]

Race

Although race is not a strong risk indicator, aortic aneurysms are more frequent and more commonly rupture in whites. In the ADAM study, black race (compared with white) was associated with a lower prevalence of AAA (odds ratio: 0.49, 0.35-0.69). Lillienfield et al reported a 3.3-fold increase in rupture rate for white men when compared to nonwhite men.

Family History

Familial clustering of abdominal aneurysms is well described. Although family history is an independent risk factor, only 5% of the patients diagnosed with an abdominal aneurysm reported a familial occurrence of aneurysm.[2] Male relatives of AAA have a higher proportion of dilated aortas. It is estimated that men with a first degree relative with AAA experience a 10-fold increased risk of developing an aneurysm, most frequently located in the abdominal aorta. Bengtsson et al reported a meta-analysis of seven sibling studies using a 3.0 cm definition of AAA and showed that the frequency of abdominal aneurysms was 16.9% (12-20%) in men and 2.9% (1-5%) in women. Genetic variation on chromosome 16, increased proteolysis, and structural abnormalities in the genes for the collagen (I-VI) family or their modifying enzymes, are under investigation as the cause for "familial" aneurysms.

Cigarette Smoking

Cigarette smoking is the strongest modifiable risk factor associated with AAA in most screening studies. In the ADAM study, the odds ratio for an aneurysm of 4.0 cm or larger compared with normal aorta (< 3.0 cm) was 5.57 (4.24-7.31).[2] This association increased significantly with the number of years of smoking and decreased with the numbers of years after quitting smoking.[2] Current smoking was associated with an increased risk even after adjustment for the number of years of smoking. Other aspects associated with a higher risk for AAA includes number of cigarettes currently smoked and the depth of inhalation. Powell et al demonstrated that smoking is also associated with rapid aneurysm growth rate. In his series, the median aneurysm growth rate in smokers was 17 mm/year as opposed to 9 mm/year in nonsmokers. Plasma cotidine and tar yield of cigarette (mg) were also investigated, but showed no correlation with increased prevalence of AAA or an increased growth rate. It is estimated that 78% of all aneurysms 4.0 cm or higher in the ADAM study population were directly attributed to cigarette smoking, which suggests that this habit is responsible for most clinically important asymptomatic aneurysms.

Hypertension

Although the mechanical role of hypertension in the pathogenesis of aneurysms may seem obvious (Laplace's Law), studies investigating the association of blood pressure levels and aneurysm risk produce conflicting results. In the ADAM study, the association of AAA with hypertension was only marginally significant (odds ratio: 1.16, 1.01-1.32). Two other screening studies have found no association, whereas a case-controlled study found hypertension to be an independent risk factor.[7] Naydeck et al recently reported a positive association between pulse pressure and risk of AAA in a cohort of elderly patients treated for isolated systolic hypertension (The SHEP study cohort).

PAOD

Claudication has been associated with an increased risk of abdominal aneurysm in some reports, but results varied depending on the definition of aneurysm. Allardice et al compared patients with PAOD to controls with similar smoking habits who had (bronchogenic carcinoma). The frequency of abdominal aneurysms was higher in patients with PAOD, reaching 17% in males. A criticism of this study is that it also included patients with peripheral aneurysms, known by its association with abdominal aneurysms. The ADAM study did not confirm the association between PAOD and aneurysm risk when the 4.0 cm criteria was used. However, there was a marginal positive association between claudication and AAA when the definition of aneurysm was changed to an aortic diameter higher than 3.0 cm.[2]

Hypercholesterolemia

The ADAM study also confirmed a positive correlation between hypercholesterolemia, coronary artery disease, and abdominal aortic aneurysm.[2] The presence of "any atherosclerosis" was also positively associated with higher prevalence estimates. Hypercholesterolemia was associated with a 1.54-fold and coronary artery disease with a 1.62-fold increase in the risk of AAA.[2] In an autopsy study of 8,000 men, hypercholesterolemia was associated with a 2.3-fold increase in the prevalence of abdominal aneurysms when compared to patients with normal lipid levels.

Negative Risk Factors

A negative association between AAA and diabetes was identified in the ADAM study.[2] The effect of diabetes on large arteries is known to be distinct from atherosclerosis; increased aortic stiffness and medial calcification, present in these patients, could stabilize the aorta and resist aneurysmal dilatation. Chronic obstructive pulmonary disease (COPD), which was positively associated with AAA in the multivariate analysis model, had no significant association when adjustment was made for the number of years smoking.[2] Therefore, the results from screening and necropsy surveys that previously demonstrated an association between lung elasticity and risk of rupture may be explained by the presence of confounding factors such as cigarette smoking and concomitant medications (steroids). Other factors that were investigated in the ADAM study, but showed no correlation are cerebrovascular disease, cancer, deep venous thrombosis, weight, and waist circumference.[2]

Prognostic Factors for Rupture

Cigarette smoking, COPD, aortic to L-3 vertebra diameter index, symptoms and aortic blebs have been positively associated with risk of AAA rupture. Expansion rate, diastolic blood pressure, absence of PAOD, and fusiform shape of AAA are factors weakly associated with aneurysm rupture (Table 2.2).

Cronenwett reported the results of a multivariate analysis where COPD was the strongest risk factor associated with aneurysm rupture.[8] Absolute aortic diameter at the time of diagnosis and diastolic blood pressure were also positively associated (Fig. 2.3). This finding was also confirmed in necropsy studies.[4] Patients with ruptured aneurysms had larger aneurysms (8.0 vs. 5.1 cm), and more frequently had hypertension (54 vs. 28%), emphysema (67 vs. 42%), and bronchiectasis (29 vs. 15%).[4] One possible explanation for the association of pulmonary and aneurysmal disease is an increased elastolytic activity in these patients. However, Lindholt et al attributed this association to the concomitant use of medications (oral steroids), rather than a common pathway of pathogenesis. The mean annual expansion rate was 2.74 mm per year among patients with COPD, 2.72 among patients without COPD, and 4.7 mm among patients who used oral steroids compared with 2.6 mm among patients who did not use steroids (p < .05).

The Whitehall study demonstrated an association between smoking and increased risk of aneurysm rupture.[7] The relative risk increased 4.6-fold for cigarette smokers, 2.4-fold for pipe/cigar smokers, and 14.6-fold for smokers of hand-rolled cigarette.[7]

Ouriel et al associated aneurysm size, defined using the AAA and L-3 vertebra diameter index, with aneurysm risk of rupture.[9] None of the 36 patients with ruptured aneurysm had an index lower than 1.0, whereas 29% of the electively repaired aneurysms were smaller than the L-3 vertebra diameter.[8] This ratio was also slightly more accurate in predicting risk of rupture (68%) than the aortic diameter alone

Table 2.2. Prognostic factors associated with aneurysm rupture

Prognostic Factor	Strength	Reference
COPD	2	Cronenwett et al (8)
Aortic/L-3 vertebra diameter Index	2	Ouriel et al (9)
Cigarette smoking	2	Stracham et al (7)
Symptoms (pain and tenderness)	2	Cronenwett et al (8)
Aortic blebs	2	Delin et al (10)
Diastolic blood pressure	1	Cronenwett et al (8)
Fusiform aneurysm	1	Sterpretti et al (5), Cronenwett et al (8)
Aneurysm diameter > 50 mm	1	Ouriel et al (9)
Absence of PAOD	1	Cronenwett et al (8)

2: strong association and 1: weak association

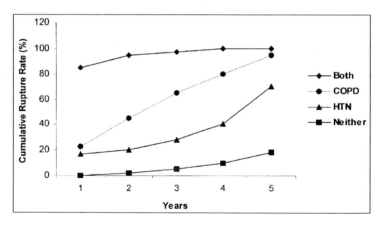

Fig. 2.3. Predicted cumulative risk for a 5.0 cm AAA depending on the presence of associated risk factors. Adapted with permission from Sampson LN, Cronenwett JL. 1995.

(60%). Eighty percent of the aneurysms that ruptured during the 4.6 year follow up period in the UK trial had a diameter of more than 5.0 cm when last recorded.[3] The expected expansion rate for an abdominal aneurysm with diameters ranging from 3-6.0 cm is estimated to be 10% of its initial size. In the UK trial the median aneurysm growth rate was 0.33 cm per year for a median initial aneurysm size of 4.6 ± 0.37 cm in the surveillance group.[3] Repair is usually recommended in patients with a sudden increase in aneurysm size of more than 5 mm in 6 months, due to an increased risk of rupture in this group of patients.[10] However, studies evaluating the prognostic role of expansion rate produced conflicting results, and it is generally accepted that AAA/L-3 vertebra index or the aneurysm diameter are more practical criteria for performing aneurysmorrhaphy.[9]

Associated Diseases and Survival

Abdominal aneurysms affect primarily older patients with comorbidities. Knowledge of the incidence of these associated diseases is fundamental when assessing the surgical risk. Patients with abdominal aneurysms have a higher incidence of cardiovascular, pulmonary and renal pathology, as confirmed by both the ADAM and the UK trial. Coronary artery disease was present in nearly 40% of patients enrolled in both studies, which explains why coronary events are responsible for most of the morbidity and mortality in these patients. The ADAM trial was limited to US veterans, which may explain some of the discrepancies in the incidence of associated diseases when compared to the UK trial that investigated the general population. Diabetes, for example, was much more frequent among US veterans (18%) than in patients participating in the UK trial (2-3%). Hypertension was also more common in patients participating in the ADAM trial (50%) when compared to those of the UK trial (40%). Hypercholesterolemia was a common associated factor in both groups of patients (53%). Other diseases reported in the ADAM study are PAOD (7%), cerebrovascular disease (12%), COPD (15%), and cancer (13%).

The 6-year life-table survival rate was 64% for both patients randomized to the surgical and surveillance arm in the UK study.[3] This result is similar to the 60% 6-year survival rate reported by the Canadian Aneurysm study.

Conclusion

Population-based screening studies and necropsy surveys have confirmed an increasing incidence of aortic aneurysms. The prevalence is estimated to be 1.4%, reaching 11.9% in older individuals. The most important factors associated with increased prevalence are male gender and cigarette smoking. Age, white race, family history, hypertension, hypercholesterolemia and coronary artery disease have a positive association with aortic aneurysms. The ADAM trial identified diabetes, female gender, and black race as factors negatively associated with aneurysms. Despite the results of the UK trial, the optimal management of patients with small aneurysms continues to be debated. The surgeon must assure mortality rates below 3% to justly elective repair of small AAA. The ADAM trial should further elucidate the management of patients with small aneurysms.

Selected Readings

1. Lawrence PF, Jones B, Gazak C et al. The epidemiology of surgically repaired aneurysms in the United States. J Vasc Surg 1999; 30:30:632-640.
   This study uses the National Hospital Discharge Summary on hospitalized US patients to investigate the frequency and mortality of aneurysms at different locations. It provides a baseline frequency and operative mortality for each aneurysm, which can be used as a standard for individual surgeons, hospitals, and to compare with new therapies, such as endovascular AAA repair.
2. Lederle F, Johnson G, Wilson SE et al. Prevalence and associations of abdominal aortic aneurysm detected through screening. The Aneurysm Detection and Management (ADAM) Veterans Affairs Cooperative Study Group. Ann Intern Med 1997; 126:441-449.

2

This VA cooperative study of 74,000 patients assessed the risk factors for patients who were screened for AAA. It found that 1.4% had an AAA >4.0 cm and that smoking was most closely associated with AAA. The data is excellent for male veterans, but does not reflect the general US population.

3. Mortality results for randomized controlled trial of early elective surgery or ultrasonographic surveillance for small abdominal aortic aneurysms. The U.K. Small Aneurysm Trial participants. Lancet 1998; 352:1649-55.

    The UK Small Aneurysm Trial prospectively and randomly compared early elective surgery with nonoperative therapy for aneurysms of 4.0 – 5.5 cm. The 30 day operative mortality was 5.8%, and the mortality at 2, 4 and 6 years was statistically similar in both groups. The safety of nonoperative management for AAA is supported by this study.

4. Bengtsson H, Bergqvist D, Sternby NH. Increasing prevalence of abdominal aortic aneurysms—a necropsy study. Eur J Surg 1992; 158:19-23.

    This retrospective study of 46,000 Swedish autopsies found a prevalence of 4,300/ 100,000 aneurysms in men and 2,100/100,000 in women. The incidence of AAA rose rapidly after age 50. Unfortunately, the size of aneurysms was not documented. However, this study shows that aneurysms are age and sex dependent.

5. Darling R, Messina C, Brewster D et al. Autopsy study of unoperated abdominal aortic aneurysms: the case for early resection. Cardiovasc Surg 1977; 56(suppl 2):161-164.

    This classic paper by Darling was one of the earliest U.S. autopsy studies of AAA incidence and rupture rates. It confirms the exponential relationship between aneurysm size and risk of rupture. It is criticized because of the selected referral population and measurement of size of AAA at autopsy, which underestimates the aortic aneurysm size in patients.

6. Sterpetti AV, Cavallaro A, Cavallari N et al. Factors influencing the rupture of abdominal aneurysms. Surg Gynecol Obstet 1991; 173:175-173.

    This Italian study of 50,000 autopsies at 2 major leading hospitals found 300 AAA, with 75% nonruptured and 25% ruptured. Risk of rupture was related to size, hypertension, and bronchiectasis. This study promoted the concept of connective tissue disease in the lungs as an associated risk factor for AAA.

7. Strachan DP. Predictors of death from aortic aneurysm among middle-aged men: The Whitehall study. Br J Surg 1991; 78:401-404.

    This British study of middle aged men with AAA analyzed the predictors of death. Smoking and diastolic hypertension were associated with death from ruptured and surgically repaired AAA.

8. Cronenwett JL, Murphy TF, Zelenock GB et al. Actuarial analysis of variables associated with rupture of small abdominal aortic aneurysms. Surgery 1985; 98:472-83.

    Cronenwett's study of patients with small AAAs, who were selected for nonoperative management, found an annual rupture rate of 6%, an annual rupture mortality of 5%, and an annual mortality from other causes of 6%. Diastolic blood pressure, initial aneurysm diameter, and COPD were independent risk factors. It was recommended that these factors be assessed before recommending nonoperative treatment of small AAAs.

9. Ouriel K, Green RM, Donayre C et al. An evaluation of new methods of expressing aortic aneurysm size: relationship to rupture. J Vasc Surg 1992; 15:12-20.

    This study by Ouriel and colleagues evaluated the relationship between absolute aneurysm size and aneurysm rupture. They found, as have other studies, that normal aortas varied in size, and suggested that the 3rd lumbar vertebral body diameter be compared to the aneurysm size, since no aneurysm ruptured when its diameter was less than the diameter of the vertebral body.

10. Delin A, Olsen H, Swedenborg J. Growth rate of abdominal aortic aneurysms as measured by CT. Br J Surg 1985; 72:530-532.

This study evaluates the growth rate, measured by CT scan, of AAA in 35 patients who had either small aneurysms or had a contraindication to surgery. The mean growth rate was 0.52 cm/year although individual rates varied, and aneurysms > 6 cm grew more rapidly than small ones.

2

CHAPTER 3

Screening for Aortic Aneurysmal Disease

William C. Krupski and Mark R. Nehler

Background

Rupture of abdominal aortic aneurysms (AAAs) is the 10th leading cause of death in the United States, accounting for slightly over 1% of deaths in men over 65 and about half of that figure in women over 65 in North America and Europe.[1] Moreover, death from rupture of a previously asymptomatic AAA has been increasing during the past three decades. The incidence (the number of new cases) of AAAs varies greatly depending on the method of detection, but incidence estimates of 20-40 cases per 100,000 persons per year are typical.[2] Physical examination (PE) is a relatively insensitive means of detecting AAAs. Chervu and colleagues from the University of Texas Southwestern found that only 93 (38%) of 243 patients undergoing aneurysm repair had their AAAs initially detected by physical examination (PE).[3] Overall, 55 (23%) AAAs were not palpable on preoperative PE, even when the diagnosis was known. Whereas ultrasonography (US) is often considered the gold standard for diagnosis of AAAs, Lederle and the Aneurysm Detection and Management (ADAM) Veterans Affairs Cooperative Study group found substantial differences between AAA measurements both by US and computed tomography (CT) examinations; variations in AAA measurements of 0.5 cm or more were not uncommon.[4]

Prevalence (the number of existing cases) of AAAs is age-dependent; in adult autopsy studies prevalence ranges from 1-6%, but in a recent U.K. study, AAAs were present in 2% of men aged 65-75 years, and 9% for those older than 75.[5] In an autopsy study from the Massachusetts General Hospital, AAAs were found in 2% of 24,000 consecutive post mortem examinations.[6] Similar studies in unselected populations, using postmortem examinations, US studies, and CT scans have reported a similar prevalence of about 2-3%.[7-9] Johnson and associates found more aneurysms in white men (4.2%) than in white women, black men, and black women (all about 1.5%)[8] AAAs occur considerably more frequently than thoracic aneurysms. Lilienfield and colleagues reported that the ratio of abdominal: thoracic aneurysms was 7:1 in men and 3:1 in women.[10] The number of new cases of AAAs among residents of Rochester, Minnesota, during 1976-1980 was about seven times higher than the incidence of racic aneurysms.[11] Repair of arterial aneurysms constitutes about 13% of the vascular experience of general surgical residents, and probably accounts for an even higher percentage of operations performed by vascular surgeons in practice.[12]

The occurrence of AAAs appears to be increasing. Two separate Mayo Clinic studies examining the decades from 1951-1980 showed a 3-fold increase in AAA prevalence from 12.2 per 100,000 to 36.2 per 100,000.[11,13] Some of this increase in frequency may be related to improved detection owing to technological advances (most importantly more widespread use of ultrasonography and CT for the diagnosis of a variety of disorders), but the magnitude of the difference suggests an authentic increase.[14] The aging of the population also plays a role in the increasing incidence. For example, in a European autopsy study, aneurysms occurred with a constantly increasing frequency in men after 55 years of age, peaking at 5.9% in 90 year-olds.[15] Women developed an increased incidence of aneurysms after age 70, peaking at 4.5% in 90 year-olds. Mortality data also suggest a real increase in the prevalence of AAAs. Since 1951 the number of deaths due to ruptured aneurysms in individuals under age 65 has remained low but rates have risen in older age groups. Compared with 30 years earlier, a 1984 study in England and Wales revealed a 20-fold and 11-fold increase in deaths from ruptured aortic aneurysms for men and women, respectively.[16] The ratio of male:female death rates decreases from 11:1 in younger age groups to 3:1 in the octogenarians. Curiously, deaths most commonly occur in the winter months, like those from coronary artery disease.[17] It is intriguing that aneurysms are increasingly common whereas deaths from coronary heart disease, which shares the same risk factors, have decreased by 20% in the past decade.[18]

Abdominal aortic aneurysms commonly remain asymptomatic until they rupture. More than 50% of patients with rupture die before they reach the hospital and overall in-and out-of hospital mortality rates from ruptured AAAs are as high as 85-95%, even in modern series.[19] In contrast, elective repair of AAAs carry < 5% mortality rates in most centers. Several institutions have reported mortality rates less than 1 or 2%.[20,21] Of note, the long-term survival and quality of life after surgical treatment of AAAs are comparable to those of matched population controls.[22] Thus, early detection and treatment of AAAs may improve chances of survival for patients with an asymptomatic AAA.[23]

However, the question of whether ultrasonic screening for AAAs in asymptomatic individuals is warranted remains controversial. In 1991, the Canadian Task Force on Periodic Health Examination evaluated the literature to provide recommendations on this problem and concluded that there is insufficient evidence to recommend routine screening programs using physical examinations or ultrasonography.[24] Based on the same literature, Harris endorsed a national screening program to reduce mortality from AAAs.[25] The U.S. Preventative Services Task Force gave AAA screening a "C" recommendation, meaning that there was insufficient evidence to recommend for or against screening.[26] In contrast, Scott and colleagues reported a 55% reduction in AAA ruptures in men, but the associated 41% reduction in AAA-related deaths did not reach statistical significance, despite the randomized study size of more than 15,000 subjects.[27] More recently Wilmink et al in the U.K. concluded that screening for asymptomatic AAAs reduced the incidence of rupture by 49%.[28] Based on their data and several assumptions, these authors concluded that in order to save one life from a ruptured AAA, 2,000 men would need to be screened and 10 elective operations performed.

Economic Deliberations

The economic cost of ruptured aneurysms is staggering. Pasch and colleagues from Rochester, New York, estimated that in 1984 dollars, $50 million and 2,000 lives could have been saved if aneurysms had been repaired before they ruptured.[29] Breackwoldt and associates reviewed financial data of 102 patients undergoing elective and emergent abdominal aortic aneurysm repair between 1986 and 1989.[30] Postoperative length of stay, net revenue, total standard charges and net profit or loss margins were the principal analyzed variables. A net loss of $409,459 was noted for the entire series. Although emergent operations (mostly for ruptured AAAs) made up only 12% of the procedures, they accounted for 73% of the losses, with an average loss of $24,655 per patient. The mean financial loss among survivors of emergent AAA repair was $36,672 per patient. Predictably, length of stay correlated closely with overall costs.

Based on such fiscal considerations, it would seem prudent to screen individuals for AAAs and repair them electively. However, given the variable incidence of aneurysms, determination of cost-effectiveness is complicated. In a thoughtful discussion of the cost-benefit analysis of AAA screening, Quill and associates noted that in 1985, there were 28,536,000 persons over age 65 in the United States.[31] During that year 12,499 U.S. deaths were caused by ruptured AAAs in the same age group (admittedly a "soft" statistic considering the rarity of postmortem examinations in recent decades). Using an average cost of $150 for an abdominal US examination, these investigators calculated that it would cost about $4.3 billion to scan all persons at risk. This amount to a cost of $360,000 per life saved, provided that all patients found to have an AAA underwent operation and there were no operative deaths (another unlikely assumption). Frame and associates recently concluded that screening for AAA in men ages 60-80 years is "cost-effective but of small benefit."[32] However, the accuracy of this conclusion is debatable; the manuscript is based on references identified from bibliographies of pertinent articles and the cost and effectiveness of various protocols. Moreover, we found the article nearly incomprehensible.

If, however, the population screened is comprised of patients with increased risk of having AAAs, the cost-benefit ratio improves. For example, if patients with concomitant peripheral vascular disease are screened (with a prevalence of AAA approaching 10%), Quill et al. Calculated that US screening would save 1500 lives at a cost of $78,000 per life saved.[31] The National Academy of Sciences has estimated that the average cost of death is $200,000,[33] thereby suggesting that US screening for AAA is cost-effective in carefully selected groups (see below).

The British literature also supports the cost-effectiveness of screening programs for detection of AAAs in selected individuals. Scott has estimated a cost of only £300 per aneurysm identified in high-risk populations.[34] Because the cost of US screening was minimal (£5 per scan), and the cost of operation also low (£2000), Collin found that it would cost only £9000 per life-saved by a screening program.[35] In an interesting examination of this tissue, Thurmond and Semler conjectured that the cost of 25-54 US examinations plus one elective operation would equal the cost of one emergency operation for a ruptured AAA; thus, they concluded that scanning would be cost-effective if the prevalence of aneurysms was 1.8-4.0%[36]

Screening Programs

A multitude of studies have been reported concerning US screening for AAAs. In general, investigations can be grouped as

1. small general population studies,
2. screening older men for AAAs,
3. risk-factor-related subgroup analyses (e.g., hypertensives, patients with coronary artery disease (CAD), patients with familial histories of AAAs),
4. subjects with other manifestations of peripheral arterial disease (PD) (e.g., carotid artery occlusive disease, patients with intermittent claudication), or
5. large multicenter population-based studies. A caution in interpretation of all these publications is that many of the studies were based on hospital-referred subjects, thus introducing potential bias.

Small General Population Screening Studies

One of the first and most widely quoted modern series of AAAs was rerouted by Nevitt and associates from Mayo Clinic in Rochester, Minnesota.[37] Whereas this was not truly a screening study, the uniformity and stability of the population in Rochester has led to designation of this article as a benchmark. The authors concluded that in their population-based study, aneurysms do not expand at the generally accepted rate of 0.4-0.5 cm per year.[38,39] In the Mayo Clinic study, the cumulative incidence of rupture was 6% after 5 years and 8% after 10 years; the median diameter expansion rate was only 0.21 cm per year. Much criticism has been leveled at this study; among the cited weaknesses are

1. the small number of patients studied (181);
2. the average small size (91% < 5 cm in diameter);
3. a 25% 5-year rupture rate in aneurysms >5 cm in diameter (death rates not provided);
4. a substantial number of patients who die during the study period underwent autopsies, thus potentially underestimating rupture rates; and
5. only 103 of the 176 patients had two or more US examinations, 8 of whom had an AAA rupture.

In spite of the many confounding variables in this report, it led many to suggest that screening studies are not cost-effective because of the low rate of expansion and rupture.

Subsequently, a number of investigators reported relatively small or pilot studies for detection of AAAs in asymptomatic patients in general practices.[19,40-43] As indicated previously, some of these reports suffer from hospital-based referral practices that could skew results, but many were community-based involving patients referred by family practitioners. The results of these small, general population studies are shown in Table 3.1.

Table 3.1. AAA prevalence in small general population studies

Ref	1st author	Year	Location	# Aortas visualized	Population Men & Women	AAAs ≥ 3 cm, Number (%)			
						Total	3-4 cm	4-5 cm	5-6+ cm
40	Scott	1988	Chichester, UK	1312	60-80 y.o.	76(5.8)	—	—	—
41	Scott	1991	Chichester, UK	4122	65-80 y.o.	179(4.3)	124(3)	30(0.7)	25(0.6)
19	Akkersdijk	1991	Hague, Netherlands	1687	50-89 y.o.	82(4.9)[1]	—	—	—
42	Brown	1996	Kingston, Ontario	492	40-89 y.o.	NS[2] 211	249	NS	
43	Kahn	1996	Milwaukee, WI	343	20-80 y.o.	75(19%)[3]			

1 11.4% in Men > 60 y.o.
2 Patients followed for enlarged aortas
3 Patients having US for clinical suspected AAA

Screening Older Men for AAAs

The prevalence of AAAs and incidence of rupture of AAAs is greater for men than women in virtually all reported studies. This has led to the strategy of screening men—particularly older men—for asymptomatic AAAs.[44,49] One particularly interesting longitudinal study, the Whitehall Study, based in London, U.K., examined 18,403 male civil servants at age 40-46 years.[50] Although routine ultrasonography was not performed, death certificates for all enrollees were reviewed. There were 99 deaths attributed to aortic aneurysm during 18 years of follow-up. Hypertension and smoking were strongly associated with death from AAAs, whereas height, adiposity, plasma cholesterol, diabetes, angina, or intermittent claudication were not risk factors. Table 3.2 summarizes the results of AAA screening studies of older men.

Screening Selected Populations at Risk for AAAs

The cost-effectiveness of screening for AAAs may be improved by identifying selected populations at risk for this disorder (Table 3.3). For example, patients with hypertension or coronary artery disease may have high prevalences of AAAs, because these diseases are frequently present in patients who are found to have AAAs.[51] Although hypertensive patients may be more likely to develop AAAs, reports are conflicting. One European study indicated a 75 prevalence of AAAs in hypertensive men over 50,[52] whereas an investigation in Sweden found only one of 245 hypertensive patients had an aneurysm (0.4%).[53] About five per cent of individuals with symptomatic coronary artery disease have aneurysms.[36,54]

In addition, screening relatives of patients with AAAs discloses more aneurysms than screening unselected populations. In 1977, Clifton reported increased likelihood of developing AAAs in first order relative, describing a family in which all three male siblings had undergone operation for ruptured aneurysms.[55] In a Swedish study, 87 siblings from 32 different families of AAA patients underwent US screening.[56] Their median age was 63 years (range 39-82). Aortic dilatation (> 29 mm) was found in ten brothers (29%) and three sisters (6%). These results were confirmed by Adamson et al in the U.K. who screened 28 families (25 brothers and 28 sisters) of patients with known AAAs.[57] Aneurysms were significantly more likely to occur in smokers, male relatives, and when probands were relatively young (< 60 years of age). Similar findings were reported by Webster and associates in Pittsburgh.[58] These investigators screened 103 first-degree relatives of patients with AAAs. Of siblings aged 55 years or older 5/20 men (25% and 2/29 women (6.9%) were found to have a previously undiagnosed abdominal aortic aneurysm. Verloes and associates studied familial and genetic aspects of AAAs in 313 multigenerational pedigrees of patients with AAAs.[59] Although routine US screening was not performed, information was obtained by questionnaire and telephone inquiry. There were 276 sporadic cases 9264 men, 12 women; 81 cases belonged to multiplex pedigrees. Compared to sporadic cases of AAAs, familial AAAs occurred in younger individuals, ruptured at younger ages, and had a substantially greater risk of rupture (32.4% vs 8.7% (p < 0.0001). Relative risk for male siblings of a male proband was 18. The reader is encouraged to review Table 3.3 of this manuscript, which provides a wealth of data regarding different studies of pedigrees of patients with AAAs.

Table 3.2. AAA prevalence in men by ultrasound screening

Ref	1st author	Year	Location	# Aortas visualized	Population	AAAs ≥ 3 cm, Number (%)			
						Total	3-4 cm	4-5 cm	5-6+ cm
44	Collin	1988	Oxford, UK	426	65-74 y.o. men	23(5.4)	11(2.6)	10(2.3)	5(2.5)
45	Lederle	1988	Minneapolis, MN	201	60-75 y.o. male veterans HTN CAD[1]	18(9)	8(4)	5(2.5)	5(2.5)
46	O'Kelly	1989	Stroud, UK	906	65-74 y.o. men in family practitioner registry	71(7.8)[2]	—	14(1.5)	—
47	Bengtsson	1991	Malmo, Sweden	364	Men born in 1914 from Malmo, Sweden	39(10.7)[3]			
48	Krohn	1992	Oslo, Norway	500	60-89 y.o. men in Norwegian HMO	41(8.2)[4]			
49	Smith	1993	Birmingham, UK	2597	65-75 y.o. men in an urban community	219(8.4)[5]			

1 HTN = Hypertension; CAD + Coronary Artery Disease
2 AAA defined as ≥ 2.5 cm
3 AAA defined as 25-70 mm; 3.3% had AAAs > 4 cm
4 5.8% "small" (3 cm) AAA; 2.4% "large" AAA (≥ 4 cm)
5 AAA defined as > 29 mm; 79 (3.0%) had aortic diameters > 4.0 cm

Table 3.3. Screening populations at special risk for AAAs

Ref	1st author	Year	Location	# Aortas visualized	Population	AAAs ≥ 3 cm, Number (%) Total	3-4 cm	4-5 cm	5-6+ cm
53	Lindholm	1985	Lund, Sweden	245	Men and women 50-70 y.o. with hypertension	1(0.4)			
52	Twomey	1986	Italy	200	Men > 50 with hypertension	14(7)			
36	Thurmond	1988	Portland, OR	120	≥ 50 y.o. men and women in cardiology clinic	27(23)	21(18)	6(5)[1]	—
56	Bengtsson	1989	Malmo, Sweden	87	39-82 y.o. siblings of AAA patients[2]	13(15)	10(12)	1(1)	2(2)
57	Adamson	1992	London, UK	53	43-83 y.o. siblings of AAA patients[3]	6(11)	—	—	—
58	Webster	1992	Pittsburgh, PA	103	1st degree relatives of AAA patients[3]	7(7)[4]	—	—	—
59	Verloes	1996	Liege, Belgium	313 pedigrees	Questionnaire and phone inquiries, not US of 1st degree relatives of AAA patients	18[5]			

1   > 4 cm
2   29% in brothers, 6% in sisters
3   Significant association with smoking, male sex and proband age < 60
4   Includes "focal bulge" as small as 1.9 cm; incidence increased to 25% in men > 55 y.o.
5   Relative risk for male siblings with a male proband (see text)

3

Subsequent studies confirmed the observation that AAAs can be familial, generating elegant research involving the molecular genetics of arterial aneurysms.[60,61] Genes responsible for synthesis and degradation of collagen and elastin are fundamental focal points in this research. Investigators have suggested that autosomal dominant, autosomal recessive, and sex-linked inheritance modes of transmission are possible.[62] About 18% of patients with AAAs have a first degree relative also affected.[7,63] In Marfan's syndrome, which is associated with arterial dilations and dissections of the entire aorta, mutations in the fibrillin-1 gene (FBN1) on chromosome 15 have been identified.[64] In patients with Ehlers-Danlos syndrome, who are at risk for sudden death from rupture of large arteries, defects in they type III collagen gene (COL3A1) have been described.[65]

Screening Subjects with Other Manifestations of PAD

The coexistence of other vascular disorders in the study population substantially increases the prevalence of aortic aneurysms (Table 3.4). Roughly, 10% of patients with peripheral or cerebrovascular disease have AAAs.[66-68] Patients with peripheral arterial aneurysms (especially those involving the popliteal artery) have a prevalence of aortic aneurysms approaching 50%.[69] Galland and colleagues in Great Britain performed abdominal US examinations in 242 patients with peripheral vascular disease.[70] AAAs were found in 34 (14%); half of these aneurysms were > 4 cm in diameter. The presence of aortoiliac disease increased the likelihood of AAA. In another study from the U.K., 104 patients with claudication or rest pain were surveyed for AAA.[71] Eight (7.7%) aneurysms were discovered ranging from 2.8-6.9 cm in diameter. Allardice et al, also in the U.K., screened one hundred consecutive patients with claudication compared with a control group.[68] In the control group the incidence of AAA was 2%. In the study group, 20% of the men and 12% of the women had aortic aneurysms or ectasia. Of note, of the abnormal aortas identified by US, only 31% were palpable. Bengtsson and associates in Malmo, Sweden, screened 372 patients with claudication for AAAs, using abdominal US in 183 patients.[72] The overall frequency of AAAs was 13.7%. More recently, Carty et al found that hemodynamically significant carotid artery disease was a definite marker for an increased incidence of abdominal aortic aneurysm in a prospective study of 131 patients.[73] Eleven infrarenal aneurysms (8.4%) were detected; four in patients with positive carotid studies (11%) and seven in those with negative studies (7%). Size ranged from 3.0-7.5 cm.

Large Scale Screening Programs for AAA

Six large-scale screening programs (three combined with trials to investigate the prognosis and optimal management of small asymptomatic AAAs) were introduced in this decade in The Netherlands, United Kingdom, Canada, and the United States. Although follow-up regimens and precise size differed, the studies are quite similar in design. The Canadian Small Aneurysm Trial has been discontinued because of inadequate patient accrual, and it will not be discussed.

The Rotterdam Study is a prospective follow-up study designated to investigate determinants of the occurrence and progression of chronic diseases in the elderly.[74]

Table 3.4. AAA prevalence in patients with additional manifestations of PAD

Ref	1st author	Year	Location	# Aortas visualized	Population	AAAs ≥ 3 cm, Number (%) Total	3-4 cm	4-5 cm	5-6+ cm
67	Allardice	1988	London, UK	100	Men and women with symptomatic PAD[1]	10(10)	—	—	—
71	Bengtsson	1989	Malmo, Sweden	183	34-74 y.o. men and women with claudication[2]	25(14)	—	—	—
70	Berridge	1989	Nottingham, UK	104	Men and women with claudication and rest pain	8(7.7)[3]	—	—	—
69	Galland	1991	Reading, UK	242	38-95 y.o. men and women with claudication and rest pain	34(14)[4]	17(7)	10(4)	7(3)
72	Carty	1993	Saginaw, USA	131	40-93 y.o. men and women with carotid disease	11(8.4)[5]	8(6)	—	3(2.4)

1 PAD defined as peripheral arterial disease invclving either the lower extremities (claudication [82%], rest pain [11%]) or cerebrovascular disease [2%]
2 AAA defined as > 29 mm
3 AAA defined as ≥ 3.5 cm or > 5 mm that adjacent vessel
4 AAA defined as > 3.5 cm or > 1.5 times the aorta at the level of the renal arteries
5 AAA defined as at least 3 cm in diameter

A total of 10,215 men and women aged 55 and older who live in this district have been invited by their general practitioners to enter a study; overall response rate was 78%. To assess the age-and sex-specific prevalence and risk factors for AAAs 5,419 subjects (42% men; 58% women) underwent abdominal ultrasonography (5,285 aortas visualized). An aneurysm (defined as a distal aortic diameter of 35 mm or more or a dilatation of the distal aorta of 50% or more) occurred in 2.1% of the study population (4.1% in men; 0.7% in women). Subjects with an AAA were more likely to be smokers and they had higher serum cholesterol levels and higher prevalence of cardiovascular disease compared with subjects without AAAs.

Another U.K. study took place in the Huntingdon District of Cambridge and Huntingdon. During a 5-year period from 1991-1996, 13,148 men were screened by ultrasonography (with a 74% response rate and an additional 6% lost to follow-up).[28] In all, 469 (3.5%) small AAAs (diameter between 3.0 and 4.5 cm) were found and 58 (0.4%) large AAA (diameter > 4.5 cm) were detected. During the 5-year period, there were 78 ruptured AAAs (62 in men; 16 in women). Death rates from ruptured AAAs were significantly greater in those unscreened than those screened.

Scott and associates have been leaders in screening programs for AAAs. Several of their previous studies have been discussed.[34,40,41] Their largest investigation of the influence of screening on the incidence of ruptured AAAs—a 5-year randomized controlled study—involved 15,775 men and women aged 65-80 years.[75] These patients were randomized to US screening for AAAs versus an age-and sex-matched control group. Of the 7887 invited for screening, 5394 (64.4%) accepted. AAAs were found in 218 (4.0% overall and 7.6% in men). The incidence of rupture was reduced by 55% in men in the group invited for screening, compared with controls. The incidence of rupture in women was low in both groups.

The UK small Aneurysm Trial, similar to the US Department of Veterans Affairs Study, was designated to determine the optimal treatment strategy for small AAAs (4.0-5.4 cm in diameter).[76] 1090 patients aged 60-76 years with asymptomatic AAAs (4.0-5.5 cm in diameter) were randomized to early elective surgery (n = 563) or ultrasonographic surveillance (n = 527) 30-day operative mortality in the early-surgery group was 5-8%, which led to a survival disadvantage for these patients early in the trial. The authors concluded that open surgical repair for AAAs of 4.0-5.5 cm in diameter is not indicated. A thoughtful editorial about this report was written by Cronenwett and Johnston.[77] In brief, they pointed out:

1. the 5.8% elective operative mortality was disappointing and higher than the 2% mortality projected in the study design;
2. the rupture risk of these small aneurysms was low—1% per year; the UK trial did suggest that early surgery was more beneficial in the subgroup of patients with 4.9-5.5 cm AAAs;
3. optimal life expectancy did not play a role in patient selection.

The U.S. small aneurysm study is designated by the acronym ADAM (Aneurysm Detection and Management) and the details of the study design have been reported.[78] This prospective randomized clinical trial is being carried out by the Department of Veterans Affairs Cooperative Studies Program in 15 VA Medical Centers with proven track records in aneurysm surgery. In brief, aneurysms discovered

Table 3.5. AAA prevalence in large general population studies

Ref	1st author	Year	Location	# Aortas visualized	Population	AAAs ≥ 3 cm, Number (%) Total	3-4 cm	4-5 cm	5-6+ cm
74	Pleumeekers	1995	Rotterdam, Netherlands	5283	> 50 y.o. men and women	112(2.1)[1]	153(2.9)	53(1%)	32(0.6%)
28	Teun	1999	Huntingdon, UK	9658[2]	50-90 y.o. mostly men	469(4.8%)	124(3)	30(0.7)	25(0.6)
75	Scott	1995	Chichester, UK	5394	65-80 y.o. men and women claudication and rest pain	218(4.0)[3]	138(2.5)	46(0.09)	34(0.06)
76	The UK Aneurysm Trial Participants[4]	1998	93 UK hospitals	1090 AAAs	60-76 y.o. men and women	5.8% early operative mortality			
79	Lederle	1997	VAMC Multicenter, USA	73,451	50-79 y.o. men and some women	1031(1.4%)[5]			

1 AAA defined as 35 mm >50% distal aortic dilatation: 4.1% incidence in men, 0.7% in women;
2 Includes 25 no-response rate, 6% lost to follow-up rate, and nonvisualized aorta of 13,147 originally invited men; 78 ruptured AAAs (62 in men; 16 in women)
3 7.6% incidence in men; incidence of rupture reduced by 55% in screened men compared with controls
4 1090 patients with known small AAAs randomized to early surgery or serial follow-up; early surgery provided no long-term advantage
5 AAA 4 cm or larger

by US screening are categorized by size. Patients with AAAs 3.0-3.9 cm are followed using serial abdominal ultrasonography. Patients with aneurysms measuring 4.0-5.4 cm in diameter (as confirmed by CT scan) are carefully evaluated with respect to operative risk. If they are good candidates for operative repair, these patients are randomized to expeditious elective surgery or serial ultrasonography/CT scans. Patients in this group, designated "selective surgery," are offered operative repair of AAAs if they expand rapidly, enlarge to 5.5 cm or become symptomatic. Aneurysms of 5.5 cm are offered an elective repair unless they are unqualified for operation because of comorbid conditions. The primary outcome measure is all cause death, and secondary outcome measures are AAA-related death, morbidity, and general health status. Although the final results of the U.S. study will not be known until the year 2,000 prevalence and associations of AAAs detected through screening have been reported.[79] This is the largest and most thoroughly analyzed screening study published to date. In brief, an AAA of 4.0 cm or larger was detected in 1031 (1.4%) of 73,451 veterans aged 50-79 years of age with no history of AAA. Smoking was the risk factor most strongly associated with AA. Female gender, black race, and presence of diabetes were negatively associated with AAA.

Table 3.5 (found on opposite page) demonstrates the variability in the frequency of identification of aortic aneurysms in large-scale screening programs. The discrepancy in prevalence can be attributed largely to differences in definitions of aneurysms and—most importantly—variance in the populations studied. Owing to economic considerations, it is unlikely that mass population screening will ever be implemented. However, based on available data, the individual physician should carefully consider recommending US screening for AAAs in first degree relatives of patients with aneurysms (over age 50), and patients over 50 with hypertension, coronary artery disease, and peripheral vascular disease—particularly if body habitus makes aortic palpation difficult.

Conclusion

In summary, consideration should be given to screening those with a family history of aneurysm, patients between 55 and 80 with peripheral vascular disease, elderly make cigarette smokers, and those with known extremity artery aneurysms, such as popliteal and femoral. However, cost-effectiveness of any specific screening strategy remains to be established.

Selected Readings

1. Lederle FA, Johnson GR, Wilson SE et al for the Aneurysm detection and management (ADAM) Veterans Affairs Cooperative Study Group: Prevalence and associations of abdominal aortic aneurysm detected through screening. Ann Int Med 1997; 126:441-49.
2. Veroles A, Sakalihasan N, Koulischer L et al. Aneurysms of the abdominal aorta: Familial and genetic aspects in three hundred thirteen pedigrees. J Vas Surg 1995; 21:646-55.
3. Chervu A, Clagett GP, Valentine RJ et al. Role of physical examination in detection of abdominal aortic aneurysms. Surgery 1995; 117:454-7.

4. Lederle FA, Wilson SE, Johnson GR et al. Variability in measurement of abdominal aortic aneurysms. J Vasc Surg 1995; 21:945-52.

5. Scott RAP, Ashton HA. Abdominal aortic aneurysms screening: acceptance rates, false negative rates, and age-related incidence in 21116 patients. Br J Surg 1993; 80:518.

6. Darling RC, Messina CR, Brewster DC et al. Autopsy study of unoperated abdominal aortic aneurysms. The case for early resection. Circulation 1977; 56(Suppl II): II-161-II-167.

7. Johnsen K, Koepsell T. Familial tendency for abdominal aortic aneurysms. JAMA 1986; 256:1934-1936.

8. Johnson G Jr, Avery A, Mcdougal G et al. Aneurysms of the abdominal aorta: Incidence in blacks and whites in North Carolina Arch Surg 1985; 120:1138-1142.

9. Leopold GR, Goldberger LE, Bernstein EF. Ultrasonic detection and evaluation of abdominal aortic aneurysms. Surgery 1972; 939:939-943.

10. Lilienfield CE, Gunderson PD, Sprafka JM et al. Epidemiology of aortic aneurysms: 1. Mortality trends in the United States, 1951-1981. Arteriosclerosis 1987; 7:637-643.

11. Melton LJ, Bickerstaff LK, Hollier LH et al. Changing incidence of abdominal aortic aneurysms: A population-based study. Am J Epidemiol 1984; 120:379-386.

12. Wheeler HB. Myth and reality in general surgery. Bull Am Coll Surg 1993; 78:21-27.

13. Bickerstaff LK, Hollier LH, Van Peenen HJ et al. Abdominal aortic aneurysms: The changing natural history. J Vasc Surg 1984; 1:6-12.

14. Ernst CB. Abdominal aortic aneurysms. N Engl J Med 1993; 328:1167-1172.

15. Bengtsson H, Bergqvist D, Sternby NH. Increasing prevalence of abdominal aortic aneurysm: A necropsy study. Eur J Surg 1992: 158;19-23.

16. Fowkes FR, Macintyre CCA, Ruckley CV. Increasing incidence of aortic aneurysms in England and Wales. BMJ 1989; 298:33-35.

17. Castleden VM, Mercer JC. Abdominal aortic aneurysms in Western Australia: Descriptive epidemiology and patterns of rupture. Br J Surg 1985; 72:109-112.

18. Stern MP. The recent decline in ischemic heart disease mortality. Ann Intern Med 1979; 91:630-636.

19. Akkersdik GJM, Puylaert JBCM, de Vries AC. Abdominal aortic aneurysm as an incidental finding in abdominal ultrasonography. Br J Surg 1991; 78:1261-63.

20. Bernstein EF, Dilley RB, Randolph HFIII. The improving outlook for patients over 70 years of age with abdominal aortic aneurysms. Ann Surg 1988; 207:318-21.

21. Crawford ES, Saleh SA, Babb JW III et al. Infrarenal abdominal aortic aneurysm: Factors influencing survival after operation performed over a 25-year period. Ann Surg 1981; 193:699-702.

22. Multirangura P, Stonebridge PA, Clason AE et al. Ten-year review of nonruptured aortic aneurysms. Br J Surg 1989; 76:1251-4.

23. Collin J. Screening for abdominal aortic aneurysms. Br J Surg 1985; 72:851-853.

24. Periodic health examination. 1991 update: 5. Screening for abdominal aortic aneurysms. Can Med Assoc J 1991: 145:783-89.

25. Harris PL. Reducing the mortality from abdominal aortic aneurysms: Need for a national screening programme. Br Med J 1992; 305: 697-99.

26. U.S. Preventive Services Task Force: Guide to clinical preventative services, 2nd Ed. Baltimore: Williams and Wilkins, 1996.

27. Scott RA, Wilson NM, Ashton H et al. Influence of screening on the incidence of ruptured abdominal aortic aneurysms: 5-year results of a randomized controlled series. Br J Surg 1995; 82:1066-70.

28. Teun BM, Wilmink MD, Quick CRG et al. The influence of screening on the incidence of ruptured abdominal aortic aneurysms. J Vasc Surg 1999; 30:203-8.

29. Pasch AR, Ricotta JJ, May AG et al. Abdominal aortic aneurysm: The case for elective resection. Circulation 1984; 70 Suppl I; I-1-I-4.

30. Breckwoldt WL, Mackey WC, O'Donnell TF Jr. The economic implications of high-risk abdominal aortic aneurysms. J Vasc Surg 1991; 13:798-804.

31. Quill DS, Colgan MP, Summer DS. Ultrasonic screening for the detection of abdominal aortic aneurysms. Surg Clin North Am 1989; 69:713-720.

32. Frame PS, Fryback DG, Patterson C. Screening for abdominal aortic aneurysms in men ages 60-80 years: A cost-effective analysis. Ann Intern Med 1993; 119:411-416.

33. Richardson EL. The creative balance. New York: Holt, Rinehart and Winston 1977:138.

34. Scott RAP. Ultrasound screening in the management of abdominal aortic aneurysms. Int Angiol 1986; 5:263-266.

35. Collin J. Screening for abdominal aortic aneurysms. Br J Surg 1985; 72:851-853.

36. Thurnmond AS, Semler HJ. Abdominal aortic aneurysm: Incidence in a population at risk. J Cardiovasc Surg 1986; 27: 457-460.

37. Nevitt MP, Ballard DJ, Hallett JW. Prognosis of abdominal aortic aneurysms: A population-based study. N Engl J Med 1989; 321: 1009-14.

38. Bernstein EF, Chan EL. Abdominal aortic aneurysm in high-risk patients: Outcome of selective management based on size and expansion rate. Ann Surg 1984; 200:255-63.

39. Cronenwett JL, Murphy TF, Zelenock GB et al. Actuarial analysis of variables associated with rupture of small abdominal aortic aneurysms. Surgery 1985; 98:472-83.

40. Scott RAP, Asshton HA, Kay DN. Routine ultrasound screening in management of abdominal aortic aneurysm. BMJ 1988; 296:1709-1710.

41. Scott RAP, Ashton HA, Kay DN. Abdominal aortic aneurysm in 437 screened patients: prevalence, development and management over 6 years. Br J Surg 1991; 78:1122-1125.

42. Brown PM, Pattenden R, Vernooy C et al. Selective management of abdominal aortic aneurysms in a prospective measurement program. J Vasc Surg 1996; 23:213-22.

43. Kahn CE, Quiroz FA. Positive predictive value of clinical suspicion for abdominal aortic aneurysm. J Gen Intern Med 1996; 11:756-8.

44. Collin J, Walton J, Araujo L et al. Oxford screening programme for abdominal aortic aneurysm in men aged 65-74 years. Lancet 1988; 2:613-15.

45. Lederle FA, Walker JM, Reinke DB. Selective screening for abdominal aortic aneurysms with physical examination and ultrasound. Arch Intern Med 1988; 148:1753-56.

46. O'Kelly TJ, Heather BP. General practice-based population screening for abdominal aortic aneurysm: A pilot study. Br J Surg 1989; 76:479-80.

47. Bengtson H, Bergqvist D, Ekberg O et al. A population based screening of abdominal aortic aneurysms (AAA). Eur J Vasc Surg 1991; 5:53-57.

48. Krohn CD, Kullmann G, Kvernebo K et al. Ultrasonographic screening for abdominal aortic aneurysm. Eur J Surg 1992; 158:527-30.

3

49. Smith FCT, Grimshaw GM, Paterson IS et al. Ultrasonic screening for abdominal aortic aneurysm in an urban community. Br J Surg 1993; 80:1406-9.

50. Strachan DP. Predictors of death from aortic aneurysm among middle-aged men: The Whitehall Study. Br J Surg 1991; 78:401-404.

51. Spittell JA. Hypertension and arterial aneurysm. J Am Coll Cardiol 1983; 1:533-40.

52. Twomey A, Twomey E, Wilkins RA et al. Unrecognized aneurysmal disease in male hypertensive patients. Int Angiol 1986; 5:269-271.

53. Lindholm L, Ejlertsson G, Forsberg L et al. Low prevalence of abdominal aortic aneurysm in hypertensive patients: A population based study. Acta Med Scand 1985; 218:305-307.

54. Cabellong S Jr, Moncrief CL, Pierre DR et al. Incidence of abdominal aortic aneurysms in patients with atheromatous arterial disease. Am J Surg 1983; 146:575-579.

55. Clifton MA. Familial abdominal aortic aneurysms. Br J Surg 1977; 64:765-766.

56. Bengtsson H, Norrgard O, Angquist KA et al. Ultrasonic screening of the abdominal aorta among siblings of patients with abdominal aortic aneurysms. Br J Surg 1989; 76:589-591.

57. Adamson J, Powell JT, Greenhalgh RM. Selection for screening for familial aortic aneurysms. Br J Surg 1992; 79:897-898.

58. Webster MW, Ferrell RE, St. Jean PL et al. Ultrasound screening of first-degree relatives of patients with an abdominal aortic aneurysm. J Vasc Surg 1991; 3:9-14.

59. Verloes A, Sakalihasan L, Koulischer L et al. Aneurysms of the abdominal aorta: Familial and genetic aspect in three hundred thirteen pedigrees. J Vasc Surg 1995; 121:646-55.

60. Tilson MD, Seashore. Fifty families with abdominal aortic aneurysms in two or more first-order relatives. Am J Surg 1984; 147:551-553.

61. Norrgard O, Angquist KA, Rais O. Familial occurrence of abdominal aortic aneurysms. Surgery 1984; 95:650-656.

62. Tilson MD, Seashore MR. Human Genetics of abdominal aortic aneurysm. Surg Gynecol Obstet 1984; 158:129-132.

63. Webster MW, St Jean PL, Steed DL et al. Abdominal aortic aneurysm: Result of a family study. J Vasc Surg 1991; 13:366-372.

64. Lee B, Godfrey M, Vitale E et al. Linkage of Marfan syndrome and a phenotypically related disorder to two different fibrillin gene. Nature 1991; 352:330-334.

65. Kuivaniemi H, Trompt G, Prockop DJ. Mutations in collagen genes; causes of rare and some common diseases in humans. FASEB J 1991; 5:2025-2026.

66. Cabellon S Jr, Moncrief CL, Pierre DR et al. Incidence of abdominal aortic aneurysms in patients with atheromatous arterial disease. Am J Surg 1983; 146:575-579.

67. Graham M, Chan A. Ultrasound screening for clinically occult abdominal aortic aneurysm. Can Med Assoc J 1988; 138:627-630.

68. Allardice JT, Allwright GJ, Wafula JMC et al. High prevalence of abdominal aortic aneurysm in men with peripheral vascular disease: Screening by ultrasonography. Br J Surg 1988; 75:240-242.

69. Anton GE, Hertzer NR, Beven EG et al. Surgical management of popliteal aneurysms: Trends in presentation, treatment, and results from 1952-1984. J Vasc Surg 1986; 3:125-131.

70. Galland RB, Simmons MJ, Torrie EPH. Prevalence of abdominal aortic aneurysm in patients with occlusive peripheral vascular disease. Br J Surg 1991; 78:1259-1260.

71.   Berridge DC, Griffith CDM, Amar SS et al. Screening for clinically unsuspected abdominal aortic aneurysms in patients with peripheral vascular disease. Eur J Vasc Surg 1989; 3:421-422.

72.   Bergstsson H, Ekberg O, Aspelin P et al. Ultrasound screening of the abdominal aorta in patients with intermittent claudication. Eur J Vasc Surg 1989; 3:497-502.

73.   Carty GA, Nachtigal T, Magyar R et al. Abdominal duplex ultrasound screening for occult aortic aneurysm during carotid arterial evaluation. J Vasc Surg 1993; 17:696-702.

74.   Pleumeekers HJC M, Hoes AW, van der Does E et al. Aneurysms of the abdominal aorta in older adults: The Rotterdam study. Am J Epidemiol 1995; 142:1291-9.

75.   Scott RAP, Wilson M, Ashton A et al. Influence of screening on the incidence of ruptured abdominal aortic aneurysm: 5-year results of a randomized controlled study. Br J Surg 1995; 82:1066-70.

76.   The UK small Aneurysm Trial Participants. Mortality results for randomized controlled trial of early elective surgery or ultrasonographic surveillance for small abdominal aortic aneurysms. Lancet 1998; 352:1649-1655.

77.   Cronenwett JL, Johnston KW. The United Kingdom Small Aneurysm Trial: Implications for surgical treatment of abdominal aortic aneurysms. J Vasc Surg 29:191-3.

78.   Lderle FA, Wilson SE, Johnson GR et al. Design of the abdominal aortic aneurysm detection and management study. J Vasc Surg 1994; 20:296-303.

79.   Lederle FA, Johnson GR, Wilson SE et al. Prevalence and associations of abdominal aortic aneurysm detected through screening. Ann Int Med 1997; 126:441-49.

CHAPTER 4

The Pathophysiology of Aortic Dissection

James I. Fann and D. Craig Miller

Aortic dissection is a common cardiovascular catastrophe, affecting upwards of 9000 patients annually in the United States.[1-5] Even with modern diagnostic modalities, a substantial fraction of patients with aortic dissection die without a correct diagnosis. Untreated, acute aortic dissection is highly lethal with a mortality of 8% within the first 6 hours, 13% within 12 hours, 21% within 24 hours, and 74% in the first 2 weeks. Therefore, it is of paramount importance that the physician maintain a high index of suspicion for this condition, so that appropriate therapy can be promptly instituted.

Although there were multiple postmortem reports of this entity in the 16th century, the first comprehensive account of aortic dissection was provided by Morgagni in 1761. In 1819, Laennec named this disorder aneurysm dissequant, or dissecting aneurysm, a misnomer since true aneurysm formation is not the primary process; thus, the more accurate term is aortic dissection. Early attempts at treatment of aortic dissection were generally unsuccessful. In 1955, DeBakey and colleagues described the modern surgical approach to aortic dissection using graft replacement.[6] In 1965, Wheat et al stressed the importance of pharmacologic management of patients with aortic dissection.[7]

This chapter focuses on the etiology and pathophysiology of aortic dissection and briefly describes conventional surgical and endovascular approaches to acute aortic dissection.

Classification and Etiology

Aortic dissection classification is extremely important since the pathophysiology and optimal therapy of these patients are predominantly determined by the acuity and type of dissection.[2] Aortic dissection involving the ascending aorta regardless of the distal extent are termed type A (Stanford), ascending, or type I/II (DeBakey) (Fig. 4.1). Those without ascending aortic involvement are considered type B (Stanford), descending, or type III (DeBakey). Aortic dissection is considered acute if onset of symptoms occurred within 14 days of presentation and chronic if greater than 14 days.

Three mechanisms have been implicated in the development of aortic dissection.[4,5,8] Firstly, aortic dissection often results from an initial intimal tear with secondary extension into the media, thereby separating the intima from adventitia. Once blood enters the aortic media, the time required for the pulsatile flow to dissect the entire aorta may be extremely brief. Multiple hemodynamic and physical factors

---

Aortic Surgery, edited by Jeffrey L. Ballard. ©2000 Landes Bioscience.

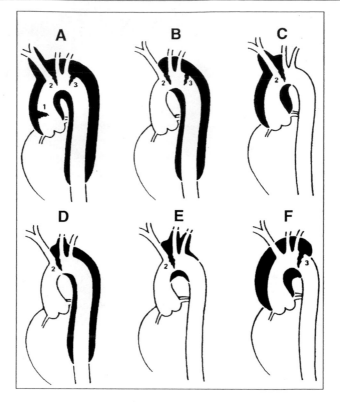

Fig. 4.1. Illustrations of different types of aortic dissections. Examples a, c, and f are considered Stanford type A aortic dissections (involvement of the ascending aorta). Note that the primary intimal tear may be located in the ascending aorta (a-1), transverse arch (a-2, c-2) or proximal descending thoracic aorta (f-3). Examples b, d, and e are considered Stanford type B dissections; that is, the ascending aorta is not involved. The intimal tear may originate in the arch (b-2, d-2, e-2) or the descending thoracic aorta (b-3). (Modified from Miller DC. Surgical management of aortic dissections: Indications, perioperative management, and long-term results. In: Doroghazi RM, Slater EE, eds. Aortic Dissection. New York: McGraw-Hill, 1983: 193-243.)

lead to the initial development and subsequent propagation of the dissection. These include the rate of rise of systolic pressure, diastolic recoil pressure, mean arterial pressure, and structural integrity of the media. Extension of the dissection requires underlying medial laxity and/or degeneration.[4,5] Although this particular mechanism is common and thought to be the main cause of aortic dissection, an intimal tear by itself does not necessarily lead to aortic dissection, and a dissecting hematoma may develop without a defined intimal tear. An important, but less common, etiology for the development of aortic dissection is hemorrhage due to ruptured vasa vasorum into a diseased media followed by propagation along the course of the aorta; a secondary intimal may or may not develop.[4,5,8] Hirst et al found that 4% of patients had no identifiable intimal tear in a series of 505 autopsy cases of aortic dissection.[7] Distinct features of "aortic dissection without intimal rupture" on imaging studies, such as computer tomographic scan (CT), magnetic resonance imaging (MRI) and/or transesophageal echocardiography (TEE), are the lack of an intimal tear and the presence of an intramural hematoma (IMH).[8] The natural history of IMH is unpredictable; it can heal with little evidence of a previous medial disruption, or it can progress to frank aortic dissection years later. Finally, a third and rare mechanism of localized aortic dissection is the result of penetrating atherosclerotic ulcer extending through the intima with resultant hematoma formation within the media. CT demonstrates intimal disruption with an ulcer, a localized hematoma and limited propagation of the false lumen. In contrast to conventional type B aortic dissection, where the intimal defect is typically located immediately distal to the left subclavian artery, dissection due to a penetrating atherosclerotic ulcer usually originates in the mid or distal descending thoracic aorta.

Aortic dissection is more common in men than women with a ratio of 3 to 1. A common predisposing factor for the development of aortic dissection is hypertension.[2-5] Because the tensile strength of the aortic wall is partly dependent on the media, processes (e.g., hypertension) that accelerate the degeneration of medial components, such as elastic tissue and smooth muscle cells, may lead to development of aortic dissection. Other risk factors for aortic dissection include heritable connective tissue disorders (e.g., the Marfan syndrome) and congenital anomalies (e.g., bicuspid aortic valve and aortic coarctation). In some cases, a mutation on chromosome 15 of the fibrillin-1 (FBN-1) gene has been found in patients with the Marfan syndrome.[9] Fibrillin, a structural component of connective tissue microfibrils, is important in maintaining the integrity of the aorta as well as a variety of organ systems. Other genetic and autoimmune disorders, such as Turner's syndrome, Noonan's syndrome, polycystic kidney disease, giant-cell aortitis, systemic lupus, and relapsing polychondritis, are associated with aortic dissection. Iatrogenic aortic dissection occurs infrequently in the region of aortic cross-clamp placement, aortotomy or site of vein graft anastomosis. Although blunt chest trauma may lead to aortic dissection, the extent of dissection in a structurally normal aorta is usually limited.

Pathophysiology

Type A dissection, seen in relatively younger patients, is usually associated with elastic tissue degeneration and an underlying connective tissue abnormality. More common in older patients, type B dissection is usually associated with degeneration and loss of medial smooth muscle cells. Approximately 60-70% of all cases of aortic dissection involve the ascending aorta (type A dissection). Typically, the intimal tear occurs just distal to the sino-tubular ridge, corresponding to the cephalad extension of the aortic valve commissures.[4,5] The intimal tear is generally transverse and involves one-half to two-thirds of the aortic circumference and rarely the entire aorta. The intimal tear commonly extends from the right lateral aortic wall coursing along the greater curvature of the ascending aorta. The dissection process usually propagates in a distal direction, but retrograde extension occurs not infrequently. Less commonly, occurring in approximately 25% of cases, the intimal tear originates from the descending thoracic aorta just distal to the left subclavian artery.[4,5] In approximately 10% of patients with aortic dissection, the origin is in the aortic arch; the abdominal aorta is affected rarely in 2% of cases. This distribution appears to be the reverse of atherosclerosis, the incidence of which progressively increases from the ascending to the abdominal aorta.

The most frequent cause of death in patients with aortic dissection is aortic rupture, which is often located near the site of primary intimal tear.[4,5] Because the pericardium covers the ascending aorta up to the origin of the innominate artery, rupture of any portion of the ascending aorta leads to leakage into the pericardial sac and cardiac tamponade. Aortic arch rupture tends to extend into the mediastinum. Descending thoracic aortic dissection commonly ruptures into the pleural cavity, more often on the left than right. Other important complications include retrograde propagation of the dissecting process into a coronary artery leading to acute myocardial ischemia. Dissection involving the aortic valve commissures can result in acute valvular regurgitation (Fig. 4.2). Additionally, aortic dissection may result in pulmonary artery compression and retrograde perforation into the atria or ventricles leading to aorto-atrial or aorto-ventricular fistulae.

Extension of the dissection into an artery arising from the aorta may result in compromised perfusion with ischemia or necrosis of the end-organ or tissue. Although occasionally sheared off, the true lumen of larger arteries tend to be compressed either at their origins or somewhere along their course by the false lumen. In some cases, the orifice of smaller arteries can be sheared off in such a fashion that distal blood flow originates from the false lumen and is unimpeded. Reentry sites communicating between the true and false lumen of the aortic dissection often correspond to the sheared off branch ostia. Extensive atherosclerosis or anatomic constraints, such as aortic coarctation, may limit the progression of the dissecting process.[4,5] In younger patients, aortic dissection usually involves the entire thoracic and abdominal aorta, whereas in older patients the dissection tends to be more localized, perhaps due to a greater degree of atherosclerosis. Peripheral vascular complications, including stroke, paraplegia, peripheral pulse loss, and impaired renal or visceral perfusion, occur in approximately 30-50% of patients with aortic dissection.[10-13] In a small fraction of patients with acute dissection, the process "heals" and becomes chronic.[4,5] Usually, chronic dissections have an identifiable distal reentry site, typically in the distal descending thoracic aorta, abdominal aorta or iliac artery. The natural history of the aortic false lumen includes thrombosis, endothelialization with a double-barrel aorta or aneurysm formation.

Clinical Presentation and Diagnosis

Acute aortic dissection has been termed "the great masquerader", since patients may develop symptoms suggestive of almost any other acute medical or surgical disease.[2,3] Aortic dissection should be considered in a case of abrupt arterial occlusion corresponding with an acute illness involving seemingly unrelated organ systems.

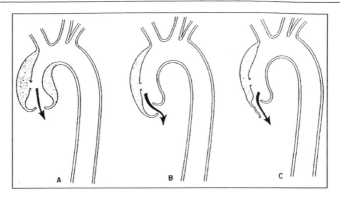

Fig. 4.2. Mechanisms of aortic regurgitation in aortic dissection. A. Circumferential tear with widening of aortic root and separation of aortic cusps. B. Displacement of one aortic cusp substantially below the level of the others by the pressure of the dissecting hematoma. C. Actual disruption of the annular leaflet support leading to a flail cusp. (Reproduced with permission from Slater EE. Aortic dissection: presentation and diagnosis. In: Doroghazi RM, Slater EE, eds. Aortic Dissection. New York: McGraw-Hill, 1983: 61-70.)

Classically, acute dissection is associated with severe, lancinating chest or interscapular pain with craniad or cephalad migration. Although the patient appears shocky with poor peripheral perfusion, the blood pressure is frequently elevated. Other symptoms and signs relate largely to which distal aortic tributaries become involved. Potentially fatal complications are those related to aortic rupture and aortic branch compression by the dissecting hematoma, leading to compromised end-organ perfusion. A complete examination of all peripheral pulses is critical, and blood pressure in both arms and legs should be assessed. A full neurologic examination is performed. If the patient is hypotensive, aortic rupture should be suspected.

The best diagnostic test is that which can be performed accurately and expeditiously in a given hospital. A chest radiograph is usually nondiagnostic. The goal of the initial diagnostic modality is to confirm the diagnosis of dissection and determine whether the ascending aorta is involved. Involvement of the ascending aorta can be determined with a high degree of accuracy using TEE, contrast-enhanced CT, MRI and aortography. TEE has emerged as a critical diagnostic tool and can determine the type and extent of the aortic dissection (Fig. 4.3). TEE remains limited in its inability to visualize the distal ascending aorta or superior transverse arch. Also, there may be artifacts leading to a falsely positive result in patients with large ascending aortas. CT is also reasonably accurate in the diagnosis of aortic dissection and can provide anatomic information for classification; however, it cannot consistently define the intimal tear (Fig. 4.4). MRI is highly accurate in the diagnosis of aortic dissection and provides delineation of the pathoanatomy (Fig. 4.5). Its main disadvantage, however, is that it cannot be performed in patients who are hemodynamically unstable and are on ventilatory support. Aortography is highly accurate in

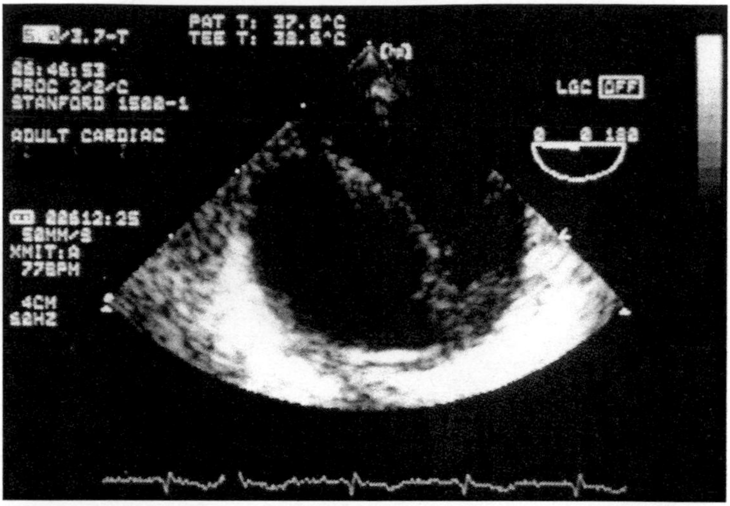

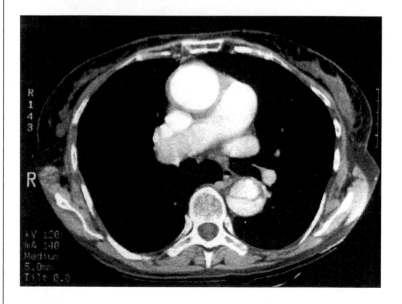

Fig. 4.3. Transesophageal echocardiographic image demonstrating a dissection flap separating the true and false lumens in a patient with acute type B dissection.

Fig. 4.4. Contrast-enhanced computed tomographic scan of a patient with an acute type B dissection.

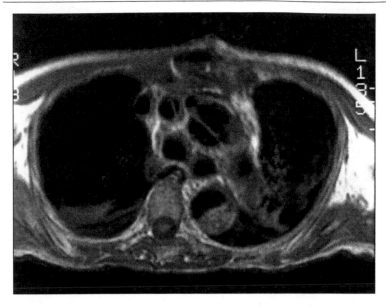

Fig. 4.5.Magnetic resonance image of a patient with acute type A dissection with involvement of the aortic arch vessels and the descending thoracic aorta.

4

the diagnosis of aortic dissection but has been largely superseded by less invasive techniques, such as TEE and MRI (Fig. 4.6). Aortography, however, provides information concerning the perfusion of aortic branches. A false negative angiogram may occur with a thrombosed false lumen, indistinct opacification of the false lumen or simultaneous opacification of the false and true lumens thereby obscuring the intimal flap.

Therapy of Acute Aortic Dissection

Acute Type A

Because of lethal complications if untreated, therapy for patients with acute type A dissection is emergency surgical replacement of the ascending aorta in essentially all cases; the few contraindications include very advanced age or other severe debilitating or terminal illnesses.[2] The surgical procedure includes ascending aortic replacement with a polyester graft and resection of the primary intimal tear, if possible. Cardiopulmonary bypass is established via femoral artery and vein cannulation. In order to avoid external cross-clamp trauma to the distal ascending aorta, we routinely employ profound hypothermic circulatory arrest with an open graft to distal ascending aortic anastomosis. After completion of the distal ascending aortic anastomosis, perfusion for cardiopulmonary bypass is achieved in an antegrade fashion to avoid the possibility of malperfusion. In acute aortic regurgitation, an attempt should be made to save the native aortic valve whenever possible, unless the patient has the

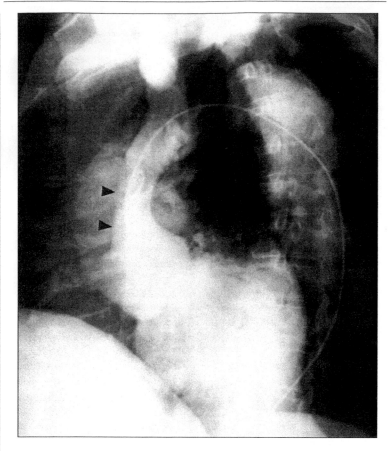

Fig. 4.6. Oblique aortogram of a patient with acute type A dissection demonstrating the intimal flap between the true and false lumens (arrows).

Marfan syndrome or severe annuloaortic ectasia, in which case concomitant aortic valve replacement should be performed. In our experience, the patient's native valve can be preserved in over 80% of patients with acute type A dissection.

In a subset of patients with acute type A dissection with preoperative malperfusion, Deeb et al[14] reported their experience with an initial endovascular approach to reperfusion, using aortic fenestration and arterial stenting where indicated, followed by surgical repair once the completely recovered from the consequences of malperfusion.[14] Mean delay to surgical repair was 20 days (range 2-67 days). Of the 20 patients undergoing this approach, 3 (15%) died preoperatively: one of retrograde dissection and rupture and 2 of reperfusion injury. Seventeen patients underwent surgical repair with two deaths yielding an operative mortality rate of 12%. Although the overall mortality was significant at 25% using this approach, they concluded that patients with an acute type A dissection and malperfusion can undergo percutaneous reperfusion, delaying surgical repair until the reperfusion injury resolves.[14]

Acute Type B

The optimal management (surgical, medical, endovascular, or a combination thereof) of patients with acute type B dissection is less clearly defined. Intensive medical therapy alone is generally advocated initially for patients with uncomplicated acute type B dissection.[15] The basis of medical treatment is the reduction of mean, peak and diastolic recoil arterial pressure and dP/dt while maintaining adequate cerebral, coronary and renal perfusion. Pharmacologic therapy includes intravenous beta-blockers (e.g., esmolol) and arterial vasodilators (e.g., sodium nitroprusside). Since nitroprusside or other arterial vasodilators can increase arterial dP/dt, concurrent administration of beta-blockers is essential. Surgery may be indicated in cases of dissection progression, impending rupture, refractory hypertension, a sizable localized false aneurysmal component, or continued pain. Partial femoral-femoral cardiopulmonary bypass is utilized, the intimal tear is resected, if possible, and the proximal descending thoracic aorta is replaced with a polyester graft. For patients with peripheral vascular complications of aortic dissection, novel endovascular techniques to stent compromised arterial branches or to create aortic fenestrations between the true and false lumens have been employed successfully.[11,12]

It should be recognized that strict medical management and reserving surgery for acute type B patients who fail medical treatment produces the paradoxical situation in which the indications for surgery represent the identical factors that portend increased surgical risk and mortality rates. Thus, in selected, low risk patients with acute type B dissection, the long-term outcome may be better if a more aggressive early surgical approach is carried out.

Selected patients with acute type B dissection have been successfully treated with an endovascular approach directed at stent-graft coverage of the primary entry tear.[16,17] Dake et al utilized endovascular stent grafting across the primary entry tear for the management of acute aortic dissection originating in the descending thoracic aorta in 19 patients.[16] The stent-grafts were made of self-expanding stainless-steel covered with woven polyester or polytetrafluoroethylene. In 4 patients, there was retrograde involvement of the ascending aorta (type A), and in 15 patients, the dissection was limited to the descending thoracic aorta (type B). The dissection involved aortic branches in 14 patients (74%), and symptomatic compromise of multiple branch vessels in 7 patients (37%). Complete thrombosis of the thoracic aortic false lumen was achieved in 15 patients and partial thrombosis was achieved in 4. Revascularization of ischemic branch vessels, with relief of symptoms, occurred in 76% of the obstructed branches. Three of the 19 patients died within 30 days, for an early mortality rate of 16%. At a mean follow-up of 13 months, there were no deaths and no instances of aneurysm or aortic rupture.[16] Nienaber et al[17] reported successful endovascular stent-grafting in 12 patients with type B dissection. TEE and angiography confirmed sealing of the entry tear during the procedure. At a mean follow-up of 3 months, thrombosis of the false lumen was confirmed in all patients as assessed by MRI. There were no instances of paraplegia, stroke, embolization, side-branch occlusion or infection in the stent-graft group. These early observations suggest that endovascular stent-grafting directed at coverage of the primary intimal tear may be a therapeutic option in selected patients with thoracic aortic dissection.

Long-Term Follow-Up

After the initial medical, surgical, endovascular and/or combined therapy, patients should be maintained on lifelong antihypertensive and negative inotropic medication, such as beta-blockers and calcium channel antagonists, even if they do not have a defined history of hypertension. Close medical follow-up including blood pressure regulation is required. Prior to discharge from the hospital, a repeat or baseline imaging study, such as CT or MRI, should be performed. If comparison with an available previous scan reveals no change, it is reasonable to wait 3 months before obtaining another scan. Serial surveillance scans are essential in the follow-up of these patients indefinitely in order to detect potential problems, since approximately 15-30% of late postoperative deaths are due to rupture of another part of the thoracic or abdominal aorta. Additionally, the natural history of the false lumen of the aortic dissection is continued dilatation leading to aneurysm formation. In general, surgical graft replacement of the thoracic aorta is considered when the aneurysm approaches 6 cm in diameter, depending on the overall health of the patient.

Selected Readings

1. Bickerstaff LK, Pairolero PC, Hollier LH et al. Thoracic aortic aneurysms: A population-based study. Surgery 1982; 92:1103-1108.
    This often quoted paper from the Mayo Clinic is one of the first thorough evaluations of the incidence of thoracic aortic aneurysms and dissections in a defined patient population over a 30 year period. The majority of the patients who underwent pathologic examination had aortic dissection as the etiology of aneurysmal dilatation. Of the 72 patients who developed thoracic aortic aneurysmal disease, 53 ruptured. Interestingly, the 5 year actuarial survival for patients with aortic dissection as the etiology of the aneurysmal dilatation was only 7%, if untreated.

2. Miller DC. Surgical management of aortic dissections: Indications, perioperative management, and long-term results. In: Doroghazi RM, Slater EE, eds. Aortic Dissection. New York: McGraw-Hill, 1983: 193-243.
    This chapter provides a comprehensive discussion of aortic dissection from the surgical prospective. Particularly important are the sections on preoperative evaluation and surgical technique, the principles of which have remained largely unchanged over the years. Modifications since this publication include newer techniques of cardiopulmonary bypass, hypothermic circulatory arrest and various means of spinal cord protection.

3. DeSanctis RW, Eagle KA. Aortic dissection. Curr Probl Cardiol 1989; 14:227-278.
    This review is all-inclusive and provides an excellent basis for the understanding of aortic dissection—its etiology, diagnosis and treatment.

4. Roberts WC. Aortic dissection: Anatomy, consequences, and causes. Am Heart J 1981; 101:195-214.
    This is a historically important paper on aortic dissection by one of the foremost authorities on the subject. Particularly interesting is the discussion of pathophysiology of aortic dissection.

5. Hirst AE, John VL, Kime SW. Dissecting aneurysm of the aorta: A review of 505 cases. Medicine 1958; 37:217-279.

   This article, perhaps the most historically significant work on the subject of aortic dissection in this past century, provides a comprehensive compilation of the presentation and pathology of over 500 patients.

6. DeBakey ME, Cooley DA, Creech O. Surgical considerations of dissecting aneurysms of the aorta. Am Surg 1955; 142:586.

   This paper has become a surgical classic in the treatment of aortic dissection.

7. Wheat MW, Palmer RF, Bantley TD et al. Treatment of dissecting aneurysms of the aorta without surgery. J Thorac Cardiovasc Surg 1965; 50:364-373.

   This paper is the medical counterpoint to reference 6 and provides the principles of aggressive medical (or nonsurgical) management of aortic dissection.

8. Robbins RC, McManus RP, Mitchell RS et al. Management of patients with intramural hematoma of the thoracic aorta. Circulation 1993; 88(II):1-10.

   Intramural hematoma is presumed to occur as a result of rupture of vasa vasorum with hemorrhage into the media or rupture of atherosclerotic plaque. Thirteen patients with intramural hematoma (3 with ascending aortic or arch involvement and 10 with descending thoracic aortic involvement) are reported from Stanford University and University of Wisconsin between 1983 and 1992. Patients with ascending aortic involvement, persistent pain or expansion of the intramural hematoma should undergo surgical graft replacement.

9. Tsipouras P, Del Mastro R, Sarfarazi M et al. Genetic linkage of the Marfan syndrome, ectopia lentis, and congenital contractural arachnodactyly to the fibrillin genes on chromosomes 15 and 5. N Eng J Med 1992; 326:905-9.

   Using specific markers for the fibrillin genes, the authors performed genetic linkage analysis in 28 families with the Marfan syndrome and 8 families with phenotypically related disorders. They concluded that the Marfan syndrome appears to be caused by mutations in a single fibrillin gene on chromosome 15. Ectopia lentis was also linked to the fibrillin gene on chromosome 15, whereas contractural arachnodactyly was linked to the fibrillin gene on chromosome 5.

10. Fann JI, Sarris GE, Mitchell RS et al. Treatment of patients with aortic dissection presenting with peripheral vascular complications. Ann Surg 1990; 212:705-713.

    This article focuses on the peripheral vascular complications of a total of 272 patients who underwent surgical management of aortic dissection at Stanford University. In this early series, 85 patients developed one or more peripheral vascular complications, most of which improved with surgical aortic repair. As reflected in references 11 and 12, endovascular techniques have since been successfully employed to treat vascular complications of aortic dissection in certain patients and may represent the treatment of choice for some patients with these devastating complications.

11. Slonim SM, Nyman U, Semba CP et al. Aortic dissection: Percutaneous management of ischemic complications with endovascular stents and balloon fenestration. J Vasc Surg 1996; 23:241-253.

    This paper, along with reference 12, describes the Stanford experience with endovascular treatment of ischemic complications of aortic dissection. Endovascular stenting and balloon fenestration have become relatively safe and effective means of addressing the problem of peripheral vascular complications of aortic dissection. This is the therapy of choice for some patients.

12. Slonim SM, Nyman UR, Semba CP et al. True lumen obliteration in complicated aortic dissection: endovascular treatment. Radiology 1996; 201:161-166.

13. Slater EE, DeSanctis RW. The clinical recognition of dissecting aortic aneurysm. Am J Med 1976; 60:625-633.

This paper provides a superb summary of the clinical presentation of patients with aortic dissection.

14. Deeb GM, Williams DM, Bolling SF et al. Surgical delay for acute type A dissection with malperfusion. Ann Thorac Surg 1997; 64:1669-1675.

This article discusses an alternate approach to patients with peripheral vascular complications of aortic dissection—namely, the malperfusion is treated with endovascular techniques, delaying surgical repair until the reperfusion injury resolves. The potential difficulty with this approach is avoiding aortic rupture during the resolution phase of the malperfusion.

15. Glower DD, Fann JI, Speier RH et al. Comparison of medical and surgical therapy for uncomplicated descending aortic dissection. Circulation 1990; 82 (suppl IV):39-46.

This retrospective report based on the combined Stanford and Duke series addresses the issue of optimal therapy of patients with uncomplicated type B aortic dissection. Recognizing the limitations of such an analysis, the data suggest that medical or early surgical therapy is associated with equivalent outcomes.

16. Dake MD, Kato N, Mitchell RS et al. Endovascular stent-graft placement for the treatment of acute aortic dissection. N Engl J Med 1999; 340 (20):1546-1552.

This article evaluated the novel concept of endovascular stent-grafting to treat acute aortic dissection originating in the descending thoracic aorta in 19 patients. In selected patients, this approach may become an important therapeutic modality.

17. Nienaber CA, Fattori R, Lund G et al. Nonsurgical reconstruction of thoracic aortic dissection by stent-graft placement. N Engl J Med 1999; 340 (20):1539-1545.

Similar to reference 16, this paper reports successful treatment of patients with descending thoracic aortic dissections using endovascular stent-grafting, suggesting that this may become a therapeutic option for certain patients.

CHAPTER 5

Carotid Screening Before Aortic Surgery

Brian L. Ferris and Gregory L. Moneta

Improvements in medical management, perioperative care and operative technique have lead to a reduction in morbidity and mortality following aortic surgery. Significant complications, however, continue to occur in this group of older, higher risk patients. Among the potential complications of aortic surgery, stroke following aortic reconstruction is clearly a devastating event. The resulting morbidity and disability of stroke seriously impact the intended prophylaxis of elective aortic aneurysm repair or potential improvement in ambulation following aortoiliac reconstruction for ischemia. Possible reduction in the occurrence of perioperative stroke following aortic surgery requires an understanding of the severity and prevalence of correctable risk factors for stroke and the incidence of perioperative stroke in patients undergoing aortic repair.

The proposed risk factors leading to postoperative stroke include, but are not limited to, carotid stenosis, age, comorbid conditions and intraoperative events such as hemorrhage, shock, cardiac ischemia, prolonged hypotension and anticoagulation. Among these preoperative and intraoperative risk factors, it is the identification and potential correction of internal carotid artery (ICA) stenosis, in addition to careful medical management, that may lead to a reduction in the occurrence of perioperative stroke following aortic aneurysm repair and aortoiliac reconstruction for occlusive disease. Diagnosis and treatment of ICA stenosis in this group of patients also carries the potential to reduce the long term risk of stroke resulting from ICA stenosis by identifying patients who are candidates for carotid endarterectomy based on the presence of carotid stenosis alone.

The relationship between the severity of ICA stenosis and the risk of stroke with and without concurrent symptoms of cerebral ischemia has been well established. As a group, patients with asymptomatic stenosis of the ICA have been shown to have an annual 2% risk of ipsilateral stroke.[1,2] In contrast, the association of ICA stenosis with symptoms of transient or nondisabling cerebral ischemia yields an approximate annual risk of 13% for the development of any stroke.[3,4]

The incidence of stroke following aortic reconstruction is low. Prior to the widespread application of carotid endarterectomy, reported series documenting the occurrence of postoperative complications following aortic reconstruction confirmed its rare occurrence. However, the incidence exceeds that of stroke following common general surgical procedures such as colon resection, hernia repair and cholecystectomy. Diehl et al analyzed perioperative risk factors in 557 patients that may lead to

Aortic Surgery, edited by Jeffrey L. Ballard. ©2000 Landes Bioscience.

complications following abdominal aortic reconstruction.[5] The overall incidence of perioperative stroke was 1.1% and the incidence of fatal stroke was 0.2%. Subset analysis did not reveal a significant difference in the occurrence of perioperative stroke between those patients who underwent elective abdominal aortic aneurysm repair, emergent abdominal aortic aneurysm repair, or elective aortic reconstruction for aortoiliac occlusive disease.

In a study by Johnston and Scobie of 666 patients undergoing elective abdominal aortic aneurysm repair the incidence of perioperative cerebral events was 0.2% in patients asymptomatic for cerebrovascular disease and 3.1% in patients with a history of TIA, CVA or previous carotid surgery. The authors point out the low (0.6%) overall risk of a cerebrovascular event following aortic aneurysm surgery and that most cerebrovascular risk factors are not amenable to treatment.[6,7] Similar overall low rates of perioperative stroke have been reported by others in patients undergoing peripheral vascular surgery, including aortic aneurysm repair and reconstruction for occlusive disease.[8,9]

Despite the low prevalence of perioperative stroke following aortic reconstruction patients who present with previous symptoms of cerebral or ocular ischemia prior to undergoing aortic surgery clearly require duplex examination of the carotid arteries as part of their preoperative evaluation. Furthermore, a history of cerebral ischemic symptoms is not uncommon in patients undergoing aortic surgery. Previous symptoms of cerebral ischemia are found in 10-15% of patients undergoing aortic reconstruction.[6]

The role of carotid endarterectomy combined with medical management of atherosclerotic risk factors to reduce the risk of future stroke in selected patients with symptomatic ICA stenosis has been clearly established by the results of the North American Symptomatic Carotid endarterectomy Trial (NASCET). NASCET confirmed the role of carotid endarterectomy to reduce the risk of future stroke in patients with symptomatic 50-69% angiographic ICA stenosis and asymptomatic 70-99% angiographic ICA stenosis. A 70-99% stenosis of the ICA combined with nondisabling symptoms of cerebral ischemia is associated with a 17% absolute reduction of any stroke in two years when treated with carotid endarterectomy and medical management when compared to medical management alone.[3] There is also a 6.5% absolute risk reduction of ipsilateral stroke at 5 years with the application of carotid endarterectomy and medical management to 50-69% stenosis of the ICA associated with symptoms of nondisabling cerebral ischemia.[4]

The Asymptomatic Carotid Atherosclerosis Study (ACAS) has also established a modest benefit of carotid endarterectomy combined with medical management to reduce the risk of ipsilateral stroke at 5years in appropriately selected patients with > 60-99% ICA stenosis and no associated cerebral ischemic symptoms.[1] The detection of asymptomatic ICA stenosis requires screening for carotid artery stenosis with duplex scanning. The efficacy of duplex scanning to accurately detect ICA stenosis of > 60-99% has been established by the work of our group and others.[10,11]

Overall, the cost effectiveness and yield of duplex scanning to detect asymptomatic ICA stenosis in the general population is low. This is due to the low prevalence of significant ICA stenosis in the general population.[12] Patient cohorts with a greater incidence of significant ICA stenosis, however, potentially may benefit from screening for asymptomatic ICA stenosis.

Patients who undergo aortic reconstruction represent a population where the incidence of asymptomatic carotid occlusive disease is higher than the general population.[6] Miralles et al recently confirmed the increased incidence of severe, asymptomatic ICA stenosis in 58 patients undergoing abdominal aortic aneurysm repair who also underwent carotid duplex screening preoperatively.[13] The prevalence of 50-99% ICA stenosis was reported using Duplex criteria with 94% sensitivity and 92% specificity. Twenty-one percent of the 58 patients were found to have a 50-99% stenosis of at least one ICA. Subset analysis of patients undergoing aortic reconstruction for aneurysm, as well as occlusive disease, suggested a higher prevalence of > 50-99% ICA stenosis in patients operated for aortoiliac occlusive disease versus aneurysm disease (32% vs. 21%). The difference, however, was not statistically significant. This trend of a high prevalence of asymptomatic high-grade carotid stenosis in patients with extracerebral manifestations of atherosclerosis has also been observed in patients who undergo peripheral bypass surgery. Up to 20% of patients in these populations have also been reported to have > 50% ICA stenosis.[14]

While the benefit of carotid endarterectomy to reduce the risk of stroke has been established by the Asymptomatic Carotid Artery Study (ACAS),[1] the benefit of the preoperative diagnosis and correction of asymptomatic, severe ICA stenosis to prevent perioperative stroke following aortic reconstruction remains unproven. Although patients with carotid artery stenosis (Fig. 5.1) can have strokes following aortic aneurysm repair, reviews of patients undergoing noncardiopulmonary bypass surgery in general have not conclusively correlated the occurrence of perioperative stroke to the presence of severe ICA stenosis.[8,15]

Deville et al reported the detection and treatment of > 70-99% ICA stenosis in 283 patients who underwent elective aortic reconstruction for abdominal aortic aneurysm over a 14 year period.[16] Nine patients (3%) reported a history of previous stroke. Two patients (1%) reported symptoms of previous transient ischemic attacks. Two patients (1%) had prior carotid endarterectomy. All patients who underwent elective aortic reconstruction received preoperative duplex ultrasound examination of the extracranial circulation. Duplex ultrasound determined a > 70-99% ICA stenosis in 6 patients (2%). Only 3 of these patients had prior symptoms of cerebral ischemia. Following selective carotid arteriography in all 6 patients, 2 (1%) carotid endarterectomies were performed for 80-99% ICA stenoses prior to aortic reconstruction. Thirty-day mortality following aortic reconstruction was 2.8% and no deaths were attributed to stroke. Stroke occurred in 10% of patients during 5-year follow-up.

It therefore appears that surgical treatment of asymptomatic ICA stenosis detected prior to aortic reconstruction cannot be relied upon to significantly reduce the incidence of perioperative stroke following aortic surgery. However, duplex scanning of the carotid arteries can be applied to characterize ICA occlusive disease as there exists a greater prevalence of severe asymptomatic ICA stenosis in the population of patients who undergo aortic reconstruction. Appropriate patients can then be selected who would benefit from carotid endarterectomy to reduce the long-term risk of

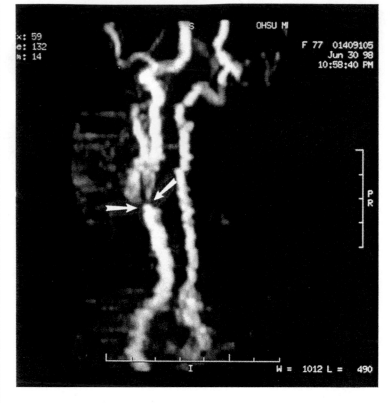

Fig. 5.1. Magnetic resonance angiogram (MRA) from a 72-year-old female who had a left brain stroke 72 hours following uncomplicated elective infrarenal aortic aneurysm repair. The MRA confirms a high-grade left internal carotid artery stenosis.

stroke. Reduction of perioperative stroke following aortic surgery may be possible in a small number of patients who present with previous and relatively recent symptoms of cerebral ischemia and who are determined to have a significant ICA stenosis during the preoperative evaluation.

Selected Readings

1. Executive Committee for the Asymptomatic Carotid Atherosclerosis Study. Endarterectomy for Asymptomatic Carotid Atherosclerosis. JAMA 1995; 273:1421-1428.

This pivotal publication of the Asymptomatic Carotid Atherosclerosis Study documents a modest benefit of carotid endarterectomy for the prevention of late stroke in patients with > 60-99% asymptomatic internal carotid artery stenosis. It is this publication, along with the fact that the prevalence of high-grade carotid stenosis is increased in patients with aortic aneurysm disease that justifies preoperative screening. The purpose of screening is to identify patients who may benefit from prophylactic endarterectomy to prevent long-term stroke. Data do not exist to establish the benefit of prophylactic endarterectomy in the prevention of perioperative stroke following aortic aneurysm repair.

2. European Carotid Surgery Trialists Collaborative Group. Risk of Stroke in the Distribution of an Asymptomatic Carotid Artery. Lancet 1995; 345:209-222.

3. North American Symptomatic Carotid Endarterectomy Trial Collaborators. Beneficial Effect of Carotid Endarterectomy in Symptomatic Patients with High Grade Carotid Stenosis. N Engl J Med 1991; 325:445-453.
This landmark publication from the North American Symptomatic Carotid Endarterectomy Trial conclusively demonstrates benefit of carotid endarterectomy in patients with nondisabling cerebrovascular symptoms and high-grade internal carotid artery stenosis. It is one of the most important papers ever published concerning a vascular surgical procedure and clearly establishes the role of carotid endarterectomy in patients with symptomatic carotid artery disease.

4. Barnett HJM, Taylor DW, for the North American Symptomatic Carotid Endarterectomy Trial Collaborators. Benefit of Carotid Endarterectomy in Patients with Symptomatic Moderate or Severe Stenosis. N Engl J Med 1998; 339:1415-1425.
This landmark publication from the North American Symptomatic Carotid Endarterectomy Trial conclusively demonstrates benefit of carotid endarterectomy in patients with nondisabling cerebrovascular symptoms and high-grade internal carotid artery stenosis. It is one of the most important papers ever published concerning a vascular surgical procedure and clearly establishes the role of carotid endarterectomy in patients with symptomatic carotid artery disease.

5. Diehl JT, Cali RF, Hertzer NR et al. Complications of Abdominal Aortic Reconstruction. Ann Surg 1983; 197:49-56.

6. Johnston KW and Scobie TK. Multicenter Prospective Study of Nonruptured Abdominal Aortic Aneurysms: I. Population and Operative Management. J Vasc Surg 1988; 7:69-81.
This important paper in a prospective fashion characterizes the prevalence of cerebrovascular symptoms and cerebrovascular complications in a group of over 660 patients undergoing aortic aneurysm repair.

7. Johnston K. Multicenter Prospective Study of Nonruptured Abdominal Aortic Aneurysm. Part II. Variables Predicting Morbidity and Mortality. J Vasc Surg 1989; 9:437-447.
This important paper in a prospective fashion characterizes the prevalence of cerebrovascular symptoms and cerebrovascular complications in a group of over 660 patients undergoing aortic aneurysm repair.

8. Barnes RW, Liebman PR, Marszalek PB et al. The Natural History of Asymptomatic Carotid Disease in Patients Undergoing Cardiovascular Surgery. Surgery 1981; 90:1075-1083.
This classic paper was among the first to prospectively document the prevalence and natural history of asymptomatic carotid disease in patients undergoing peripheral vascular surgery. Its findings call into question performance of prophylactic carotid endarterectomy in an effort to reduce perioperative stroke prior to noncerebrovascular peripheral vascular surgery.

9. Gerraty RP, Gates PC, Doyle JC. Carotid Stenosis and Perioperative Stroke Risk in Symptomatic and Asymptomatic Patients Undergoing Vascular or Coronary Surgery. Stroke 1993; 24:1115-1118.

5

10. Moneta GL, Edwards JM, Hatsukami T et al. Screening for Asymptomatic Internal Carotid Artery Stenosis: Duplex Criteria for Discriminating 60-99% Stenosis. J Vasc Surg 1995; 21:989-994.

11. Carpenter JP, Leta FJ, Davis JT. Determination of Sixty Percent or Greater Carotid Artery Stenosis by Duplex Doppler Sonography. J Vasc Surg 1995; 22:697-705.

12. Colgan MP, Strock GR, Sommer JD et al. Prevalence of Asymptomatic Carotid Disease: Results of Duplex Scanning in 348 Unselected Volunteers. J Vasc Surg 1988; 8:674-678.

13. Miralles M, Corominas A, Cotillas J et al. Screening for Carotid and Renal Artery Stenosis in Patients with Aortoiliac Disease. Ann Vasc Surg 1998; 12:17-22.

14. Gentile AJ, Taylor LM Jr, Moneta GL et al. Prevalence of Asymptomatic Carotid Stenosis in Patients Undergoing Infrainguinal Bypass Surgery: A Cross-Sectional Study. Arch Surg 1995; 130:900-904.

15. Moneta GL, DeFrang R, Porter JM. Perioperative Stroke. In: Complications in Vascular Surgery. Bernhard VM and Towne JB (eds.) Quality Medical Publishing, St. Louis 1991:443-455.

16. Deville C, Kerdi S, Madonna F et al. Infrarenal abdominal aortic aneurysm repair: Detection and treatment of associated carotid and coronary lesions. Ann Vasc Surg 1997; 11:467-472.

5

CHAPTER 6

Cardiac Screening Before Aortic Surgery

Douglas J. Wirthlin and Richard P. Cambria

The incidence of concomitant coronary artery disease (CAD) and aortic pathology is such that few would dispute the need of some level of cardiac evaluation prior to aortic surgery. Over half (40-60%) of patients presenting with abdominal aortic aneurysm (AAA) harbor CAD and less than 10% have normal coronary anatomy. More importantly, approximately one third of patients present with severe but surgically correctable cardiac disease, and of these patients, half (15% of total patients) demonstrate few to no clinical signs of CAD.[1]

Concomitant CAD impacts both the perioperative period and long-term survival such that cardiac complications are the leading cause of morbidity and mortality both early and late following aortic surgery. In current practice, the mortality following elective aortic operation is only 0-5%, yet one half to two thirds of perioperative deaths relate to cardiac disease. For example, in the Canadian multicenter study of over 600 elective AAA repairs, overall hospital mortality was 4.8% and two thirds of perioperative deaths were caused by cardiac complications.[2] In the author's review of over 300 aortic reconstructions at the Massachusetts General Hospital similar findings were observed, i.e., perioperative mortality and morbidity though rare, was attributed primarily to cardiac disease.[3] Moreover, patients without overt CAD or with previous coronary revascularization experience decreased perioperative mortality (less than 2%) compared to those with significant yet uncorrected CAD (approximately 7%). Hence, if perioperative outcomes are to improve beyond the already low 0-5% mortality, significant CAD must be identified and treated.

Similar to perioperative outcome, recent natural history studies have identified CAD as the major cause of long-term morbidity and mortality following aortic surgery. For example, after aortic surgery, less than one third of patients with severe uncorrected CAD survive 5 years whereas patients having undergone both AAA and coronary artery bypass grafting (CABG) enjoy a near 75% 5-year survival. Of late deaths following aortic surgery, approximately half are caused by myocardial infarction and near 60% directly relate to cardiac disease. Accordingly, long-term survival of patients after aortic reconstruction is inferior to that of an age-matched cohort and thus preoperative cardiac evaluation and operative treatment should take into account the long-term impact of concomitant CAD.

It is this clinical dilemma, CAD concurrent with aortic pathology, that has motivated the past 15-20 years of work devoted to developing methods of preoperative cardiac risk stratification (CRS), i.e., clinical scoring systems, objective

Aortic Surgery, edited by Jeffrey L. Ballard. ©2000 Landes Bioscience.

noninvasive cardiac tests, and invasive cardiac evaluation and treatment. The purpose of CRS is to identify patients with significant CAD in whom changes in management such as, heightened perioperative monitoring, altered operative plan, or coronary revascularization, would improve perioperative and long-term outcome following aortic surgery. Thus, the key question facing the surgeon during preoperative cardiac evaluation of patients with aortic disease is, will additional information regarding coronary anatomy and cardiac function (i.e., cardiac testing) alter medical management? However, despite voluminous literature available, the answer to this questions remains controversial and opinions range from those who advocate clinical assessment without any objective testing to those who practice mandatory objective cardiac testing. This controversy in part stems from unresolved questions such as, what is the pathophysiology of perioperative MI, and does preoperative coronary revascularization improve overall outcome? Therefore the practical questions of when to obtain and how to best utilize cardiac testing may be difficult to delineate.

To address these questions, this chapter will review the following topics, pathophysiology of perioperative MI, clinical evaluation and clinical markers of CAD, noninvasive cardiac testing, and invasive cardiac evaluation and treatment. In addition, this chapter will provide an algorithm for preoperative cardiac evaluation, which in the author's experience offers an effective approach to CRS prior to aortic surgery.

Pathophysiology of MI

The exact pathophysiology of MI is unknown and this lack of understanding may limit the ability to predict and prevent perioperative MI. Classically, perioperative MI was thought to be related solely to fixed obstructing coronary lesions that impair oxygen delivery in the setting of increased oxygen demand in the perioperative period. This is based partially on observations that post operative MI correlates strongly with prolonged periods of ischemia. However, multiple factors cause perioperative ischemia and whether perioperative MI is caused more by increased oxygen demand or decreased oxygen delivery is unknown (Fig. 6.1). Moreover, like MI in the ambulatory setting, there is evidence that perioperative MI, especially when fatal, may be caused by unstable coronary plaques that rupture and lead to coronary thrombosis. Interestingly, often times the severity of underlying stenosis detected by coronary angiography can not accurately predict the subsequent infarct-related territory suggesting that the pathophysiology of fatal perioperative MI is not entirely related to a fixed obstructing lesion. Rather, severe coronary stenoses may be a marker of more diffuse disease and presence of unstable plaques. This is supported by observation that patients with severe CAD are at highest risk for fatal perioperative MI. Hence, preoperative noninvasive testing which is based on altering myocardial oxygen supply and demand to identify hemodynamically significant lesions may be targeting an inaccurate mechanism of perioperative MI. Nonetheless, current noninvasive tests can accurately identify multivessel CAD which in turn, may be a marker of unstable plaques. In the author's review of preoperative thallium scanning and perioperative cardiac events, multiple regions of reperfusion appeared to correlate with unstable plaques and fatal perioperative MI. Unfortunately, as of yet, there is no specific test to identify coronary lesions susceptible to plaque rupture, and

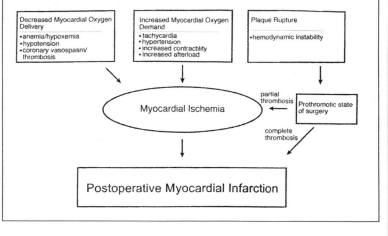

Fig. 6.1. The pathophysiology of perioperative MI is complex and involves multiple perioperative changes, which alter the balance between oxygen delivery and demand. Recently, plaque rupture has been shown to cause fatal perioperative MI.

development of such a test may be the next major advance in preoperative cardiac screening.

Clinical Evaluation and Clinical Markers of CAD

Despite incomplete understanding of perioperative MI, clinical evaluation and identification of clinical markers of CAD are very effective at stratifying perioperative risk and predicting cardiac events. Accordingly, all patients considered for aortic surgery should undergo at least clinical evaluation of cardiac risk, which includes a thorough history and physical exam and ECG. Clinical evaluation also involves consideration surgery-specific factors (nature and urgency of aortic pathology and operative plan) that might impact perioperative and long-term outcome. In the author's review of variables that correlate with postoperative outcome, cardiac risk was primarily attributable to readily identifiable CAD risk factors (patient-specific) rather than to the specific type of vascular operation (surgery-specific). In fact, perioperative and late adverse cardiac events were more frequent in patients undergoing infrainguinal versus aortic procedures.[3] Nonetheless, surgery-specific considerations play a significant role in preoperative cardiac evaluation and formulation of an overall plan.

Surgery-Specific Considerations

The most important surgical consideration, urgency of aortic disease and relative versus absolute indication for aortic operation, tempers the level of preoperative cardiac evaluation and influences the extent of operative intervention. For example, the surgical imperative of a ruptured AAA or acutely thrombosed aorta allows no more than a cursory clinical evaluation of cardiac disease whereas management of an asymptomatic AAA allows time for a complete cardiac evaluation. Moreover, elective AAA is by definition prophylactic and is only rational if the patient has a reasonable life expectancy. Thus, the threshold for obtaining additional cardiac testing should be lowered as the indication for intervention becomes less absolute, particularly as patients reach extremes of chronological or physiological age with modest-sized aneurysms. More importantly, because these considerations require surgical judgement, clinical evaluation of cardiac risk should not be delegated entirely to the cardiologists or medical consultant.

Other important surgical considerations specific to aortic operations include, aortic cross clamping and duration of surgery. The physiologic response to aortic cross clamping has been clearly documented, i.e., abrupt rise in systemic vascular resistance and cardiac afterload, and decrease in cardiac index. Infra-renal aortic clamping is relatively well tolerated in healthy patients, however in patients with cardiac disease, especially those with left ventricular ejection fraction less than 35%, the physiologic alterations of clamping are magnified and can lead to global ventricular dysfunction and myocardial ischemia. Supra-celiac aortic clamping also increases the magnitude of hemodynamic changes with aortic occlusion and carries the added impact of development of transient coagulopathy. Prolonged aortic clamping (> 45 minutes) has been shown to correlate with postoperative MI, however in Cambria's review of 202 aortic reconstructions, cross-clamp time (greater than 90 minutes) did not correlate with perioperative morbidity, rather prolonged operative time (greater than 5 hours) was the single significant correlate of major cardiopulmonary complications.[4] Thus, anticipated supraceliac clamping or infrarenal clamping in patients with left ventricular dysfunction and extensive dissection with prolonged operative time should heighten the surgeon's concern for perioperative complications and lower the threshold for objective preoperative cardiac testing (Table 6.1).

Clinical Markers of CAD

Similar to surgery-specific considerations, clinical markers of CAD have been identified that correlate with both perioperative and long-term cardiac complications. Identification of these markers using multivariate analysis led to development of a number of clinical scoring systems that can estimate perioperative cardiac risk based on clinical evaluation (history, physical, and ECG). The most notable scoring system, the Goldman Multifactorial Index,[5] has been useful for estimating risk of a broad-based population of general surgical patients, but is less effective in estimating risk for a more homogeneous but higher-risk subset of patients, such as those undergoing major vascular procedures. Moreover, 15% of vascular patients will harbor occult CAD and will not demonstrate major markers of CAD such as recent MI, unstable or new onset angina, or poorly controlled left ventricular (LV) dysfunction. Accordingly, Eagle and coworkers analyzed cardiac events occurring in 200 consecutive vascular operations, the majority of which were aortic reconstructions, and identified 5 independent predictors of postoperative ischemic events.[6] These clinical markers of CAD include Q wave on the preoperative EKG (prior documented MI), a history of angina, a history of ventricular arrhythmias requiring therapy, diabetes requiring therapy other than dietary, and age older than 70 (Table 6.1). They observed a 3%

Table 6.1. Clinical factors which influence cardiac testing before aortic surgery

Markers of occult CAD
Q wave on ECG or history of MI
Diabetes
Age > 70 yrs
History of angina
Ventricular arrhythmia requiring treatment
Major CAD markers

Recent MI
Unstable or new onset angina
Recent or poorly controlled left ventricular dysfunction
Surgical factors
Infrarenal clamp and poor left ventricular function
Supraceliac clamp
Prolonged (> 5h) surgery anticipated

6

incidence of postoperative ischemic events in patients with none of the clinical markers compared to 50% incidence of cardiac events in patients with 3 or more markers. They also identified an intermediate risk group, patients with one or two clinical markers, in whom ischemic events occurred in 15.5% of patients, and within this group they were able to further stratify patients into high risk or low risk subgroups using results from dipyridamole thallium scanning (D-thal). Based on this investigation, Eagle and coworkers suggested that low risk patients can safely proceed to surgery without further testing whereas intermediate risk patients should undergo non invasive cardiac testing for further stratification and high risk patients should proceed directly to coronary catheterization. Thus, using Eagle's clinical markers of CAD patients can be identified as low risk (no markers), intermediate risk (1-2 markers), or high risk (3 or more markers), and the need for further cardiac testing can be determined.

In addition to Eagle's clinical markers of CAD, determination of overall functional status also predicts perioperative outcome and influences further cardiac testing. Functional status can be estimated by merely observing the patient's overall general status, an important component of the physical examination that should not be overlooked by the surgeon. Functional status can also be determined by a patient's ability to perform activities of daily living (functional capacity) and to some degree can be objectively estimated by measuring functional capacity in metabolic equivalent levels (METs), a unit measured in multiples of the baseline metabolic rate in a resting state (Fig. 6.2). For example, attending to basic needs such as eating and dressing requires 1 MET, light house work and climbing a flight of stairs require 4 METs, and participation in light recreational activities and hard house work require greater than 7 METs. Functional capacity less than 4 METs has been shown to predict perioperative MI and decreased long-term survival. Functional capacity is considered excellent if > 7 METs is achieved, moderate for 4-7 METs, and poor for less than 4 METs. In the context of preoperative cardiac evaluation, estimation of functional capacity can help stratify patients and influence further cardiac testing.

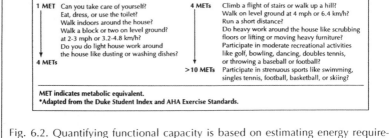

Estimated Energy Requirements for Various Activities*

| 1 MET | Can you take care of yourself? | 4 METs | Climb a flight of stairs or walk up a hill? |

1 MET — Can you take care of yourself?
Eat, dress, or use the toilet?
Walk indoors around the house?
Walk a block or two on level ground?
at 2-3 mph or 3.2-4.8 km/h?
Do you do light house work around
the house like dusting or washing dishes?
4 METs

4 METs — Climb a flight of stairs or walk up a hill?
Walk on level ground at 4 mph or 6.4 km/h?
Run a short distance?
Do heavy work around the house like scrubbing
floors or lifting or moving heavy furniture?
Participate in moderate recreational activities
like golf, bowling, dancing, doubles tennis,
or throwing a baseball or football?
>10 METs — Participate in strenuous sports like swimming,
singles tennis, football, basketball, or skiing?

MET indicates metabolic equivalent.
*Adapted from the Duke Student Index and AHA Exercise Standards.

Fig. 6.2. Quantifying functional capacity is based on estimating energy requirements for various activities.

For example, a patient with no clinical markers for CAD but very poor functional capacity (less than 4 METs) should be considered intermediate risk rather than low risk and should undergo further cardiac testing.

Noninvasive Cardiac Evaluation

After clinical evaluation, the next level of CRS is noninvasive cardiac testing. Noninvasive cardiac testing compared to clinical evaluation is a more objective and sensitive measurement of cardiac reserve and CAD. Most tests are based on stressing the myocardium with exercise or pharmacologic agents and monitoring the effect on the myocardium using continuous ECG, echocardiography or nuclear perfusion scanning. These tests, especially D-thal and dobutamine echocardiography, can objectively and to some degree quantitatively identify size and number of regions of myocardium at risk. All tests are extremely sensitive (> 90%) at predicting cardiac events but have a low positive predictive value and low specificity (10-40%). The cause for low specificity and low positive predictive value is two fold,[1] in current practice aortic surgery is already attended by a low rate of cardiac complications, and[2] investigations of non invasive cardiac testing may select high risk patients for a treatment change (cancellation of surgery, altered medical management, or coronary revascularization) rather than proceeding directly to surgery. Nonetheless, the low specificity and positive predictive value should not be a deterrent to using these tests in CRS.

As stated earlier, which patients to test and how to use data from noninvasive tests is at times unclear. In general, identifying clinical markers of CAD can determine the need for further cardiac testing, i.e., patients at intermediate risk require further testing. Moreover, the indication for obtaining additional testing should not focus solely on perioperative considerations, "getting the patient through an aortic operation," but should also seek to identify CAD that will impact long-term survival. For example, just as many AAAs are encountered during evaluation of an unrelated clinical problem, noninvasive testing during CRS may be the opportunity to uncover severe CAD that requires revascularization on its own merits. Finally, use of information obtained from noninvasive testing should not be limited to extremes of clinical decisions, i.e., surgery vs. no surgery or CABG vs. no CABG, rather more subtle management changes are possible such as altered perioperative medical management or choosing a lesser operation.

There are several noninvasive cardiac tests available for CRS including, exercise stress testing, myocardial scanning, dobutamine stress echocardiography, echocardiography, and ambulatory 48 hour Holter monitoring. The later two deserve only brief discussion. Echocardiography without dobutamine stress, provides useful information regarding ejection fraction and myocardial reserve, but by itself is not a useful test to predict perioperative coronary events and is inadequate as the sole cardiac test when noninvasive testing is indicated. Similarly, ambulatory 48 hour Holter monitoring, which monitors ST segment depression and arrhythmias, does not aid in further stratifying cardiac risk and does not have an important role in CRS.

Which preoperative test to use, exercise stress testing, myocardial imaging or dobutamine echocardiography, is somewhat determined by institutional preferences as most of these tests have similar sensitivity and specificity for predicting both perioperative and late cardiac events. In general, clinical examination followed by selective myocardial scanning (D-thal) is the most common approach to preoperative cardiac assessment and is the author's preference.

Exercise Stress Testing

Exercise stress test is the examination of choice for any patient who can achieve adequate exercise levels. The test provides an estimate of functional capacity, hemodynamic response to exercise, potential for catecholamine-induced cardiac arrhythmias, and exercise myocardial ischemic threshold. Compared to other noninvasive examinations, exercise stress test provides added information regarding objective measurement of functional capacity and cardiopulmonary reserve. Decreased functional capacity is a major prognostic determinant of both perioperative and long-term cardiac morbidity and is influenced by several factors including inadequate cardiac reserve, advanced age, transient myocardial dysfunction from myocardial ischemia, deconditioning and poor pulmonary reserve. Like other noninvasive evaluations, this test is useful to further stratify patients at intermediate risk into higher or lower risk strata. The sensitivity and specificity is dependent on the severity of stenoses, extent of CAD and level of exercise (i.e., increased severity of CAD and level of exercise increases the sensitivity and specificity). The mean sensitivity is 68% (23-100%) and the mean specificity is 77% (17-100%) for all levels of CAD, and for patients with left main disease or 3-vessel disease, the mean sensitivity and specificity increases to $86 \pm 11\%$ and $53 \pm 24\%$ respectively. The positive predictive value of an abnormal exercise test result ranges from 5-25% to predict death or MI during hospitalization or after major noncardiac surgery whereas the negative predictive value is greater than 90%. Unfortunately, 30-50% of patients with vascular disease are unable to achieve a sufficient level of exercise to test cardiac reserve, which limits the usefulness of this test. Arm ergometry may expand the application of this test in vascular patients. Nonetheless, exercise stress testing is a useful tool for CRS, and patients with exercise induced myocardial ischemia especially at low levels of activity merit invasive coronary evaluation.

Myocardial Imaging

Of the nonexercise cardiac stress tests, myocardial imaging is the most commonly used and most extensively investigated. Myocardial perfusion is estimated by scanning the relative distribution of radionucleotides (thallium-201 or 99m Tc-sestamibi) in two phases, baseline and 3-4 hours later. On the baseline scan, normally perfused myocardium demonstrates homogeneous distribution of radionucleotide whereas myocardial scar or ischemia is represented by a defect. Redistribution of thallium in an area of the initial defect differentiates ischemic myocardium from a fixed myocardial infarction. Adding dipyridamole or adenosine induces relative vasodilatation (simulates increased myocardial demand) and increases the sensitivity of detecting reversible defects. Also, sestamibi compared to thallium allows estimation of cardiac ejection fraction. Moreover, myocardial scans can be interpreted in a semiquantitative manner and evaluate the number and size of myocardial regions at risk. In the author's experience interpreting myocardial scans in a quantitative manner versus a binary manner, "positive or negative," increases the specificity of this test. For example, a single region of redistribution on myocardial scanning is associated with fewer perioperative cardiac events compared to findings of multiple regions of myocardial redistribution. The sensitivity and negative predictive value of a normal study are extremely high (98%) whereas the specificity is low (10-30%). As shown by Eagle and co-workers, the specificity of myocardial imaging increases when combined with clinical markers.[6] The specificity will further increase as myocardial scanning becomes more quantitative. In sum, myocardial scanning is a very sensitive predictor of cardiac events and patients with large single regions of redistribution or multiple regions of redistribution require further invasive evaluation.

Dobutamine Stress Echocardiography

Another nonexercise stress test, dobutamine echocardiography, has not been studied as extensively as myocardial scanning but appears to be as effective. Oxygen demand is artificially increased via dobutamine-induced tachycardia, and areas of myocardium at risk are detected based on wall motion abnormality. Interpretation of the examination is somewhat subjective and the criteria for a positive scan may vary from institution to institution. The positive predictive value for MI or cardiac death (7-23%) and negative predictive value of such events (93-100%) are similar to that of thallium scanning. Compared to most myocardial imaging scans, dobutamine echocardiography has the added advantage of providing information regarding valve function and ejection fraction. However, safety of this study is decreased in patients with left bundle branch block or known CAD. Nonetheless, dobutamine echocardiography can be used like myocardial scanning, and significant areas of stress-induced wall motion abnormalities should prompt further evaluation.

Invasive Coronary Evaluation and Intervention

Like noninvasive cardiac testing, the role of invasive coronary evaluation and preoperative revascularization remains somewhat controversial. Cardiac catheterization provides definitive information regarding coronary anatomy and provides the opportunity to intervene via Percutaneous transluminal angioplasty (PTA). Coronary angiography should only be performed if there is a high likelihood of significant disease based on combined clinical markers and noninvasive testing and if the patient is a candidate for coronary artery bypass grafting (CABG). Regarding coronary revascularization, to date there is no prospective randomized trial validating the overall efficacy of preoperative CABG yet, prior CABG clearly protects against adverse perioperative and long-term cardiac events. The overall efficacy of preoperative CABG must take into account the perioperative mortality of CABG, which can be substantial (> 5%) in elderly patients with vascular disease, the same population presenting with AAA. Moreover, the mortality benefits of coronary revascularization are not realized for 2-3 years, and there is a slight increase in mortality in the first year following CABG. Overall efficacy of preoperative CABG is also influenced by the estimated morbidity and mortality of the proposed aortic operation. The relative indication for preoperative CABG increases as the rate of perioperative mortality and morbidity following CABG decrease and the rate of cardiac events following aortic surgery increase. Based on decision analysis, preoperative CABG to reduce short-term (perioperative) risk is indicated only if the risk of aortic surgery is greater than 5% and the risk of coronary angiography followed by selective revascularization is less than 3%, a circumstance that is fairly uncommon. Hence, preoperative CABG to "get the patient through aortic surgery" is only appropriate in a small subset of high-risk patients.

CRS will identify another subset of patients who will benefit from coronary revascularization based solely on severity of CAD. The indications for CABG in these patients are the same as those for ambulatory patients, i.e., acceptable coronary revascularization risk and suitable viable myocardium with significant left main stenosis, three-vessel CAD, two-vessel CAD in conjunction with left ventricular dysfunction, two-vessel disease involving severe proximal left anterior descending artery stenosis, and intractable myocardial ischemia despite maximal medical therapy. In patients with these anatomic patterns, CABG improves long-term survival. On the other hand, the exact role of preoperative coronary angioplasty (PTCA) is less clearly defined because of limited data and limited application in the preoperative setting. PTCA is meant to treat primarily single vessel disease and the indications for PTCA are the same as those for patients in the ambulatory setting. PTCA appears to be effective in preventing cardiac events but is attended by higher restenosis rates and increased need for repeat interventions compared to CABG. The optimal time for surgery following PTCA is 30-40 days, a time when acute thrombosis is decreased and before restenosis occurs. In patients with aortic pathology requiring preoperative CABG, coronary revascularization is performed first followed by aortic reconstruction after a short recovery period (less than 2 weeks in patients with large AAA). In very rare circumstances patients present with unstable coronary syndromes concurrent with urgent aortic pathology (symptomatic AAA). In these cases, selected centers have recommended simultaneous CABG and aortic reconstruction, however proceeding with aortic reconstruction alone or performing a lesser operation such as endovascular AAA repair seems more appropriate.

Algorithm for Preoperative Cardiac Assessment

To summarize the salient principles of CRS, the author's approach to preoperative cardiac assessment, which is based on clinical evaluation and selective noninvasive testing, will be presented (Fig. 6.3). The decision tree begins with determining if further knowledge of coronary risk or anatomy will affect management. In cases in which the urgency of aortic surgery precludes cardiac evaluation or in patients who are deemed poor candidates for coronary revascularization, further evaluation is not indicated. In the majority of cases, i.e., elective aortic surgery in reasonable risk patients, cardiac evaluation is initiated with clinical evaluation and patients are categorized as low, intermediate or high risk. Low clinical risk patients have no clinical markers of CAD (Eagle markers), have had prior coronary revascularization with no recurrent coronary symptoms, or a single clinical marker, advanced age (> 70) or diabetes, in the setting of good functional capacity. Intermediate risk patients present with 1 or 2 clinical markers of CAD or harbor controlled CAD or LV dysfunction. These patients merit further noninvasive cardiac testing and undergo either exercise thallium or dipyridamole thallium scanning. High-risk patients, i.e., those with 3 or more CAD markers, major CAD markers (unstable angina) or poorly controlled LV dysfunction, should proceed directly to cardiac catheterization. In contrast, low risk patients safely undergo aortic surgery.

Further management of intermediate risk patients is based on results of noninvasive testing, i.e., no redistribution, mild redistribution, or moderate to severe redistribution. Those with no redistribution or those with mild redistribution (single small reversible defect) without LV dysfunction may proceed to surgery. Those with LV dysfunction and mild thallium defects or moderate to severe defects (multiple large areas of redistribution) require coronary arteriography.

The indications for CABG are similar to those in the ambulatory setting, i.e., left main or 3-vessel CAD, and when indicated, CABG is performed prior to aortic surgery. If the coronary anatomy is inappropriate for mechanical intervention, the relative surgical indications are once again addressed, and in patients in whom the surgical indications are absolute, surgery is performed with maximization of anti-ischemic medications and with full hemodynamic monitoring. In those in whom surgery is not absolute, surgery is deferred or a lesser operation, i.e., endovascular aortic intervention, is entertained.

Cambria and co-workers, reviewed the impact of this approach in 202 elective aortic reconstructions (Fig. 6.4).[4] Notably, the operative mortality was low (2%) with only one cardiac related death, and major cardiac morbidity only occurred in 4% of patients suggesting that this is an effective approach to CRS. Also, only 29% of patients required dipyridamole thallium scanning of which almost half demonstrated areas of redistribution, in which patients with more clinical markers of CAD were more likely to have positive thallium scans. Thus, clinical markers can effectively stratify patients and select those who require further testing. Only a small number of patients required cardiac catheterization (16 patients, 8% of total patients) and fewer (13 patients) underwent coronary revascularization (CABG 11 and PTCA 2). Finally, similar to observations of others, coronary events were more frequent in patients who did not have coronary revascularization prior to surgery.

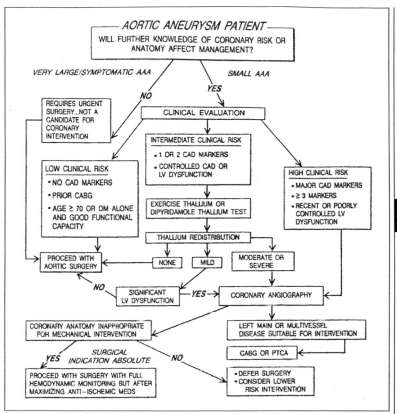

Fig. 6.3. Algorithm for preoperative cardiac assessment in patients undergoing aortic surgery.

Conclusion

Defining coronary risk prior to aortic reconstruction is an important step in the management of patients with aortic pathology to improve both the perioperative and long-term outcome. Combination of clinical markers of CAD and selective use of noninvasive cardiac testing effectively defines cardiac risk and identifies patients who would benefit from invasive cardiac evaluation. Invasive cardiac evaluation and coronary revascularization are necessary in a small percentage of patients with aortic pathology and of these patients, the majority merit CABG based solely on severity of CAD.

Selected Readings

1. Hertzer NR, Young JR, Beven EG. Late results of coronary bypass in patients with infrarenal aortic aneurysms. The Cleveland Clinic Study. Ann Surg 1987; 205:360-367.

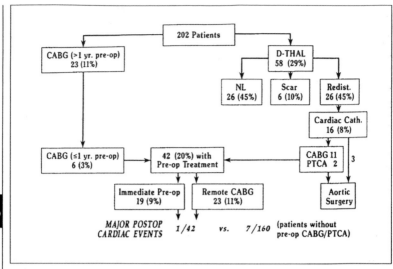

Fig. 6.4. Evaluation and treatment of coronary artery disease in a modern series of 202 patients undergoing aortic surgery.

Cardiac catheterization was performed in a consecutive series of 246 patients under consideration for elective AAA repair. Severe, surgically correctable coronary artery disease (CAD) was discovered prior to AAA repair in 78 (32%) patients, and 70 (28%) underwent pre-AAA repair coronary revascularization with four fatal complications (5.7%). Fifty-six patients in this subset had staged AAA repair during the same hospitalization with a single (1.8%) death from stroke. These data demonstrate that correctable CAD is prevalent in AAA patients and that staged CABG and AAA in selected patients is well tolerated.

2. Johnston KW. Multicenter prospective study of nonruptured abdominal aortic aneurysm. Part II. Variables predicting morbidity and mortality. J Vasc Surg 1989; 9:437-447.

    This landmark publication describes perioperative complications in a previously reported group of 666 patients who had elective repair of AAA. Vascular morbidity data included intraoperative bleeding (4.8%), postoperative bleeding that required transfusion (2.3%) or reoperation (1.4%), intraoperative limb ischemia (3.5%), graft thrombosis (0.9%), embolization (3.3%), amputation (1.2%), graft infection (1 case). General morbidity data included, but was not limited to, myocardial infarction (5.2%), congestive heart failure (8.9%), dysrhythmia requiring treatment (10.5%), respiratory failure (8.4%), renal insufficiency (5.4%). Overall mortality was 4.8%, with 3.3% incidence of cardiac related death.

3. L'Italien GJ, Cambria RP, Cutler BS et al. Comparative early and late cardiac morbidity among patients requiring different vascular surgery procedures. J Vasc Surg 1995; 21:935-944.

    This study of 547 patients quantified the relative contributions of specific vascular procedures and CAD clinical markers on perioperative and long-term cardiac risk.

Every patient underwent clinical examination and D-thal testing before aortic (n=321), infrainguinal (n=177) or carotid (n=49) reconstruction. Perioperative myocardial infarction (MI) occurred in 6% of patients who had aortic or carotid procedures and in 13% of the infrainguinal group. Significant predictors for MI were history of angina, fixed and reversible D-thal deficits, and ST segment depression during preoperative screening. Predictors of late MI included history of angina, congestive heart failure, diabetes, fixed D-thal defects and perioperative MI.

4. Cambria RP, Brewster DC, Abbott WM et al. The impact of selective use of dipyridamole-thallium scans and surgical factors on the current morbidity of aortic surgery. J Vasc Surg 1992; 15:43-51.

   This study evaluated the selective use of D-thal scans before elective aortic surgery in 202 patients based on clinical markers of CAD. Preoperative D-thal scans were performed in 29% of patients. Abnormal studies prompted coronary angiography in 11% and 9% of patients had CABG/PTCA before aortic surgery. Operative mortality for aortic reconstruction was 2% with only one cardiac related death. An additional 4% of patients had nonfatal perioperative MI or unstable angina. Variables that were demonstrated to be significant for cardiac complications included prolonged operative time (> 5hrs), reconstruction for aortoiliac occlusive disease and a history of ventricular ectopy. These data suggest that upwards of 10% of patients who require aortic reconstruction will also need an invasive cardiac procedure before the proposed vascular procedure.

5. Goldman L, Caldera DL, Nussbaum SR et al. Multifactorial index of cardiac risk in noncardiac surgical procedures. N Engl J Med 1977; 297:845-850.

   Classic study that prospectively evaluated preoperative factors that might affect the development of cardiac complications in 1001 patients over 40 years of age. Nine independent variables correlated with life-threatening and fatal cardiac complications. These variables were preoperative third heart sound or jugular venous distension, MI within six months of surgery, greater than 5 premature ventricular contractions per minute, any dysrhythmia or premature atrial contractions, age over 70 years, emergency intraperitoneal, intrathoracic or aortic procedure, significant aortic valve stenosis and deconditioned state. This study was one of the first to suggest that preoperative estimation of cardiac risk was just as important as estimating the direct surgical risk.

6. Eagle KA, Coley CM, Newell JB et al. Combining clinical and thallium data optimizes preoperative assessment of cardiac risk before major vascular surgery. Ann Intern Med 1989, 110:859-866.

   This retrospective observational study sought to determine whether clinical markers of CAD and D-thal scans were useful in predicting ischemic events after vascular surgery. Two hundred fifty-four consecutive patients referred for D-thal testing comprised the study group. Logistic regression identified five clinical predictors of cardiac complications. These variables were Q wave on ECG, history of ventricular ectopy, diabetes, age over 70 and history of angina. Patients with at least one of these factors should have cardiac stress testing before major vascular surgery.

CHAPTER 7

Diagnostic Imaging Techniques Before Aortic Surgery

Mark D. Morasch and William H. Pearce

Great strides in aortic surgery have taken place over the last 40 years. Operative mortality following surgery for aneurysmal disease has decreased substantially. Much of the improvement in outcome can be attributed to refinement in both surgical and anesthetic techniques. Progress in preoperative decision making has been facilitated by improvement in the ability to image pathology prior to surgical intervention. This has allowed for safer and more efficient treatment strategies.

Once an aortic aneurysm has been discovered and the decision has been made to proceed with reconstruction, a wide variety of imaging modalities are presently available to characterize aneurysm morphology. Most would agree that operative candidates require some form of preoperative imaging in order to appropriately plan surgical intervention. However, which specific tests are considered appropriate and the extent of preoperative imaging necessary remain controversial. In fact, some surgeons still argue that once an abdominal aortic aneurysm has been diagnosed, no further radiographic imaging is necessary as all particular circumstances can be identified and appropriately managed during the time of open surgery.

Nonetheless, a detailed knowledge of aortic morphology permits the surgeon the luxury of deciding the most appropriate approach for repair. Most importantly, radiographic imaging can provide important information regarding the proximal extent of the aneurysm. This information is critical for selecting the most appropriate operation. Transperitoneal, retroperitoneal, endolumenal and laparoscopic approaches have all been used. Knowledge of the length and quality of the proximal neck is important for planning placement of a clamp during open surgery. Aneurysmal extension into the iliac vessels may also alter one's open approach. Preoperative information regarding associated pathology can help the surgeon avoid particular pitfalls during surgery.

With the advent of minimally invasive techniques and endovascular aneurysm repair and with the increasing popularity of retroperitoneal aortic reconstruction, detailed knowledge of aortic anatomy, adjacent vasculature and other nonarterial pathology is vital. As newer approaches to aortic reconstruction become widely popular, newer, more sophisticated diagnostic imaging techniques are emerging. These have become increasingly useful for patient selection and procedural planning.

Ultrasound remains the simplest and most cost-effective tool for screening and for initial diagnosis of abdominal aneurysms. Thoracic and thoracoabdominal aneurysms are often suggested on routine chest radiographs. Both are inexpensive

Aortic Surgery, edited by Jeffrey L. Ballard. ©2000 Landes Bioscience.

and noninvasive, although only ultrasound has utility for following aneurysmal growth over time. Neither can provide the detailed information preferred for proper preoperative planning.

Cross-sectional imaging with computed tomography (CT) or magnetic resonance (MR) will clearly demonstrate aneurysm extent as well as adjacent anatomy and pathology. While both are noninvasive, can be performed on an outpatient basis, and can easily be postprocessed into three-dimensional images, they are also moderately expensive. Three-dimensional CT, like conventional angiography, requires the use of 200 cc of an intravenous nephrotoxic contrast agent. High quality three-dimensional CT reconstruction of transaxial images or conventional angiography remain a necessary addition to transaxial imaging when contemplating endovascular repair. Careful definition of lumenal contour and the aneurysm's dimensions is needed to prevent perigraft leak from poor arterial apposition or by foreshortening of the endovascular graft. Angiography remains essential for demonstrating stenosing lesions in adjacent visceral or outflow vessels. Intravascular ultrasound has the capability of defining lumenal anatomy and can also be used to measure the dimensions of the aneurysm but, like angiography, it too is an expensive, invasive diagnostic tool.

7

Selection of the appropriate imaging modality is often based upon institutional experience with particular imaging techniques as well as upon each center's preferred approach for surgical reconstruction. Regard for cost containment is also important. The surgeon must select only those studies considered necessary for surgical decision making. Presently, at Northwestern University, a number of different surgical techniques are used to repair aortic aneurysms. Patients with thoracic or infrarenal aneurysms who are deemed appropriate candidates for endovascular exclusion undergo repair using endografts placed under the auspices of Phase II or Phase III experimental protocols. All other aneurysms, including suprarenal or thoracoabdominal aortic aneurysms, normally undergo repair using traditional open techniques. Preoperative diagnostic imaging follows specific protocols designed to allocate patients with aortic aneurysms to the appropriate type of repair.

Standard Computed Tomography

Computed Tomography (CT) scans are usually performed early in the work-up of patients with aortic pathology. Noncontrast CT scans can be completed quickly in order to obtain or confirm a diagnosis and they provide useful information regarding extent and size of the aneurysm, the presence of iliac dilatation, and the existence of hemorrhage or adjacent hematoma. Noncontrast scans are limited by their inability to assess vessel patency but they are useful for patients with renal insufficiency, iodine contrast allergy or cardiac failure. Additionally, noninfused CT is useful for demonstrating significant calcification within the wall of the aorta and its branches. It can also be used to identify associated retroperitoneal, renal, hepatic or bowel pathology.

Contrast enhanced CT examinations have specific protocols that vary according to indication for the study. When the infusion is timed appropriately for a vascular study, contrast is present within the intravascular space and enhancement provides important information regarding intralumenal flow. Slice thickness and rate of acquisition can be modified depending upon the information that is desired. Standard CT scans are performed using 5mm slice thickness with an interscan delay and dynamic table incrementation. Typical contrast protocols include an initial bolus of 500 cc administered by a power injector at a rate of 2-5 cc per second followed by maintenance infusion using 0.8-1.5 cc/sec for an additional 150 cc. Thinner slice acquisition and reduced interscan delay are required to clearly identify branch vessels, and 3 mm slices are required by most endograft protocols.

Infused CT scans are essential for identifying intralumenal thrombus and perianeurysmal inflammation. In patients who present with peripheral embolism, it is important first to obtain a CT scan to localize intralumenal thrombus prior to any intralumenal manipulation with a catheter. Additionally, the presence of laminated thrombus within the aneurysm neck may have important implications regarding the appropriateness of endovascular graft repair. Contrast enhancement assists in the identification of important branch vessels and can provide information regarding their patency. Identification of extralumenal contrast can suggest the presence of ulceration, acute or chronic contained rupture or aortocaval fistulae. Clinically significant inflammation within the aortic wall occurs in approximately 6% of aneurysms and this is best identified using contrast CT scans (Fig. 7.1).

CT scans will also suggest important nonarterial pathology that may affect the decision to operate or the particular approach to intervention. The presence of diverticular disease, associated malignancies or cholelithiasis may give cause for delay or a different treatment algorithm. Particular renal anomalies including horseshoe kidney should prompt further radiographic investigation with arteriography. Congenital venous anomalies including left-sided vena cava, caval duplication, retroaortic renal veins and venous collars are not uncommon. Prior knowledge of the presence of these anomalies will prompt particular caution when placing aortic clamps.

CT Angiography

Conventional CT scans provide important transaxial images of the aorta. With the introduction of fast CT scans and a continuously moving gantry, volume data is now obtainable. Modern spiral CT scanners not only provide high quality transaxial images, but also three-dimensional reconstructions that can be postprocessed using volumetric data into both maximum intensity projection (MIPs) and shaded surface displays (SSDs). Images are obtained using contrast infusion via peripheral vein. A contrast bolus is injected at a rate of 4-5 ml/sec during a single breath-hold. The entire examination of the abdomen and the pelvis takes less than two minutes. Transaxial images obtained from the spiral CT represent 3-5 mm slices and each possess high contrast definition. As with conventional CT scans, the cross-sectional data is available and provides data regarding associated venous abnormalities and other intraabdominal pathology. Length and diameter can be measured at the CT workstation from both the transaxial images and the postprocessed reconstructions. When properly calculated, measurements obtained from CT aortography are very accurate and can be used to choose appropriately sized endograft components. Three-dimensional reconstruction of the transaxial data into SSD provides impor-

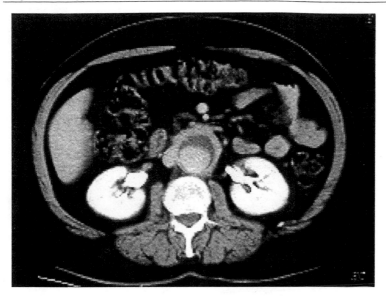

Fig. 7.1. CT scan best identifies clinically significant inflammation within the aortic wall which occurs in approximately 6% of aneurysms.

tant additional information on lumen contour, side branch pathology and aneurysm morphology (Fig. 7.2).

Shaded surface displays measure depth from calculations of reflection from an imaginary light source. These images can be rotated and viewed from arbitrary positions to view contour and branch morphology. Maximum intensity projections display the images by determining the maximal pixel value encountered along an imaginary ray and, thereby, provide data regarding aortic wall composition. Calcification appears as islands of bright spots separated from the arterial wall on a MIP (Fig. 7.3). CTA can also provide excellent definition of major arterial branches. However, when compared to standard angiography, branch vessel stenoses may not be as well defined and small accessory renal branches, lumbar vessels or the inferior mesenteric artery may not be imaged. As with conventional CT scanning, images may be sub-optimal if there is motion artifact or if metal devices or surgical clips degrade the displays.

Contrast-Enhanced Magnetic Resonance Angiography

Advances in magnetic resonance techniques used for arterial imaging are progressing rapidly. Magnetic resonance angiography (MRA) is a noninvasive diagnostic tool that uses non-nephrotoxic intravenous contrast agents to image arteries and veins. The introduction of Gadolinium (Gd-DTPA) has greatly improved the quality of MRA, and has stimulated the development of fast MR techniques to exploit the short-lived intravascular peak in the concentration of this agent.

7

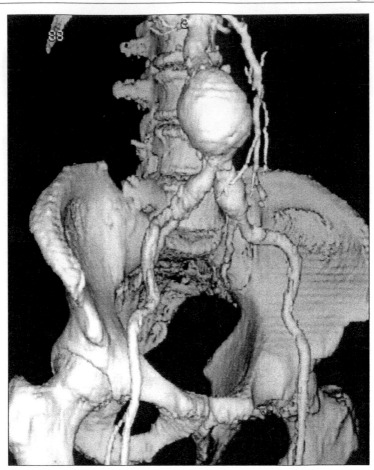

Fig. 7.2. Three-dimensional reconstruction of the transaxial data into SSD provides important additional information on lumen contour, side branch pathology and aneurysm morphology.

The technique of contrast-enhanced MRA bears a strong resemblance to CTA, which probably inspired its development. There are, however, several differences between the two techniques. Unlike CT, MR does not employ ionizing radiation. CT images are always acquired in the transverse plane but they may be reconstructed into other planes with postprocessing. Magnetic resonance angiograms may be acquired in arbitrary planes, and also reconstructed. The total volume of contrast agent injected is lower with MRI, and as mentioned above, Gd-DTPA is not nephrotoxic. MRA and CTA are prone to different artifacts. Certain artifacts on MRA are dependent on the pattern of blood flow, and these can be complex. CTA is relatively independent of the blood flow pattern.

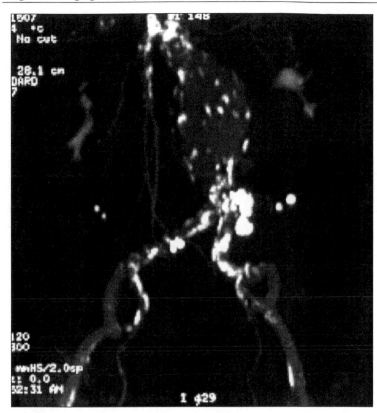

Fig. 7.3. Calcification appears as islands of bright spots separated from the arterial wall on a MIP.

The most widely used MRA techniques are based on so-called "time-of-flight" effects, whereby the signal from blood is highlighted by virtue of its flow. If flow is sluggish, visualization of blood vessels may be compromised. The mechanism whereby the signal from slowly flowing blood is suppressed is termed "saturation," and this, until recently, has severely limited direct three-dimensional, or "thick-slab," imaging of vessels. Saturation occurs due to the repeated application of radio-wave pulses essential for most MR imaging applications. If these pulses are applied at very short intervals, some tissues become refractory or "saturated," and cannot generate sufficient signal for detection. The tendency for tissues to become saturated is described by their "T1 relaxation time." Tissues with long T1 values (such as blood and most other biological fluids) need more time to relax between radio-wave pulses than do tissues with short T1 values (such as fat). MRA techniques, in general, use short intervals between pulses, and rely on high flow velocity to offset the tendency towards saturation of the blood. Although this approach often works well for normal blood vessels, diseased vessels are frequently not well seen due to slow flow. MR contrast agents such as Gd-DTPA selectively shorten the refractory period (T1) of blood, making it possible to image the vascular lumen in a manner independent of flow velocity.

Accurate timing of image acquisition is required to capture the arterial phase. Image acquisition must coincide with the arrival of contrast agent. Two different approaches have been developed to accomplish this. The first approach is to run a prescan using a small test dose. Subsequent high-resolution 3D acquisition is then timed based on this test to capture the image data while the contrast agent is in the arterial phase. The second approach is to run a combined acquisition. Two-dimensional images are acquired, reconstructed, and displayed in real-time while the bolus of contrast agent is injected. When the contrast agent is first visible the operator switches immediately to 3D acquisition. The resulting images can be analyzed to generate a velocity vs. time curve for a selected region of interest.

Cardiac-triggered measurements can be performed with the acquisition of one line of data for each cardiac phase during each heartbeat. This type of single-line at a time acquisition can also be performed with retrospective cardiac gating. It takes about 15 seconds for a bolus to reach the abdominal aorta following injection into an antecubital vein. However, there is a lot of variation from patient to patient.

Magnetic resonance angiograms are generally displayed as projections. It is important to be aware that these projections may contain information from all or only part of the volume examined. For example, if a volume of tissue, 10 cm thick and covering a 40 cm square field-of-view is acquired, then information is potentially available about all the vessels contained in that 40 x 40 x 10 cm^3 volume. However, if a full-thickness projection is collapsed and displayed, then some vascular detail may be obscured by vessel overlap. In that case, it may be desirable to collapse only a sub-volume, showing specific vessels of interest in greater detail. One caveat of this type of postprocessing is that some vessels may appear to be attenuated or absent simply because they are excluded from the displayed volume. It is important to be aware of this possibility. This can become important when imaging smaller vessels, but is not so important when imaging the aorta.

Conventional Angiography

Conventional angiography has long been considered useful in the preoperative evaluation of aortic pathology. Angiograms provide the most accurate diagnosis of adjacent branch vessels pathology and can reliably predict whether or not important branch vessels arise from the aneurysm itself (Fig. 7.4). Renal or visceral artery stenoses are best identified using multi-plane arteriography. Preoperative identification of accessory renal vessels, particularly those associated with horseshoe kidney, is particularly useful in order to plan appropriate reimplantation. Additionally, arteriography can be used to confirm patency of important inferior mesenteric and hypogastric vessel collaterals providing bowel and pelvic circulation. Patients with iliac artery occlusive disease distal to aneurysmal pathology should have an arteriogram performed to help plan complete arterial reconstruction. Angiography can also accurately diagnose and localize ulcers that may cause embolization and the rare

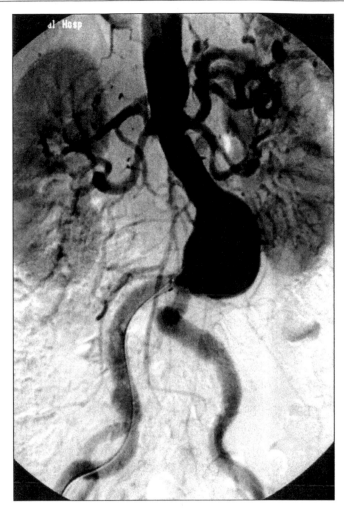

7

Fig. 7.4. Angiography provides the most accurate diagnosis of adjacent branch vessels pathology and can most reliably predict whether or not important branch vessels arise from the aneurysm itself.

aortocaval fistula. However, as images only demonstrate lumenal contour, aortography cannot identify laminated thrombus or extensive calcification. As with CT (SSD) or MR angiographic reconstruction, when significant thrombus is present aortography is limited by its inability to depict true aneurysm size and dimension. Contrast angiography is also significantly more expensive than ultrasound, CT, or MR, and it requires invasive arterial cannulation. A typical aortogram requires 150-200 cc nephrotoxic intravenous contrast. The routine use of digital subtraction techniques will limit contrast volume, diminish the time needed to complete the examination, and provide clearer images.

Intravascular Ultrasound (IVUS)

Intravascular ultrasound (IVUS) is an imaging modality that has evolved from transcutaneous and intralumenal gastrointestinal ultrasound technology. It has been adapted for uses along side other endovascular interventional technology. IVUS has the capacity to provide unique information regarding extent and morphology of aortic pathology. When compared to conventional imaging, IVUS adds a heightened level of accuracy when it comes to defining particular complex vascular anatomy. IVUS is easily applied during other types of interventional procedures and it can reduce or completely avoid the need for ionizing radiation. Currently IVUS is limited by the added expense for the instrumentation. It also requires an invasive procedure for catheter introduction.

The IVUS instrument consists of a miniature catheter with an ultrasound device incorporated into the tip and a console that processes the acquired ultrasound data to form an image. The ultrasound tip scans through a full circle to provide 360° cross-sectional images. Both mechanical and multi-element phased array catheters are available for use. Phased array catheters incorporate multiple, electronically-switched transducer elements that are arranged in a circular array. Each transducer functions at ultrasound frequencies in the 15-30 MHz range. Mechanical transducers transmit ultrasound in the 10-45 MHz range and their construct incorporates either a single rotating transducer or a fixed transducer adjacent to a rotating acoustic mirror. In both, the imaging apparatus is housed in the catheter tip and the ultrasound beam is directed perpendicular to the axis of the catheter making image quality optimal when the catheter runs parallel to the vessel wall. Vessel tortuosity results in eccentric catheter alignment that can create hyperechoic artifacts. With phased array devices, when the multiple transducer crystals are in direct contact with the structure being imaged, a bright circumferential artifact is created that obscures the anatomy. Mechanical devices slightly angle either the transducer or the acoustic mirror and can eliminate the "ring down " artifact. Mechanical devices are housed in a chamber that must be primed with a saline solution in order to minimize acoustic shadowing.

IVUS catheters are designed to pass intralumenally over guidewires. Guidewires allow for controlled maneuvering from remote introduction sites. In phased array devices, the elements are arranged around a central core and this allows for catheter construction that incorporates a central lumen. This permits catheter introduction over a guidewire. The saline filled chamber housing the mechanical device cannot accommodate a central lumen so these catheters require a monorail type configuration.

MR or CT images may not provide accurate information regarding lumenal dimensions, particularly when tortuous vessels are imaged in cross section. Similarly, 3-D MR or CT reconstructions, as well as conventional angiograms, may be limited when it comes to measuring axial lengths. Again, vessel tortuosity creates parallax which can result in underestimation of true length. With conventional angiography, eccentric plaques must be imaged in multiple planes to estimate lumenal diameter. IVUS can overcome all of these limitations. Inner vessel diameter can accurately be measured to within 0.05mm and arterial lengths can be accurately measured at the time of catheter withdrawal. IVUS can also identify particular characteristics of the vessel wall including intimal defects, medial plaques, calcification and the presence of laminated thrombus.

Imaging for Endograft Placement

The advent of new technology for remote intralumenal repair of aortic pathology has created a need for precision preoperative imaging. Accurate measurement of intralumenal dimensions and degrees of angulation are necessary for proper endograft placement and for sealing. Significant endoleaks can develop if axial alignment or coaptation of the device with the aortic neck is imprecise. Data regarding patency and tortuosity within the iliofemoral access vessels is similarly important for preoperative planning. Contrast enhanced CT that combines cross section imaging with spiral reconstruction is presently the most useful method for determining patient candidacy for endograft repair of aortic and iliac aneurysms. Third generation CT scanners can provide information regarding proximal aortic neck diameter and length, the adequacy of iliac vasculature for device introduction and for distal endograft sealing, and whether or not significant calcification or thrombus, which may preclude endorepair, is present at the implantation site. Cross-sectional imaging alone does not allow for clear definition of aortic neck angulation. Similarly, length measurements from proximal to distal implantation sites may be underestimated if tortuosity is present. However, accurate 3-D reconstruction of CT or MR images can provide this information. Contrast arteriograms, particularly if combined with IVUS technology, are still the best technique both for defining branch vessel anatomy, for demonstrating neck angulation and for determining total aortic lengths. Conventional angiography can be misleading when it comes to imaging intralumenal thrombus and vessel diameters at device implantation sites. Most clinicians still utilize intraoperative contrast cineflouroscopy for guiding endograft deployment. IVUS is the most accurate intraoperative method for determining complete endograft expansion.

Most endograft protocols require follow-up imaging at various intervals during the early postoperative years. The combination of noninfused and infused fine cut CT scanning is most useful for diagnosing continued aneurysm expansion, endograft migration, and most importantly the presence of early or late type I, II or III endoleaks. Many centers are also using CT to depict and follow proximal neck expansion over time subsequent to endograft repair.

Selected Readings

1. Galt SW, Pearce WH. Preoperative assessment of abdominal aortic aneurysms: Noninvasive imaging versus routine arteriography. Sem Vasc Surg 1995; 8:103-107. *This manuscript reviews different techniques used for the preoperative evaluation of patients with abdominal aortic aneurysms and addresses indications for proceeding to invasive aortography prior to aneurysm repair.*

2.   White RA, Donayre CE, Kopchok GE. Adjunctive use of intravascular ultrasound. In: Techniques in Vascular and Endovascular Surgery. Yao JST, Pearce WH, eds. Stamford, CT: Appleton and Lange 1998; 242-257.
      This chapter details both the mechanics and applications of the different available forms of intravascular ultrasound. Overall, an excellent comprehensive review of the topic.

3.   Zarins CK, Krievins DK, Rubin GD. Spiral computed tomography and three-dimensional reconstruction in the evaluation of aortic aneurysm. In: Yao JST, Pearce WH, eds. Progress in Vascular Surgery, Norwalk, CT: Appleton and Lange, 1997:117-128.
      This chapter gives a good overview of the techniques used to reconstruct spiral CT transaxial images into usable 3D reconstructions. It also addresses the advantages and disadvantages of these techniques and compares CT to angiography.

4.   Rubin GD, Dake MD, Napel S et al. Spiral CT of renal artery stenosis: comparison of three-dimensional rendering techniques. Radiology 1994; 190:181-189.
      This paper addresses the accuracy of CT angiography for the diagnosis of renal artery stenosis and is particularly useful in the authors discussion of different 3-D rendering techniques used for aortic imaging.

5.   Kaufman JA, Yucel EK, Waltman AC et al. MR angiography in the preoperative evaluation of abdominal aortic aneurysms: A preliminary study. JVIR 1994; 5:489-496.
      This original publication touts the use of contrast enhanced MR angiography as the most complete single method for preoperative aortic imaging. The techniques used to create optimal images are described in detail.

6.   Bartle EJ, Pearce WH, Sun JH et al. Infrarenal venous anomalies and aortic surgery: Avoiding vascular injury. J Vasc Surg 1987; 6:590-593.
      Classic paper describing the venous anomalies that can be encountered during aortic surgery and the incidences of each.

7

CHAPTER 8

Surgical Exposure for Aortic Surgery

Jeffrey L. Ballard

A well-planned surgical exposure facilitates even the most difficult peripheral vascular procedure. Awareness of the relationship of surface anatomy to underlying vascular structures ensures precise incision placement. This helps to minimize tissue trauma and reduces the likelihood of wound infection. In addition, detailed knowledge of vascular anatomy helps to prevent injury to vital structures in the operative field. In this chapter, anatomic relationships will be emphasized and vascular anatomic variations that may be encountered during common aortic exposures will be highlighted. Several alternate surgical approaches will also be described. Sources given in the reference list will supply the reader with additional detailed information.

Exposure of the descending thoracic and proximal abdominal aorta will be discussed first. This will be followed by a systematic discussion of elective and emergent surgical exposure of the abdominal aorta and its major branches. Iliac artery exposure is the final topic discussed in this chapter.

Exposure of the Descending Thoracic and Proximal Abdominal Aorta

No single approach lends itself so well to extensive exposure of the thoracic and abdominal aorta as a properly positioned thoracoabdominal incision. After pulmonary artery and radial arterial line placement and dual-lumen tracheal intubation, the patient is placed in a modified right lateral decubitus position with the hips rotated 45 degrees from horizontal. This allows exposure of both groins. A bean bag device is helpful to support the patient's position on the operating table. The free left upper extremity should be passed across the upper chest and supported on a cushioned Mayo stand (Fig. 8.1). In this way, thoracoabdominal aortic exposure is gained by unwinding the torso as described by Stoney and Wylie.

The rib interspace to enter primarily depends on the extent of thoracic aorta to be exposed. The forth or fifth intercostal space is used when the entire thoracoabdominal aorta from subclavian artery origin through abdominal aorta is to be exposed whereas the eighth or ninth intercostal space allows mid to terminal thoracic aortic exposure plus wide abdominal aortic visualization. On occasion, two interspaces (for instance, forth and ninth) may be entered under one thoracoabdominal incision to facilitate proximal descending thoracic and abdominal aortic exposure. The thoracic incision is continued across the costal margin in a paramedian plane to the level of the umbilicus (Fig. 8.1). If the terminal aorta and iliac vessels are to be exposed, the incision is extended to the left lower quadrant.

Aortic Surgery, edited by Jeffrey L. Ballard. ©2000 Landes Bioscience.

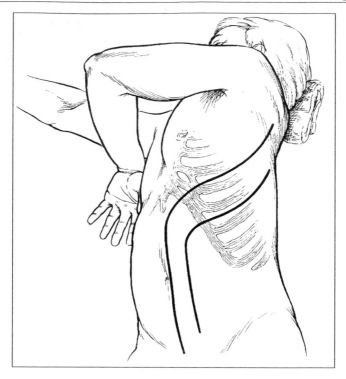

8

Fig. 8.1. Incision options for thoracoabdominal aortic procedures are based on extent of thoracic aorta to be exposed and desire to stay in an extraperitoneal plane. Reprinted with permission from Rutherford RB. Thoracoabdominal aortic exposures. In: Rutherford RB, ed. Atlas of Vascular Surgery: Basic Techniques and Exposures. Philadelphia: W.B. Saunders Company 1993:223.

With the left lung deflated, the origin of the left subclavian artery and proximal descending thoracic aorta can be gently dissected free of surrounding tissue to facilitate cross clamping. The vagus and recurrent laryngeal nerves are densely adherent to the aorta just proximal to the subclavian artery. Meticulous care should be taken not to injure these structures. Division of the inferior pulmonary ligament will expose the mid and distal descending thoracic aorta. The diaphragm is radially incised toward the aortic hiatus and the left crus of the diaphragm is divided to expose the terminal descending thoracic aorta (Fig. 8.2). Alternatively, just the central tendinous portion of diaphragm can be divided or it can be incised circumferentially at a distance of approximately 2.5 cm from the chest wall.

The left retroperitoneal space is developed in a retronephric extraperitoneal plane as surgical exposure of the thoracoabdominal aorta is best performed by mobilizing the left kidney forward. Division of the median arcuate ligament and lumbar tributary to the left renal vein will facilitate further medial rotation of abdominal viscera and left kidney.

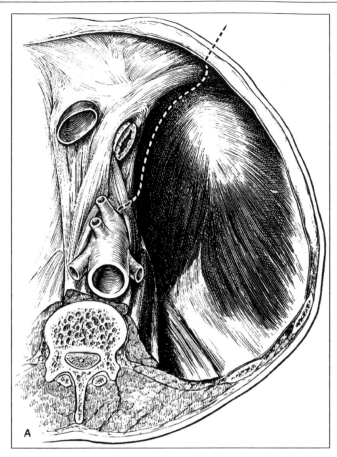

Fig. 8.2. Radial division of the diaphragm and left crus facilitates proximal abdominal aortic and visceral artery exposure. Reprinted with permission from Rutherford RB. Thoracoabdominal aortic exposures. In: Rutherford RB, ed. Atlas of Vascular Surgery: Basic Techniques and Exposures. Philadelphia: W.B. Saunders Company 1993:227.

Aortotomy is facilitated by clearing the posterolateral surface of the thoracoabdominal aorta. With this exposure, the origins of the left renal, celiac and superior mesenteric arteries can then be visualized and dissected free as indicated by the disease process present (Fig. 8.3).

Preservation of the blood supply to the spinal cord is critical in this extensive operation. Brockstein and associates have stressed the importance of the arteria radicularis magna (artery of Adamkiewicz) in providing circulation to the anterior spinal artery. This vessel is a branch of either a distal intercostal or a proximal lumbar artery. It has been identified as proximal as T-5 and as distal as L-4. However, the

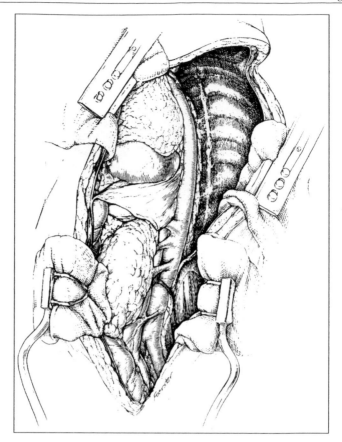

Fig. 8.3. Thoracoabdominal aortic exposure from the origin of the left subclavian artery to the common iliac arteries. Reprinted with permission from Rutherford RB: Thoracoabdominal aortic exposures. In: Rutherford RB, ed. Atlas of Vascular Surgery: Basic Techniques and Exposures. Philadelphia: W.B. Saunders Company 1993:223.

artery generally arises at the T-8 to L-1 level. Therefore, it is unwise to ligate any large intercostal or proximal lumbar artery until the aorta has been opened so that an assessment of backbleeding can be made under direct vision.

Closure of this extensive aortic exposure begins by reapproximating the diaphragm with 2-0 prolene suture. A posterior (#28F) chest tube is placed under direct vision and then the ribs are reapproximated with interrupted #1 Vicryl suture. Occasionally, a segment of the cartilaginous costal arch is excised to provide stable rib approximation. In the abdomen, the posterior rectus sheath is closed and the thoracic musculature is reapproximated in layers with 1-0 Vicryl suture. The anterior rectus sheath is closed with a running #1 PDS suture. Finally, skin is either closed with staples or a running 3-0 subcuticular suture.

Retroperitoneal Exposure of the Abdominal Aorta and Its Branch Vessels

Transperitoneal aortic exposure is generally regarded as the standard operative approach to the abdominal aorta. However, retroperitoneal aortic exposure has gained wider acceptance among vascular surgeons as it affords a more direct route to the aorta and facilitates complex aortic reconstruction above the level of the renal arteries. We and others have demonstrated that in comparison to transperitoneal aortic exposure, the retroperitoneal approach is associated with decreased perioperative morbidity, earlier return of bowel function, fewer respiratory complications, decreased intensive care and hospital stay and lower overall cost.

For this aortic exposure, the patient is positioned on the operating table with the kidney rest at waist level. After pulmonary artery and radial arterial line placement and tracheal intubation, the patient is turned to the right lateral decubitus position with the pelvis rotated posteriorly to allow exposure of both groins. The kidney rest is elevated and the operating table flexed to open the space between the left anterior superior iliac spine and costal margin (Fig. 8.4). The free left upper extremity is positioned as described earlier.

The incision begins over the lateral border of the rectus muscle approximately 2 cm below the level of the umbilicus and is carried laterally over the tip of the 12th rib (Fig. 8.5). This decreases the chance of injury to the main trunk of the intercostal nerve within the 11th intercostal space. In males, resection of a significant portion of this rib facilitates retroperitoneal aortic exposure. However, in females, 12th rib resection is not always required. The anterior rectus sheath is opened to allow transection of the left rectus abdominus muscle. Inferior epigastric vessels are divided between silk ligatures to avoid troublesome postoperative bleeding. The incision is carried laterally through the external and internal oblique muscle fibers. Careful incision of the lateral most aspect of the posterior rectus sheath will facilitate development of an extraperitoneal plane. The remaining posterior sheath is divided toward the midline and laterally, transversus abdominus muscle fibers are split toward the 12th rib.

The peritoneum is gently swept off the posterior rectus sheath, transversus abdominus fibers and diaphragm to allow safe entry into the left retroperitoneal space. This space is best entered laterally. The peritoneum and its contents are swept medially off the psoas muscle toward the diaphragm along with Gerota's fascia with the contained left kidney. With careful manual control of the left kidney/peritoneal contents and counter traction upward on the diaphragm, further medial rotation of the left kidney and viscera allows exposure of the aorta from the left diaphragmatic crus to its bifurcation. The Omni-Tract retraction system (Omni-Tract Surgical, Minneapolis, MN) is critical for maintaining this exposure.

The left renal artery is readily identified and serves as the main landmark for suprarenal as well as infrarenal aortic exposure (Fig. 8.6). Just above this level, division of the median arcuate ligament and left diaphragmatic crus facilitates exposure

8

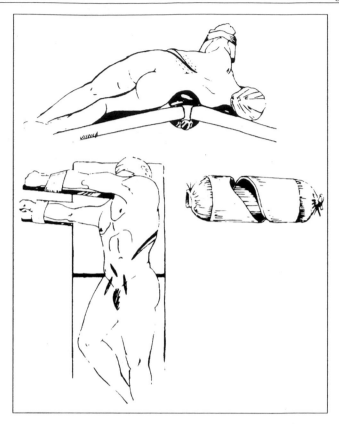

Fig. 8.4. Positioning for retroperitoneal exposure of the aorta. Top, Patient's waist is placed over kidney rest with table flexed. Bottom left, Oblique positioning of hips in relation to table facilitates groin exposure. Left upper extremity is passed across the chest and cushioned on Mayo stand. Bottom right, This position unwinds the torso. Reprinted with permission from Shepard A, Scott G, Mackey W et al. Retroperitoneal approach to high-risk abdominal aortic aneurysms. Arch Surg 1973; 126:157.

of the supraceliac aorta (Fig. 8.7). The celiac and superior mesenteric arteries can be dissected free for a significant length after carefully incising the enveloping neural tissue that surrounds both vessels. If needed, the distal thoracic aorta is readily accessible by carrying the dissection proximally between the crura and in an extrapleural plane. This extended exposure facilitates repair of suprarenal aortic disease and transaortic renal or mesenteric endarterectomy as well as antegrade bypass to these vessels.

This left flank approach is ideal for visceral and renal artery exposure. The celiac artery and proximal aspects of its major branches are readily accessible. In addition,

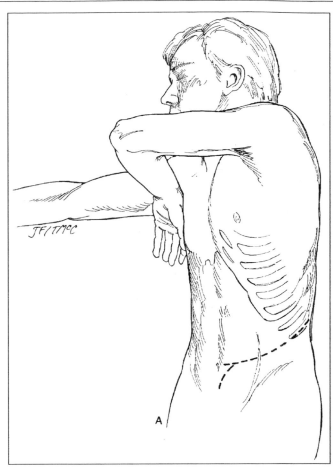

Fig. 8.5. The incision for retroperitoneal aortic exposure is carried across the flank to the 12th rib. Reprinted with permission from Rutherford RB. Thoracoabdominal aortic exposures. In: Rutherford RB, ed. Atlas of Vascular Surgery: Basic Techniques and Exposures. Philadelphia: W.B. Saunders Company 1993:196.

the splenic artery can easily be mobilized off the posterior aspect of the pancreas to facilitate extraanatomic splenorenal bypass. Hepatorenal bypass requires a right retroperitoneal approach. There are no major branches which emanate from the superior mesenteric artery for a distance of up to 5 cms distal to its origin. Therefore, bypass or endarterectomy of the superior mesenteric artery well beyond its orifice is possible without ever entering the peritoneal space. The first major branch is usually the middle colic artery, which arises from the anterior and right lateral surface of the superior mesenteric artery as it emerges from the pancreas. This branch is the usual site for an embolus to lodge. It is important to remember that in addition to a

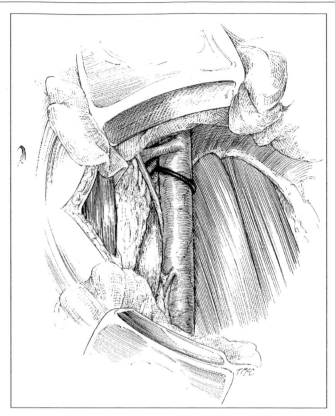

Fig. 8.6. Left renal artery serves as landmark for this dissection. Note iliolumbar venous tributary just distal to the left renal artery. Reprinted with permission from Rutherford RB. Thoracoabdominal aortic exposures. In: Rutherford RB, ed. Atlas of Vascular Surgery: Basic Techniques and Exposures. Philadelphia: W.B. Saunders Company 1993:201.

possible replaced right hepatic artery, the common hepatic artery occasionally arises from the superior mesenteric artery. In both circumstances, the replaced artery arises from the proximal aspect of the superior mesenteric artery just past its origin and courses back toward the right upper quadrant.

Dissection at the origin of the left renal artery and along the posterolateral aspect of the infrarenal aorta will expose the large communicating vein connecting the renal to the hemiazygous vein. Once this venous tributary (often two tributaries are encountered) is divided, the left renal vein can be elevated off the infrarenal aorta to facilitate cross clamping. This maneuver facilitates right renal artery exposure as the origin of this vessel comes into view with superolateral retraction of the left renal vein. This retroperitoneal surgical exposure also allows dissection of either renal artery to its branch vessels in preparation for endarterectomy or bypass.

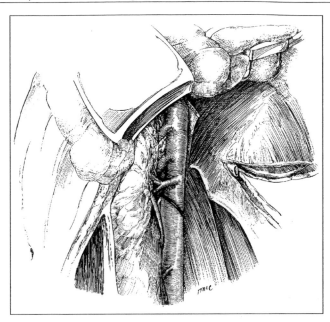

8

Fig. 8.7. Division of the median arcuate ligament and left diaphragmatic crus facilitates suprarenal and supraceliac exposure. Reprinted with permission from Rutherford RB. Thoracoabdominal aortic exposures. In Rutherford RB, ed. Atlas of Vascular Surgery: Basic Techniques and Exposures. Philadelphia: W.B. Saunders Company 1993:207.

In order to carry out transaortic renal endarterectomy with direct visualization of a clean endpoint, it is necessary to dissect the renal arteries well beyond their respective origins. In addition, the segment of aorta to be isolated must be completely mobilized with control of any adjacent lumbar arteries. This will eliminate troublesome backbleeding that can obscure vision after creating an aortotomy. Proximal exposure of the suprarenal aorta should include at least the origin of the superior mesenteric artery so that an aortic clamp can be placed above this level. This is necessary if there is little distance between the takeoff of the renal arteries and mesenteric vessels. Transaortic endarterectomy is accomplished by either transecting the aorta below the level of the renal arteries or by making a longitudinal aortotomy posterolateral to the left renal and/or superior mesenteric artery. Aortotomy can also be carried supraceliac to facilitate visceral endarterectomy. Any of these visceral vessels can also be transected well beyond the disease process to facilitate direct end-to-end bypass. The ability to extensively mobilize the renal and mesenteric arteries is a major advantage of this retroperitoneal surgical exposure.

The inferior mesenteric artery is the primary blood supply to the left colon and is located by carrying the infrarenal dissection inferiorly along the posterolateral aspect of the aorta. In some large aneurysms the thickened wall of the aorta obscures the actual origin of the inferior mesenteric artery. Division of this mesenteric vessel flush with the aorta is generally well tolerated. However, its inadvertent division distal to the left colic branch may result in sigmoid colon infarction. This complication is much more likely to occur when there is arteriosclerotic occlusion of the marginal artery of Drummond. In patients with visceral artery occlusive disease, the left colic artery communicates with the left branch of the middle colic artery to become the meandering mesenteric artery (AKA central anastomotic artery). This artery provides collateral circulation between the superior and the inferior mesenteric arteries and vice versa.

Beyond the pelvic brim, the left common and external iliac arteries are readily accessible for vascular control. Exposure of the distal anterolateral surface of the infrarenal aorta and right common and external iliac arteries is facilitated by ligating and dividing the inferior mesenteric artery flush with the aorta. It is wise to remember that the common iliac veins and vena cava are densely adherent to the posteromedial aspect of the left common iliac artery and posterolateral aspect of the right common iliac artery. Vascular control of these vessels is safest after gently elevating them off their respective underlying major vein. This maneuver also facilitates transection of the distal common iliac artery under direct vision so that end-to-end aortoiliac reconstruction can be accomplished. If the iliac anastomosis cannot be performed at this level, then it is wise to graft end-to-end to the internal iliac artery and then to jump a separate graft to the external iliac artery. With this graft configuration, even an aneurysmal internal iliac artery may be simultaneously excluded (by opening it) and bypassed to the level of its first branch vessels. This will help to maintain vital pelvic perfusion.

Wound closure is accomplished in layers using #1 Vicryl suture for the posterior rectus sheath, transversalis fascia, transversus abdominus and internal oblique muscle layers. The anterior rectus sheath and external oblique aponeurosis are closed with #1 PDS suture. Subcuticular skin closure with 3-0 Vicryl suture completes this multilayer wound closure.

Alternate Renal Artery Exposure

The distal right renal artery can be exposed through a right-sided flank incision, which is a "mirror image" of the incision described in the section on retroperitoneal exposure of the aorta. With the patient on the operating table in a modified left lateral decubitus position, the retroperitoneal space is entered laterally after division of the abdominal wall muscles. The peritoneum and contents are gently mobilized anteriorly and medially, including the right kidney enclosed in Gerota's fascia. The renal artery is palpated distally and carefully dissected free of surrounding tissue. The inferior vena cava is also identified and mobilized after ligation of two or three paired lumbar veins. The vena cava can be gently elevated to expose the right posterolateral aspect of the aorta. Partial aortic occlusion with a side-biting vascular clamp is employed for anastomosis of the proximal bypass graft. Thereafter, a distal end-to-end anastomosis completes renal artery revascularization.

Moncure and associates have described an extra-anatomic revascularization procedure for the right kidney. This exposure employs a right subcostal incision extending into the right flank. The hepatic flexure of the colon is mobilized and rotated to the left. The duodenum is kocherized toward the midline to expose the right kidney. The renal artery is located behind and just above the right renal vein. Next, the hepatic artery is palpated in the hepatoduodenal ligament and the gastroduodenal artery identified. The hepatic artery proximal to the gastroduodenal artery is dissected free. An end-to-end (or rarely end-to-side) anastomosis of the bypass graft to the renal artery is constructed first. The bypass is then brought over the hepatoduodenal ligament and anastomosed to the side of the hepatic artery to revascularize the kidney.

The left renal artery can be exposed peripherally for extraanatomic bypass by using the same incision described earlier in this section for retroperitoneal exposure of the abdominal aorta. Once the pararenal aorta is exposed, the tail of the pancreas is separated from the left adrenal gland to expose the splenic artery for bypass to the left renal artery. Inflow can also be obtained from the aorta proximal or distal to the renal artery. This bypass can originate from the side of the aorta with destination to the transected left renal artery.

Alternate Exposure of the Proximal Abdominal Aorta

A helpful modification of the standard midline abdominal incision that can be used to expose the proximal abdominal aorta without entering the chest is illustrated in Figure 8.8. An inverted hockey-stick incision is employed beginning at the left midcostal margin. The left rectus muscle is transected and the oblique and transversus muscles are divided in the direction of the skin incision. The incision is continued down the linea alba to the symphysis pubis. The left colon is mobilized by incising the peritoneum along the white line of Toldt from the pelvis to the lateral peritoneal attachments of the spleen. The spleen is gently mobilized and brought forward toward the midline by incising the splenorenal and splenophrenic ligaments.

Dissection is continued by forward mobilization of the spleen, pancreatic tail and splenic flexure of the colon between the mesocolon and Gerota's fascia taking care not to damage the adrenal gland medially or the adrenal vein at its junction with the left renal vein. This left-to-right transperitoneal medial visceral rotation affords excellent exposure of the supraceliac and visceral aorta including the renal arteries (Fig. 8.9). Division of the median arcuate ligament and diaphragmatic crura exposes the distal thoracic aorta without entering the left chest. The left kidney can be brought forward with the rest of mobilized viscera or left in situ.

Transperitoneal Exposure of the Infrarenal Abdominal Aorta

A midline abdominal incision from the xiphoid to symphysis pubis is commonly used for anterior exposure of the abdominal aorta. One major disadvantage of this approach is incomplete visualization of the proximal abdominal aorta and/or renal artery origins. This potential lack of exposure is improved by proximally extending the midline incision around the xiphoid process and completely mobilizing the third and fourth portions of the duodenum. The dissection continues through the posterior peritoneum just lateral to the duodenum and medial to the inferior mesenteric vein to avoid damaging the circulation to the left or sigmoid colon. This is particularly

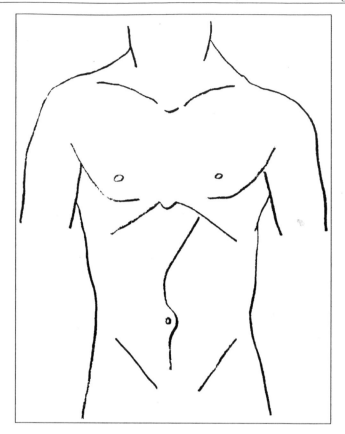

Fig. 8.8. Modified abdominal incision for transperitoneal medial visceral rotation exposure of the abdominal aorta. Reprinted with permission from Deiparine MK, Ballard JL. Correspondence re: "Transperitoneal medial visceral rotation." Ann Vasc Surg 1995; 9(6):607.

important in dealing with ruptured abdominal aortic aneurysms, where landmarks are frequently obscured by an extensive retroperitoneal hematoma. The duodenum can nearly always be visualized and used as a landmark during this exposure.

It is wise to palpate the aortic bifurcation and expose the common iliac arteries from the midline, thereby avoiding injury to the ureters. Fibers of the sympathetic nerves arch over the left common iliac artery in males, and damage to these sympathetic fibers can result in erectile dysfunction and retrograde ejaculation. The external iliac arteries can be readily identified by incising along the white line of Toldt and mobilizing the sigmoid or proximal ascending colon toward the midline. Graft limbs coursing out to this level should be passed under both the colon mesentery and ureter.

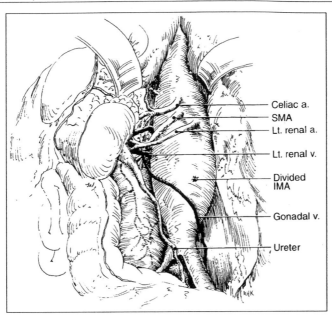

Fig. 8.9. Transperitoneal medial visceral rotation exposure of supraceliac abdominal aortic aneurysm. Reprinted with permission from Ballard JL. Management of renal artery stenosis in conjunction with aortic aneurysm. In: Wilson ES ed. Semin Vasc Surg 1996; 9:221.

8

Transperitoneal Exposure of the Renal Arteries

The left main renal artery usually arises from the posterolateral surface of the aorta at the level of the upper border of the left renal vein as it crosses the abdominal aorta. The right renal artery usually arises at a slightly lower level. Anterior exposure of the origin of either renal artery involves incision of the posterior parietal peritoneum just lateral to the fourth portion of the duodenum. Additional exposure is obtained by continuing this incision along the distal third portion of the duodenum.

The left renal vein is identified and carefully mobilized. Frequently there is a small parietal vein that terminates in the inferior margin of the left renal vein over the aorta. Otherwise there are two major venous tributaries to be identified, ligated and divided. The first is located by following the inferior margin of the left renal vein laterally to the termination of the left gonadal vein. Next the dissection is carried laterally along the superior surface of the left renal vein until the confluence of the left adrenal vein is identified. It should be ligated flush with the renal vein and divided. The entire left renal vein can then be mobilized on a silastic vascular loop.

A word of caution here. There is an important large communicating vein arising from the posterior surface of the proximal left renal vein. This vein communicates with the adjacent lumbar vein and thence to the hemiazygous system and superior vena cava. The presence of this venous collateral allows acute ligation of the left renal vein without impairment of renal function. This lumbar venous communication should be preserved if at all possible during this anterior transperitoneal approach.

Once the left renal vein is mobilized, attention should be directed to exposing the left lateral surface of the aorta above and below the level of the left renal vein. The left renal artery arising from the posterolateral surface of the aorta will thus be exposed. Autonomic nerve elements will be encountered on the renal artery but can be divided without concern. Gentle placement of a vein retractor under the left renal vein with upward retraction by an assistant greatly facilitates this exposure. A silastic loop placed about the renal artery origin aids in the mobilization and dissection of this vessel.

The right renal artery is more difficult to expose, since it passes directly behind the inferior vena cava on its course to the renal hilum. The origin of this artery is palpated as it emerges from the right posterolateral aspect of the aorta. Care should be taken not to injure the right adrenal branch which arises 5-10 mm from the origin of the right renal artery. The size of this vessel may be 2-3 mm when renal artery stenosis is present since it becomes a very important collateral to the distal right renal artery via capsular branches. In the event that the entire right renal artery and its branches must be exposed, the surgeon must completely mobilize the vena cava above and below the artery by carefully ligating and dividing all adjacent lumbar veins.

The subhepatic space is entered and the duodenum kocherized to allow exposure of the right renal vein as it joins the inferior vena cava. The renal vein is mobilized on a silastic loop to aid in identification of the main renal artery lying beneath the vein. Exposure of the renal artery is completed when this distal dissection joins the medial exposure already described.

Transperitoneal Exposure of the Abdominal Aorta at the Diaphragmatic Hiatus

Exposure of the supraceliac aorta at the diaphragmatic hiatus is life saving for early control of exigent hemorrhage in the case of ruptured abdominal aortic aneurysm. It is also useful for temporary control of the aorta during repair of aortocaval or aortoenteric fistulae and infected aortic grafts. Less frequently, this exposure is suitable for revascularization of the celiac trunk and its proximal branches or the superior mesenteric artery.

This exposure, through the lesser sac, is facilitated by downward retraction of the stomach and lateral retraction of the esophagus. The aortic pulse is palpated and the arching fibers of the diaphragm at the aortic hiatus are divided directly over the aorta. The periaortic fascia is opened and index and middle fingers are passed medial and lateral to the aorta. Gentle blunt finger dissection between the diaphragmatic fibers and the aorta will create space on either side of the aorta. This maneuver is critical as any overlying muscle fibers will allow a vascular occluding clamp to slide up and off the aorta. No effort is made to completely encircle the aorta since an intercostal or proximal lumbar artery or vein can be avulsed with troublesome bleeding. At this point, a partially opened aortic clamp is advanced over the dorsal hand

and appropriately positioned fingers to cross clamp the aorta and interrupt blood flow. This exposure is illustrated in Figure 8.10.

Celiac artery reconstruction requires more exposure. A generous incision is made in the posterior parietal peritoneum (Fig. 8.11) and the diaphragmatic crura are completely divided. The inferior phrenic arteries should be isolated, ligated and divided. The aortic branch to the left adrenal gland is also usually visualized and sacrificed. Dissection is continued distally to expose the celiac artery, which can be palpated at its origin from the anterior surface of the aorta. Dense fibers of the median arcuate ligament are divided along with the neural elements forming the celiac plexus. This tissue is quite vascular; thus, stick ties and cautery are useful for hemostasis. Once the celiac trunk has been exposed, the hepatic artery is dissected free of surrounding tissue as it courses toward the liver hilum. Sympathetic nerve fibers can be seen to entwine on the surface of this vessel. There is usually a 3-4 cm segment of the hepatic artery that is free of branches and therefore useful as a site for vascular anastomosis. The splenic artery is palpable at the superior border of the pancreas and courses to the left toward the splenic hilum. Here again there is a 4-5 cm segment free of branches that can be used for placement of a vascular anastomosis. The left gastric artery is the smallest of the three main branches of the celiac artery. It courses anteriorly to follow the lesser curvature of the stomach and should be protected during this exposure.

The supraceliac aorta can also be used as bypass origin for superior mesenteric artery reconstruction. The proximal anastomosis is made on the anterior surface of the aorta after opening the aortic hiatus as described above. A tunnel must then be created behind the pancreas using careful finger dissection. The bypass graft is passed through the tunnel and anastomosed to the distal patent superior mesenteric artery. Kinking of the bypass with replacement of bowel is unlikely in this tunneled position as can occur with retrograde aortic-to-superior mesenteric artery bypass grafts.

Anterior exposure of the superior mesenteric artery inferior to the transverse mesocolon requires opening the posterior parietal peritoneum lateral to the third and fourth portions of the duodenum (Fig. 8.8). The left renal vein is identified and mobilized as described above for exposure of the renal arteries. The left renal vein is retracted downward and the dissection carried upward on the aorta until the superior mesenteric artery origin can be palpated. It usually arises from the left side of the anterior surface of the aorta. The artery is immediately encased by the superior mesenteric sympathetic nerve plexus which must be incised for exposure. Bleeding from the vascular plexus tissue is controlled by cautery and suture ligatures. This exposure is significantly limited by the overlaying transverse mesocolon and pancreas.

Emergency Exposure of the Abdominal Aorta and Vena Cava

Vascular exposure of injured vessels within the abdomen is best carried out through a generous midline abdominal incision. Location of the encountered hematoma determines the exposure to be employed. Since the abdominal circulation arises in a retroperitoneal location, the overlying viscera will need to be rotated medially or elevated superiorly in order to expose the aorta and its major branches or the caval and portal venous circulation.

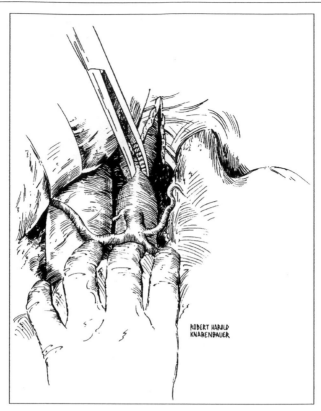

Fig. 8.10. Exposure of the abdominal aorta at the diaphragm. Reprinted with permission from Ballard JL, Killeen JD. Anatomy and surgical exposure of the vascular system. In: Moore WS ed. Vascular Surgery A Comprehensive Review. Philadelphia: WB Saunders Company, 1998:54.

Kudsk and Sheldon have classified the retroperitoneal space into three zones (Fig. 8.12). The presence of a central hematoma (zone 1) indicates injury to the aorta, proximal renal/visceral arteries, inferior vena cava or portal vein. An expanding, zone 1 retroperitoneal hematoma with extension to the left indicates a proximal aortic or adjacent major branch vessel injury. Transperitoneal left-to-right medial visceral rotation will swiftly and widely expose the aorta from the diaphragm to its bifurcation. Exposure can be facilitated by division of the left rectus muscle transversely in the left upper quadrant or by the modified abdominal incision described earlier in the chapter. The splenic flexure is mobilized including the spleen and the left kidney with rotation of these viscera to the right. The origins of the celiac, superior mesenteric, and renal arteries are likewise exposed.

The presence of a zone 1 retroperitoneal hematoma with extension into the right flank is indicative of major caval, portal venous or proximal injury to a major arterial

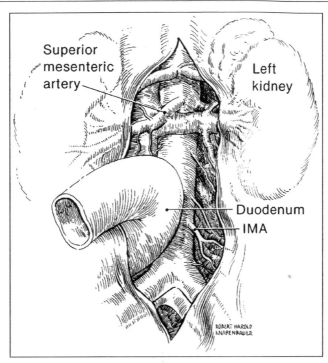

Fig. 8.11. Anterior exposure of the superior mesenteric artery. Pancreas and transverse colon are not shown but are retracted cephalad. Reprinted with permission from Ballard JL, Killeen JD. Anatomy and surgical exposure of the vascular system. In: Moore WS ed. Vascular Surgery A Comprehensive Review. Philadelphia: WB Saunders Co., 1998:55.

branch in the right upper quadrant. Exposure is gained by incising the peritoneum lateral to the ascending colon and reflecting this structure medially followed by duodenal kocherization. This right-to-left medial visceral rotation exposes the entire vena cava from the iliac confluence to the liver (Fig. 8.13).

The portal vein is inspected by incising the hepatoduodenal ligament above the duodenum. The common bile duct is retracted laterally and the hepatic artery is palpated and isolated for inspection. Thereafter the portal vein is exposed by retracting the hepatic artery toward the midline. The right side of the aorta can be inspected as well as the proximal right renal artery if rotation and mobilization of the overlying bowel is continued to the midline.

Lateral hematomas (zone 2) indicate injury to distal visceral and renal vessels. Despite their lateral location, it is wise not to enter a large hematoma to control exigent hemorrhage until central aortic exposure has been secured for possible cross clamping. Retroperitoneal pelvic hematomas (zone 3) usually indicate torn branches of the iliac vessels associated with pelvic fractures. These may not require exploration

8

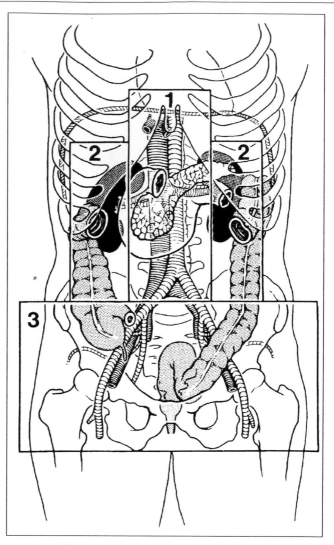

Fig. 8.12. Anatomic zones for exploration of abdominal vascular trauma. Reprinted with permission from Kudsk KA, Sheldon GF. Retroperitoneal hematoma. In: Blaisdell FW, Trunkey DD eds. Trauma Management, Vol I: Abdominal Trauma, 2nd ed. New York: Thieme Medical Publishers, Inc. 1993:400.

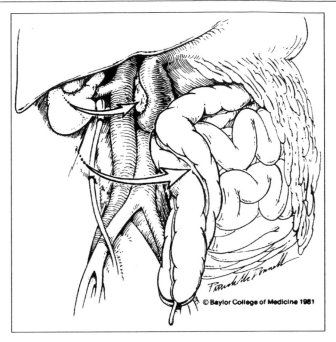

Fig. 8.13. Right-to-left medial visceral rotation. Reprinted with the permission of Dohrmann M, original illustrator.

unless the hematoma is expanding or there is evidence of large-vessel injury demonstrated by angiography.

Extraperitoneal Exposure of the External Iliac Arteries

This exposure begins with an oblique incision in the lower quadrant of the abdomen on the side of involved iliac artery occlusive disease. It is wise to start the incision near the pubic tubercle with extension obliquely lateral, staying medial to the anterior superior iliac spine of the pelvis. The external oblique aponeurosis is opened in the direction of its fibers and the incision continued into the fleshy portion of this muscle. The internal oblique and transversus abdominus muscles are divided in the direction of the incision to enter the preperitoneal space. The peritoneum is gently pushed medially to expose the external iliac artery. Exposure of the common iliac artery requires extension of the incision proximally and laterally into the flank region.

Care should be taken not to injure the ilioinguinal or genitofemoral nerves during exposure or retraction. Their location on the anterior surface of the psoas muscle is vulnerable. Combination of this incision with a curvilinear incision over the common femoral artery will permit exposure from the terminal common iliac artery to the proximal superficial or deep femoral arteries (Fig. 8.14). The iliac artery exposed

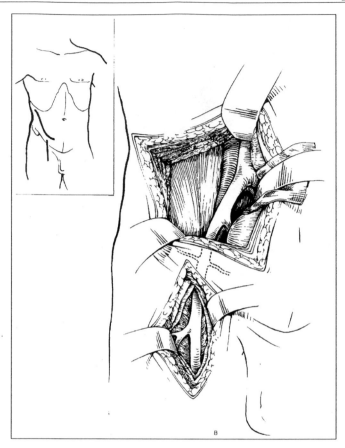

Fig. 8.14. Extraperitoneal exposure of the distal common and external iliac arteries. Counter incision at groin facilitates ilio-femoral reconstruction.

in this extraperitoneal fashion is particularly appealing as an inflow source in cases in which there is extensive scarring at the groin from previous peripheral vascular procedures.

Selected Readings

1.   Ballard JL, Killeen JD. Anatomy and surgical exposure of the vascular system. In: Moore WS ed. Vascular Surgery—A Comprehensive Review. Philadelphia: W.B. Saunders Company. 1998;44-66.
      This chapter reviews pertinent vascular anatomy and surgical exposure of the vascular system from a surgeon's perspective. Accompanying figures and radiographs nicely complement the surgical descriptions.

2.   Stoney R, Wylie E. Surgical management of arterial lesions of the thoracolumbar aorta. Am J Surg 1973; 126:157.

Dr. Stoney at the Forty-fourth Annual Meeting of the Pacific Coast Surgical Association presented this report of 4 patients who had exposure and vascular reconstruction of the thoracoabdominal aorta. This paper emphasizes the importance of proper patient position, extraperitoneal aortic exposure, preservation of spinal cord blood flow and sequential visceral perfusion.

3. Brockstein B, Johns L, Gewertz BL. Blood supply to the spinal cord: Anatomic and physiologic correlations. Ann Vasc Surg 1994; 8:394.

    This excellent review article clarifies current thought on blood supply to the spinal cord. This subject has been studied for many years, yet conflicting data and confusing nomenclature complicates understanding of this clinically important area. Thankfully, these authors have greatly facilitated this understanding.

4. Ballard JL, Yonemoto H, Killeen JD. Cost effective aortic exposure: A retroperitoneal experience. In press, Ann Vasc Surg 2000; 14:1-5.

    Retroperitoneal aortic exposure is compared to transperitoneal aortic exposure with regard to hospital and ICU days, perioperative complications and cost. These data demonstrate that one modification of the standard operative approach to infrarenal aortic aneurysm repair can greatly affect outcome. Retroperitoneal exposure for this aortic repair is associated with decreased pulmonary complications, significantly shorter ICU and hospital days and significantly decreased hospital cost compared to transperitoneal aortic exposure.

5. Sicard GA, Reilly JM, Rubin BG et al. Transabdominal versus retroperitoneal incision for abdominal aortic surgery: report of a prospective randomized trial. J Vasc Surg 1995; 21:174-83.

    In a prospective randomized trial, these authors demonstrated that in comparison to transperitoneal aortic exposure, the retroperitoneal approach was associated with decreased perioperative morbidity, earlier return of bowel function, fewer respiratory complications, decreased intensive care and hospital stay and lower cost. However, in this experience there were more wound problems associated with retroperitoneal aortic exposure.

6. Darling RC III, Shah DM, McClellan WR et al. Decreased morbidity associated with retroperitoneal exclusion treatment for abdominal aortic aneurysm. J Cardiovasc Surg 1992; 33:65-9.

    As above, these authors have championed the use of retroperitoneal aortic exposure. They too have demonstrated significant reduction in morbidity when the aorta is approached through the flank as opposed to the abdomen.

7. Uflacker R. Abdominal aorta and branches. In: Uflacker R, ed. Atlas of Vascular Anatomy—An angiographic approach. Baltimore: Williams and Wilkens. 1997; 405-604.

    This text is a quick and practical reference of vascular anatomy designed for anyone involved with anatomy, diagnosis and treatment of vascular diseases. All vascular territories are regionally depicted and correlated with function where applicable. Critical anatomic structures related to the clinical and surgical application of vascular anatomy is highlighted throughout this beautifully illustrated text.

8. Tollefson DFJ, Ernst CB. Gastrointestinal and visceral ischemic complications of aortic reconstruction. In: Bernhard VM, Towne JB eds. Complications in Vascular Surgery. St Louis: Quality Medical Publishing, Inc. 1991; 135-152.

    Despite significant advances in the field of vascular surgery, gastrointestinal complications occasionally occur. This chapter emphasizes the importance of early identification of patients at high risk for this type of complication and institution of preventative measures aimed at minimizing such events. Topics covered in this thorough review include epidemiologic considerations, relevant anatomy and pathophysiology, clinical

8

diagnosis, treatment options and preventive strategies. The last section discusses other intra-abdominal diseases that could complicate aortic reconstruction such as gallstones, pancreatitis, peptic ulcer disease and malignancy.

9.   Moncure A, Brewster D, Darling R et al. Use of the splenic and hepatic arteries for renal revascularization. J Vasc Surg 1986; 3:196-203.

During a 16-year period, 77 patients underwent 79 extra-anatomic renal artery reconstructions for treatment of renovascular hypertension, renal preservation, or both. Perioperative mortality was 6% and there was no incidence of hepatic dysfunction. Hypertension cure or improvement was achieved in 52 of 63 patients and renal function was preserved or improved in 67 of 77 patients. Remarkably, deterioration of renal function only occurred in three patients and each had had bilateral simultaneous repair. Long-term results demonstrated the safety and excellent durability of these alternate renal reconstructions.

10.   Kudsk KA, Sheldon GF. Retroperitoneal hematoma. In: Blaisdell FW, Trunkey DD, eds. Trauma Management, Vol I: Abdominal Trauma. New York: Thieme-Stratton, Inc. 1982;281.

These authors divide the retroperitoneal space into three zones to facilitate diagnosis and emergency treatment of major intra-abdominal vascular injury. The presence of a central hematoma (zone 1) indicates injury to the aorta, proximal renal/visceral arteries, vena cava or portal vein. Lateral hematomas (zone 2) indicate injury to distal visceral vessels. Retroperitoneal pelvic hematomas (zone 3) usually indicate torn branches of the iliac vessels associated with pelvic fractures. These may not require exploration unless the hematoma is expanding or there is evidence of large-vessel injury demonstrated by angiography.

CHAPTER 9

Management of Small Aortic Aneurysms

Robert A. Duensing and Samuel E. Wilson

Since the first reported aortic aneurysm resection by DuBost in 1951, the operative morbidity and mortality for aneurysm repair has steadily improved. Today, consideration of the optimal management of abdominal aortic aneurysms (AAA) requires a balance between the individualized operative morbidity and mortality and the risk of rupture. Overall operative mortality rates for elective aneurysm repair have been reported in the range of 4.5-6.5%. Most surgeons agree that repair is indicated when the maximal transverse diameter of the aneurysm reaches 5.0 cm. This opinion stems from reports of heightened rupture rates in large aneurysms observed in necropsy, retrospective, and prospective studies published in prior decades. Prohibitive morbidity and mortality rates of 40-50% encountered with operative management of ruptured aortic aneurysms is a compelling reason to perform elective repair.

Due to the evolution and ready availability of noninvasive imaging modalities such as transabdominal ultrasonography and computed tomography (CT), there has been a sevenfold increase in the detection of abdominal aortic aneurysms since 1950. It is also likely that there is a true increase in the prevalence of aortic aneurysmal disease. Identification of asymptomatic aneurysms in large screening programs have revealed that approximately 1.7% of older men have abdominal aortic aneurysms larger than 4.0 cm, with 25% of these greater than 6.0 cm.

The natural history of aortic aneurysms is that of enlargement and the best predictor of rupture is the transverse diameter. Growth rate variability and unpredictable rupture rates reported for small aneurysms have complicated management strategies for this subgroup. The goal of aneurysm repair is to remove the potential for life threatening rupture without invoking a prohibitively high risk of death or major morbidity that would not have otherwise been present without surgery. With these considerations in mind, it is apparent that the management of smaller diameter lesions is unsettled compared to large aneurysms. In fact, this has become one of the most controversial topics in vascular surgery. In an effort to develop guidelines for the treatment of small aortic aneurysms, three randomized multi-center trials were constructed, two of which are completed and one is nearing completion.

This chapter will discuss the incidence, natural history, rupture potential, and management strategies available for patients with small aneurysms of the infrarenal aorta.

Incidence and Risk Factors

A noted increase occurred in the number of men who had the diagnosis of abdominal aortic aneurysm admitted to hospitals from 1968-1983. Causal relationships between an increased incidence of AAA and improved screening and diagnostic techniques have been examined in retrospective studies. In fact, the conclusions of these reports indicate that a real increase in the prevalence of infrarenal AAA has occurred over the past decade.

The incidence of abdominal aortic dilation varies depending on the population from which data is extracted. In autopsy series, infrarenal aneurysms have been reported to occur in 1.5% of that population. This rate increases to 4.6% in unselected patients screened with abdominal ultrasound. When screening patients with known vascular disease, this rate rises from 5% in patients with coronary artery disease to 9.6% in patients with peripheral vascular disease, and is the highest in the 53% of patients who have popliteal or femoral artery aneurysms.

Screening programs using abdominal ultrasonography provide the best account of asymptomatic aneurysms. The prevalence of AAAs greater than 4.0 cm ranges from 0.9-3.3% in data obtained in ultrasound screening studies. This variation in rate is affected by the population being studied and influenced by the relative degree of certain known risk factors, such as age, atherosclerotic disease and smoking. Overall, the prevalence of small aneurysms is higher than larger aneurysms. In one large screening study that identified 3366 patients with asymptomatic aneurysms from a population of 73,451 persons, 1.4% had AAA 4.0 cm or greater, 0.5% greater than 5.0 cm, 0.3% greater than 5.5 cm, 0.19% greater than 6.0 cm, 0.07% greater than 7.0 cm and 0.03% at least 8.0 cm. In this study, more than one-third of patients who had aortic dilation had aneurysms greater 4.0 cm, while only one-sixth were larger than 5.0 cm; a greater than 50% difference in occurrence. This has significant implications when considering size as a threshold for aneurysm repair.

Most of the information regarding risk factors for abdominal aortic aneurysms is the result of large population based multivariate analyses in case-control studies and univariate analyses in prospective reports. Evidence has demonstrated that cigarette smoking is a significant and consistent risk factor for AAA formation. Other important risk factors include coronary artery disease, family history and hypertension. Characteristics such as diabetes and female gender have been identified as negative risk factors.

Natural History and Risk of Rupture

Rupture of abdominal aortic aneurysms is the 10th most common cause of death for men over age 55. Abdominal aortic aneurysms are responsible for approximately 15,000 deaths per year in the United States, including deaths related to both repair and rupture. Data describing the natural history of small AAAs is limited mainly because most surgeons repair aneurysms once they reach 5.0 cm or show evidence of rapid expansion. Prior to the development of aneurysmorrhaphy, long term survival of patients with AAAs was limited. Subsequent studies by Debakey et al showed a clear survival benefit in patients who underwent aneurysm repair versus no operation. In 1966, Szilagyi et al unveiled a relationship between long term survival and aneurysm diameter. In this retrospective study, patients with aneurysms less than 6.0 cm experienced a 5 year survival of 47.8% compared to a mere 6% for patients with aneurysms greater than 6.0 cm. However, this study was based on physical exam to determine aneurysm size and cannot be directly translated into observations of aneurysm size determined with modern techniques, such as ultrasonography and computed tomography. Some contemporary data regarding the natural history of small AAAs has been provided by Cronenwett et al. Sixty-seven patients with asymptomatic AAAs chosen for nonoperative management due to a combination of advanced age, cardiac risk factors and small aneurysms were observed with serial ultrasonography. Cumulative 5-year survival in these patients was 52%. There was a 28% mortality from other causes and 20% of deaths were from aneurysm rupture. The annual mortality rate due to rupture and other causes in this study was 6% and 5%, respectively. Other studies have demonstrated the importance of myocardial infarction as a cause of mortality in patients with small aneurysms. Szilagyi et al identified myocardial infarction as the cause of death in 36% of patients with AAAs less than 6.0 cm compared to 31% mortality due to aneurysm rupture. The converse was observed in patients with aneurysms greater than 6.0 cm.

Risk of aneurysm rupture is related to the maximum measured anterior-posterior or transverse diameter. The rupture risk is most accurately determined from prospective studies; however, ethical reasons prohibit such studies due to the presumed survival advantage with repair of large aneurysms. Data from retrospective studies have provided helpful guidelines concerning rupture in small aortic aneurysms. An autopsy study by Darling et al found aneurysm rupture as the cause of death in 10% of patients with aneurysms 4.0 cm or smaller, 25% of aneurysms 4.1-7.0 cm, and 46% of aneurysms 7.1-10.1 cm. Another autopsy study by Sterpetti et al demonstrated a rupture rate of 5%, 39%, and 65% for aneurysms measuring less than 5.0, 5.1-6.9, and 7.0 or larger, respectively. However, measurement of aneurysm diameter at autopsy may underestimate the actual diameter compared to living patients measured radiographically when the vascular system is expanded.

Collective review of the literature concludes that an increase in rupture rate parallels an increase in aneurysm size. Some reviewers conclude that aneurysms 5.0-5.9 cm have a 25% chance of rupture over a 5 year period, while aneurysms 6.0 and larger have a rupture rate ranging from 35-75% over 5 years. An accurate estimate of rupture rate is difficult for aortic aneurysms less than 5.0 cm, mainly because of the difficulty in gathering data in this group of patients. The main limitation in natural history studies of small aneurysms is that 40-61% of patients who are observed serially with radiographic studies leave the observation group for aneurysm repair due to rapid diameter expansion of the aneurysm, symptoms, or reaching a prohibitive size. Nevitt et al demonstrated a 3% rupture risk over 10 years in patients with asymptomatic aneurysms less than 5.0 cm. Nearly one-quarter of the study patients subsequently required repair due to early operation selection criteria. However, a study by Guirguis et al demonstrated a rupture rate of 2% of patients with aneurysms ranging 4.0-4.9 cm, of which only 6% of all 300 patients in the study were removed from observation for operation. Annual rupture rates for aneurysms 5.0 cm or less have been reported to be 0.4-5.4% per annum according to gathered literature.

Due to the limitations in acquiring data regarding rupture rates in small aneurysms, an accurate estimation is not currently available. It is reasonable to conclude that aneurysms less than 5.0 cm can rupture; however the rate is much less than that of larger aneurysms. Table 9.1 summarizes three prospective reports of rupture rates in small aneurysms less than 5.0 cm.

Management

Prior to the advent of safe repair techniques, rupture accounted for two-thirds of deaths in patients with abdominal aortic aneurysms. The ability to screen aneurysms in asymptomatic patients using noninvasive methods has led to increased detection at smaller diameters. In order to minimize death from rupture, surgeons are compelled to answer the question: What diameter is the threshold for elective repair of patients with asymptomatic infrarenal abdominal aortic aneurysms? The answer must take into account three considerations that will optimally balance the risk of not repairing smaller aneurysms with the risk of death or significant morbidity related to the repair. First, what is the potential for rupture in patients with small aortic aneurysms? Second, what is the anticipated operative mortality, and third, what is the general health and life expectancy of the individual patient?

Operative mortality has continually declined over the past five decades since the first repair in 1951 to an average of less than 5% in centers with significant vascular experience. As a result, a subcommittee appointed by the Society for Vascular Surgery and the International Society for Cardiovascular Surgery has recommended elective repair for low operative risk patients with AAAs as small as 4.0 cm. Due to the high risk of rupture in aneurysms 6.0 cm or larger, elective resection is generally advocated even in high operative risk patients. The rationale for repair at smaller diameters stems from low elective mortality rates and the potential to avoid aneurysm rupture, which has an overall mortality of 78%. However, whether to repair aortic aneurysms in their early stage, or proceed with serial radiographic monitoring until specific criteria for repair have been met has become an important question both in terms of patient outcome and cost-effectiveness.

The size limits that define small abdominal aortic aneurysms historically have been referred to those with a maximal transverse diameter measured radiographically of less than 5.0 cm. This size reference is based on a generally accepted standard of operative repair for aneurysms larger than 5.0 cm due to their prohibitively high rupture rate. Five-year survival rates were shown by Szilagyi et al to increase markedly, from 6% in patients with aneurysms 5.0 cm or larger without repair, to 47.2% in those after repair.

Measurement of abdominal aortic aneurysm size is primarily obtained using transabdominal ultrasonography or computed tomography. The accuracy of these modalities is critical. Thus, the potential for measurement variation of ultrasonography within the same patient, between ultrasound and CT, and between CTs is important. Until recently, the few studies examining the variations of ultrasonography measurement were mainly related to technical considerations such as operator technique, equipment, time of testing and image reader techniques. In a study by Lederle et al, ultrasound measurements were smaller than CT scan measurements at

Table 9.1. Summary of rupture risk for abdominal aortic aneurysms less than 5.0 cm

Author	Number of patients	Rupture rate
Sterpetti et al	297	5%
Darling et al	64	12%
Bernstein and Chan	67	3%
Nevitt et al	130	0%
Glimaker et al	110	1%
Ouriel et al	214	5%
Guirguis and Barber[10]	300	2%
Faggioli et al	135	9%

a standardized central CT measurement center by an average of 0.27 cm in 258 patients. In this same study, which is the only reported review on the variability of CT scans on AAA diameter, differences of 0.5 cm were observed in 17% of CT scans when the same scan was interpreted by different readers. Additionally, variations occurred between separate interpretations of the same CT scan by one reader, although 90% differed by 0.2 cm or less. Since the decision to repair an asymptomatic patient's aneurysm depends mainly on diameter, the implication of measurement variability becomes increasingly important.

Death after aneurysm rupture is certain unless operative repair occurs expeditiously. Even in the best circumstances, expected operative mortality rates in patients who present with aneurysm rupture approach 50%. Therefore, elective repair of a known asymptomatic aneurysm prior to rupture is the ultimate treatment goal. Assessment of operative mortality is an important aspect in decision making regarding operative verses nonoperative management of asymptomatic aneurysm patients. During the first decade of elective infrarenal aneurysm repair, operative mortality ranged between 13 and 18%. Currently, 30-day operative mortality rates have been reported to vary from 0-10%. Operative mortality rates of surgeons who are active in aneurysm surgery are at the lower end of the spectrum ranging from 4.5-6.5%.

Several factors are responsible for these declining mortality rates, most of which are due to improved preoperative evaluation of operative risk factors, perioperative management, surgical techniques and prosthetic materials, and postoperative care. An additional factor that has contributed to improved operative mortality is the increased number of repairs performed on asymptomatic aneurysms and smaller size compared to four decades ago. Early detection of aortic aneurysms using ultrasound and CT has provided surgeons with a new population of patients who are generally younger and have less severe comorbid factors that effect operative mortality. Such factors include the presence of cardiac disease, hypertension, renal insufficiency and chronic obstructive pulmonary disease. Age has been implicated as a determinant of operative risk. More importantly, is the general health of the individual patient. Studies examining patients 80 years and older have demonstrated a 50% mortality rate due to rupture of their aneurysmal disease. Conversely, comparable operative mortality rates have been obtained in elderly patients of low operative risk due to comorbid factors. As a result, age alone should not be a determinant to aneurysm repair.

Most surgeons agree that patients with aneurysms measuring 5-6 cm may undergo operative repair in the instance of low operative risk. This approach is based on operative mortality rates of less than 5% reported by experienced surgeons. Balanced against a rupture rate of 25-41% over 5 years in this size range, the operative mortality poses less risk to the patient. This view is supported by recommendations from a RAND/Academic Medical Center Consortium expert panel which recommended repair of AAAs larger than 5.0 cm. Szilagyi et al demonstrated prolongation of life in patients with aneurysms less than 6.0 cm who underwent operative repair. In this study, patients were stratified by size; the 5-year survival was 66.7% after aneurysm repair compared to 47.8% in patients observed without operation. Due to an increase in operative risk and mortality, patients with significant comorbid factors that would contribute to a high operative risk and subsequently outweigh the risk of rupture should be observed with serial ultrasound or CT at 6-month intervals until a 6.0 cm maximal transverse diameter is reached. At 6.0 cm, the risk of rupture exceeds the operative risk in most patients despite significant comorbidities. Additionally, aneurysms that enlarge by 0.5 cm or more within 6 months documented by serial radiographic studies should also undergo repair. Lastly, patients who develop symptoms of aneurysm leak or rupture obviously require urgent surgical attention. In this subset of patients, a selective repair approach and the ominous risk of rupture mandates the accessibility of a surgical team with the capability to perform aortic aneurysm repair at any time.

The management of patients with aneurysms less than 5.0 cm is less clear because of the inability to accurately predict rupture rates in these smaller aneurysms. Two management approaches have evolved and include immediate surgery once an aneurysm of any size is detected, and observation using serial imaging techniques until signs or symptoms of rupture develop or a diameter threshold is reached (usually 5.0 cm). Three multicenter randomized prospective trials have evolved to help provide guidelines for the management of small aneurysms. The first concluded trial was the Canadian Aneurysm Study. Unfortunately, this study was discontinued early due to inadequate recruitment. Nonetheless, important information was obtained from those patients who were enrolled in the trial. The second multicenter trial conducted in the United Kingdom (UK) was successfully completed and reported in 1999. The third, currently underway in the United States, is the Aneurysm Detection and Management (ADAM) Study that scheduled to conclude in 2000. Results of these trials are summarized in Table 9.2.

The Canadian Aneurysm Study enrolled 666 patients prior to its discontinuation. From the data collected an operative mortality rate of 4.7% was determined. After early discontinuation of the trial, a total of 680 patients underwent aneurysm repair, with an overall 6-year survival of 60.2%. Only 1.5% of these deaths were related to aneurysmal disease. The UK Small Aneurysm trial randomized 1090 patients aged 60-76 years with asymptomatic aneurysms of 4.0-5.5 cm determined by ultrasound screening to either aneurysm repair or ultrasound surveillance at regular intervals. The 30-day operative mortality rate was 5.8%. Sixty-one percent of the

Table 9.2. Summary of multicenter prospective randomized trials of small abdominal aortic aneurysms

Results	Canadian Study	UK Trial	ADAM Study
Total patients	680	1090	1350
Follow-up (months)	72	72	60
Operative mortality	4.7%	5.8%	tba
Total survival			
Surveillance	—	64%	tba
Operative	60.2%	64%	tba
AAA related mortality			
Surveillance	—	23%	tba
Operative	1.5%	21%	tba
AAA repair	680	800	tba
Surveillance		321/527(61%)	
Operative		520/563 (92%)	

tba=to be announced
AAA=Abdominal aortic aneurysm

patients in the selective arm eventually met criteria for aneurysm repair with a 7.1% operative mortality rate. Risk of rupture in the surveillance group with aneurysm diameters ranging 4.0-5.5 cm was only 1% per year. The survival for both management groups at 6 years was 64%. The relatively low rupture rate and 5.8% operative mortality rate in this trial led to the conclusion that early surgery offered no advantage in long term survival, thus supporting the approach of ultrasound surveillance in patients with small aneurysms. The ADAM Study is an ongoing trial of patients aged 50-79 years of acceptable operative risk with AAAs measuring 4.0-5.4 cm by screening ultrasound. Similar to the UK Study, surveillance is continued with serial ultrasound until criteria for repair, such as rapid expansion, symptoms or a size of 5.5 cm are met. The target of 1350 randomized patients has been achieved and the trial is nearing its completion. The main goal of the study is to determine mortality from all causes as well as aneurysm related morbidity and mortality.

Until results of the remaining trial are accessible, information from prospective studies on the selective management of small aneurysms are helpful. The results of some important studies are summarized in Table 9.3. These reports differ from the multicenter trials in that a larger diameter of 6.0 cm was used as the criterion for patient removal from the surveillance group. Consequently, rupture rates in these studies may be higher than if a smaller aneurysm threshold was used. Nonetheless, a reasonable management approach is possible based on data available today. It is apparent that strict criteria for operative repair applied to the general population of patients with aneurysms may lead to inappropriate management strategies. Indeed, the decision for immediate aneurysm repair or surveillance requires individualized consideration based on all of the factors discussed previously. With this approach in

Table 9.3. Summary of studies on the selective management of abdominal aortic aneurysms

	Total patients	Follow-up (months)	Elective repair	Operative mortality	AAA related mortality	Non-AAA related mortality
Bernstein/Chan	99	29	41%	5%	4%	34%
Sterpetti et al	54	24	43%	9%	9%	26%
Littooy et al	149	35	39%	3%	7%	19%
Cronenwett et al	73	37	36%	4%	3%	36%
Kingston Study	268	42	43%	2%	1%	14%

AAA=Abdominal aortic aneurysm

mind, certain guidelines can be extracted from previous experience on the management of small aortic aneurysms.

Young, healthy patients with aneurysms 4.0-5.0 cm may experience improved long-term survival with immediate surgery. This strategy is based on minimal to no comorbid factors affecting operative risk and the likelihood of an exceptionally low operative mortality. Unfortunately, this group is the minority in the population of aneurysm patients. For the majority of patients with small aneurysms, in which exceptional operative mortality cannot be assured, surveillance is most appropriate. The threshold for repair then should be dictated by the presence and degree of comorbidities that might affect operative risk. Patients with minimal risk factors will benefit from aneurysm repair once the diameter reaches 5.0 cm. A threshold of 6.0 cm is more likely to optimize long-term survival in patients with multiple and/or severe illness. Overall, the surgeon's decision must carefully consider multiple factors, including operative risk, rupture risk, age and expected longevity, and patient desire.

The Advent of Endoluminal Aortic Stented Grafts

Another technique currently in clinical trials worldwide that has demonstrated considerable promise is aortic aneurysm exclusion using stent-graft devices placed through an endoluminal route. This procedure requires common femoral or external iliac artery exposure followed by fluoroscopic guided deployment of the stented-graft. There are several device designs, each of which claim specific advantages. Results using this technique are encouraging, however limitations regarding aneurysm characteristics are significant. Accumulated data from 12 of the largest clinical studies published from 1995-1997 reveal an initial success rate of 65-80%. However, the 10-25% rate of perigraft leak poses the threat of continued aneurysm growth with rupture a distinct possibility. Overall perioperative mortality rates ranged from 0-28%, but this includes data from devices in early stages of design. While the perioperative mortality rates will likely improve with more sophisticated technology and experience, the primary efficacy measured by prevention of aneurysm rupture over time is yet to be determined.

The potential advantage of endoluminal aneurysm repair relies on the fact that an intraabdominal operation and prolonged aortic occlusion is avoided. This has significant implication to high risk patients with cardiovascular disease, obstructive lung disease, advanced age, and multiple previous abdominal operations which effect operative morbidity and mortality. Therefore, the risk-to-benefit ratio may be improved by endoluminal grafts for patients in whom risks outweigh benefits of open operation. This is particularly applicable to patients with small aneurysms. If operative mortality rates with endovascular aortic grafts prove to be less then conventional open repair, the long-term survival of patient with aneurysms less than 5.0 cm may be enhanced with immediate endoluminal repair, obviating the possibility for rupture. Additionally, high risk patients with aneurysms of 5.0-6.0 cm diameter and a 25-41% rupture rate may benefit from aneurysm exclusion using these new techniques. Despite some less than glowing early results, endoluminally placed aortic stent-grafts for aneurysms is only in the initial stages of development. Final results await larger perioperative experience and long-term survival data.

Selected Readings

1. Lederle FA. Current issues in the management of small abdominal aortic aneurysms. Chronic Diseases in Canada, Proceedings of the Workshop on the Control of Abdominal Aortic Aneurysm 1994; 15 (4S):S38-S39.
   This brief review highlights Dr. Lederle's presentation at the Proceedings of the Workshop on the Control of Abdominal Aortic Aneurysm in May, 1994. The presentation summarizes some of the important reports to date that should be used when developing a management strategy for patients with abdominal aortic aneurysms.

2. Lederle FA. Management of small abdominal aortic aneurysms. Ann Int Med 1990; 113(10):731-732.
   A concise summary describing the controversy surrounding management of aneurysms ranging from 4-6 cm. Several randomized trials comparing immediate surgery with selective surgery within this size range are discussed.

3. Castleden WM, Mercer JC et al. Abdominal aortic aneurysms in Western Australia: Descriptive epidemiology and patterns of rupture. Br J Surg 1985; 72:109-112.
   This excellent retrospective study examines hospital discharge records and operations for 1237 patients with abdominal aortic aneurysms over 11 years in Western Australia. An increase in the prevalence of diagnosis of abdominal aortic aneurysms was noted from 74.8 per 100,000-117.2 per 100,000 and 17.5 per 100,000-33.9 per 100,000 men and women, respectively over 55 years old. Interestingly, this study demonstrates significant correlations between both emergency admission with aortic aneurysms and rupture with winter months in Western Australia.

4. Lederle FA, Wilson SE et al. Design of the abdominal aortic Aneurysm Detection and Management Study. J Vasc Surg 1994; 20:296-303.
   This article describes the impetus and design of the Aneurysm Detection and Management (ADAM) Study, a randomized clinical trial currently in progress at the Department of Veterans Affairs Cooperative Studies Program. Objectives include determination of the best management strategy for abdominal aortic aneurysms ranging from 4.0-5.4 cm in diameter: immediate repair or serial ultrasonography at 6 month intervals until a 5.5 cm diameter threshold, rapid expansion, or symptoms occur.

9

5.   Greenhalgh RM. Small Abdominal Aortic Aneurysm Trials. In: Trials and Tribulations of Vascular Surgery. Greenhalgh RM, Fowkes FGR, eds. London: WB Saunders Company 1996:203-215.

      A descriptive summary of three randomized clinical trials concerning the management of small abdominal aortic aneurysms. The main focus is on the design of the United Kingdom Trial and some early results, however, two other important studies, The Canadian Aneurysm Trial and the Aneurysm Detection and Management (ADAM) Study, are well outlined.

6.   Taylor LM, Porter JM. Basic data related to clinical decision-making in abdominal aortic aneurysms. In: Basic Data Underlying Decision Making in Clinical Vascular Surgery. Porter JM, ed. 1986; 1(4):502-503.AUTHOR: Please provide Publisher and city.

      Clinical decision making should be based on surgical judgement, experience and data from relevant basic and clinical studies. Due to the vast amount of resources and information available, organization of meaningful data can be difficult. This text is constructed specifically to summarize information from quality studies and arranged to allow easy reference to important vascular problems.

7.   Lederle FA, Johnson GR, Wilson SE et al. Prevalence and associations of abdominal aortic aneurysm detected through screening. Ann Int Med 1997; 126:441-449.

      This large Veteran's Affairs cohort study used multivariate analysis to identify factors independently associated with abdominal aortic aneurysm (AAA). Cigarette smoking had the strongest association with AAA – not surprising!

8.   Cronenwett JL, Katz DA. Decision making in the management of abdominal aortic aneurysms. In: Vascular Surgery, Theory and Practice. Callow AD, Ernst CB, eds. Stamford: Appleton and Lange 1995:965-976.

      This chapter emphasizes key considerations a surgeon must examine when constructing a management strategy for patients with abdominal aortic aneurysm. The authors thoroughly examine current data that is important in deciding which patients will benefit from elective abdominal aortic aneurysm repair.

9.   Mitchell MB, Rutherford RB, Krupski WC. Infrarenal abdominal aortic aneurysms. In Vascular Surgery, 4th ed. Rutherford RB, ed. Philadelphia: W.B. Saunders Co., 1995:1032-1059.

      This chapter provides a comprehensive description of infrarenal abdominal aortic aneurysm from diagnosis to operative technique and postoperative care. Particularly superb tables of comparative literature review add significantly to the text.

10.   Mortality results for randomized controlled trial of early elective surgery or ultrasonographic surveillance for small abdominal aortic aneurysms. The UK Small Aneurysm Trial participants. Lancet 1998; 352:1649-1655.

      This study, along with the Aneurysm Detection and Management study and the Canadian aneurysm study, is amongst the largest prospective randomized trials that specifically examines the management strategy, surgery versus surveillance, for abdominal aortic aneurysms 4.0-5.5 cm in diameter. The findings fail to demonstrate a distinct long-term survival advantage for early surgery for aneurysms within this size range.

11.   Johnston KW et al. Nonruptured abdominal aortic aneurysm: Six-year follow-up. Results from the multicenter prospective Canadian aneurysm study. J Vasc Surg 1994; 20:163-170.

      This paper describes early and late survival rates for 680 patients involved in a large prospective randomized trial on patients with abdominal aortic aneurysms. The study identifies increased heart-related and cerebrovascular causes of death in the aneurysm

9

group compared to the general population. Additionally, vascular complications from aneurysm repair or recurrent aneurysms were an uncommon cause of late mortality.

12. Faggioli GL, Stella A, Gargiulo M et al. Morphology of small aneurysms: Definition and impact on risk of rupture. Am J Surg 1994; 168:131-135.

This prospective study of 135 patients evaluated the relationship of small abdominal aortic aneurysm morphology to rupture risk. The presence of aortic blisters was the only independent morphologic predictor of rupture compared to those aneurysms without the lesions.

9

CHAPTER 10

Aortic Surgery in the Very Elderly

Jeffrey L. Ballard

For the most part, the elderly can be treated surgically for their vascular disease in much the same fashion as a younger patient. The expected results, particularly in terms of improved longevity and lifestyle, are similar. However, it must be recognized that morbidity and mortality rates steadily increase with each decade over 65 years of age. Not infrequently, an initial problem cascades into a constellation of complications resulting in death. Proper recognition of this increasing morbidity is nowhere more important than in the treatment of aneurysmal or occlusive aortic disease in the very elderly.

An old vascular axiom wisely states that the current symptoms manifested by any given patient represent only the clinically evident tip of the vascular iceberg. Thus, the experienced vascular surgeon should not only focus on the aortic disease but also on the less clinically evident generalized atherosclerosis process. This generally silent process, particularly in the very elderly, might otherwise prove entirely too clinically evident in the perioperative course. Coexistence of other cardiovascular disease is thus expected and should be thoroughly evaluated before surgical treatment of the presenting problem. The elderly patient presenting with the diagnosis of an abdominal aortic aneurysm (AAA) has a distinct risk of having associated coronary artery disease, both symptomatic and occult. There is also a risk of finding asymptomatic severe carotid occlusive disease and an incidence of associated lower extremity vascular disease. Thus, even the sequence of repair of concomitant vascular problems should be carefully considered in this vulnerable age group.

Concomitant Vascular Disease in the Elderly

The association between coronary artery disease and aortic aneurysmal disease is probably the most intensively studied situation of concomitant vascular disease. Between 50 and 70% of elderly patients presenting to the vascular surgery clinic will have clinically evident coronary artery disease (history of myocardial infarction, angina, ECG evidence of old infarct, etc.). In fact, 10-15% of these will have clinically occult but significant and possibly correctable coronary artery disease. Other authors have noted a relatively high frequency of impairment of left ventricular function on intensive hemodynamic monitoring, clinically occult but significant reduction in ejection fraction found on routine screening and ST segment depression indicating segmental ischemia on routine ST segment monitoring of peripheral vascular patients. It is therefore not surprising that myocardial infarction is the single largest factor for both perioperative and long-term mortality in aortic surgery. In light of this data, we routinely obtain dobutamine stress echocardiograms in

Aortic Surgery, edited by Jeffrey L. Ballard. ©2000 Landes Bioscience.

patients preparing for aortic surgery. Advantages of this strategy are that an ejection fraction can be calculated and the myocardium can be stressed all in one examination.

The incidence of asymptomatic carotid occlusive disease in patients presenting with aortic disease is not insignificant. Therefore, we routinely obtain a screening carotid duplex examination on all patients presenting with aortic disease. Justification for routine screening is based on total patient management for the long-term. Moderate (45-70%) internal carotid artery lesions are noted and followed with serial duplex studies. If a severe (> 70%) asymptomatic internal carotid artery lesion is discovered, it is probably in the patient's best interest to have it repaired. In our practice, carotid endarterectomy for severe asymptomatic disease precedes elective aortic surgery.

There is also a known association between atherosclerotic disease of the aorta and lower extremities. If mild symptoms are present then a screening arterial Doppler examination is useful if no more than a baseline prior to partial or complete correction of potential iliac stenoses during aortic reconstruction. If there are moderate-to-severe symptoms present, and particularly if femoral pulses are decreased or absent, then preoperative arteriography will definitely add useful information. In fact, routinely performed angiography in aneurysm patients will demonstrate roughly half to have peripheral stenoses. On the other hand, routine arteriography in this setting is costly and not without risk. Therefore, we reserve this test for patients with suspected renovascular hypertension or decreased/absent femoral pulses. Otherwise, CT scanning is our preoperative imaging study of choice for patients presenting with aortic aneurysms. Finally, arteriographic or noninvasive vascular laboratory screening is essentially unwarranted if there are palpable pedal pulses and/or no symptoms warranting intervention.

10

Operative Indications

The basic indication for elective repair of an abdominal aortic aneurysm is size ≥ 5 cm in a patient expected to survive greater than one year despite concomitant medical comorbidities. Recognize that this "magic" 5 cm size is based on an aneurysm being twice the reference size of a "normal" male aorta which is 2.0-2.5 cm in diameter. Thus, the relative indication for surgical repair is the same for a woman with a 4.0 cm infrarenal aortic aneurysm whose aorta measures 1.7 cm in diameter at the renal arteries. Patients with small aneurysms (3.5-5.0 cm) who are in good medical condition are also candidates for repair depending on their circumstances. For instance, a hypertensive patient with well controlled chronic obstructive pulmonary disease will benefit from repair as the risk of rupture in this group is significant if the aneurysm is allowed to expand. Similarly, a good risk patient who travels frequently may opt to have a small aneurysm repaired rather that risk rupture in unfamiliar surroundings. AAA repair is also generally indicated for associated complications such as infection, rupture, leakage or distal embolization.

Disabling claudication is a common indication for aortic reconstruction in patients with severe aortoiliac occlusive disease. Patients with concomitant outflow (lower extremity) lesions should have in-flow corrected first. This is because lower extremity symptoms may abate after correction of in-flow and there may be no need for more distal arterial reconstruction. This is particularly true if the in-flow procedure is combined with femoral endarterectomy and profundaplasty. On the other hand, if the aortoiliac lesions are amenable to stent deployment than this may obviate the need for an open procedure altogether. The reader is referred to Chapters 11 and 13 for a more thorough discussion of this topic.

There are no firm official recommendations as to an age cut-off on any of these scenarios but most vascular surgeons would probably add the qualifier of "not very elderly" to the small aneurysm category. Thus, a small abdominal aortic aneurysm in a patient over age 75 would likely be followed with serial duplex ultrasound examinations and demonstrated to be enlarging before repair is recommended. This is based on detailed analysis of the cost-benefit ratio of small aneurysmorrhaphy in the elderly. Age over 75 years shifted the operative mortality significantly enough to outweigh the projected benefit of protection from small aneurysm rupture.

Sequencing Concomitant Vascular Procedures

In the very elderly patient with concomitant aortic aneurysm and cardiovascular disease, the higher risk situation is handled first. Left main/left main equivalent coronary disease, unstable angina, recent myocardial infarction with destabilization would all be indications for coronary bypass to precede aneurysm repair. Significant 3-vessel coronary artery disease with good ejection fraction is a judgment call; aneurysmorrhaphy can be safely performed in urgent situations (i.e., aneurysms that are extremely large, painful or acutely contained ruptures). Conversely, and particularly if the aneurysm is small and/or recently diagnosed, elective coronary bypass followed by aneurysm repair is prudent. Nonurgent aortic disease in conjunction with significant coronary artery disease, reduced ejection fraction (particularly to < 30%) and salvageable myocardium would indicate the need for coronary bypass first. This treatment algorithm is based on the ability to improve ejection fraction and impact both longevity and perioperative myocardial infarction rate during aortic reconstruction.

Others and we have shown that patients with severely compromised left ventricular function can be nursed through aortic surgery with acceptable perioperative myocardial infarction and mortality rate. However, the posthospital mortality rate is 30-50% in the first year, obviating much of the benefit of aneurysm repair. This would then indicate that unless the heart can also be repaired, there is little benefit to aneurysm repair in this setting and particularly in the very elderly patient. Furthermore, there are data that indicate that an ejection fraction < 28% with coronary disease unsuitable for repair constitutes a contraindication to aneurysm repair or aortic bypass, based on prohibitive operative and six-month mortality.

There are no hard and fast data for establishing which operation goes first for the elderly patient with both an aneurysm and severe asymptomatic carotid disease. Obviously, if either is symptomatic then that would take precedence. One ultimately balances the risk of interval aneurysm rupture versus the possibility of stroke during a major aortic procedure. There is, however, no clear theoretic basis for either a stroke occurring during aneurysm repair or for an aneurysm to rupture immediately following endarterectomy. Our judgement has been to repair the carotid artery first and then during the same hospitalization to repair the aneurysm or reconstruct severe aortoiliac occlusive disease.

Finally, we consider an aneurysm to be a life-threatening condition while lower extremity vascular disease is at worst a limb-threatening problem. Consequently, aneurysms that are clearly twice the size of their reference diameter should be repaired first. If a true foot salvage situation exists, then a concomitant (preferably two-team approach) in-flow/outflow procedure may be done or the patient can have the secondary lower extremity revascularization a few days after aortic reconstruction.

There is a theoretic risk for lymphatic contamination of the aortic graft from a distal septic focus (if present) which might suggest that distal bypass and control of the septic focus should be done first followed by aortic grafting. However, the situation of incurring an infected aortic tube or aortoiliac graft from a distal limb septic source has only been described for synthetic grafts associated with a groin incision. No cases exist of more proximal nongroin incision aortic tube or aortoiliac grafts becoming infected in this setting. If aortofemoral grafting is indicated for aortic reconstruction, it is a moot point as to which recognized risk for groin-wound graft infection is greater; the distal septic focus or a redo case involving the same groin incision days/weeks later.

The other special situation that might arise is the combination of distal emboli, foot-threatening ischemia and aortic aneurysmal or occlusive disease. Here, repair of a large aneurysm or severely ulcerated aorta should certainly precede any distal bypass. In the case of a small embolizing aneurysm, if the limb threat is severe, one could make a case for doing the necessary distal limb revascularization first and repairing the aneurysm second, based on the perceived low threat of interval aortic rupture. Theoretically, further emboli from the aneurysm or diseased aorta could occur in the interim, so the time interval between operations should be short.

Loma Linda University Experience

From April 1980 to November 1997, 69 octa- or nonagenarians had aortic aneurysm repair at Loma Linda University Medical Center. There were 56 patients who had elective aneurysm repair and 13 patients who had ruptured aneurysm repair. Mean age was 83 years (range 80-92 years). In the nonruptured group, there were 39 (69.6%) males and 17 (30.4%) females. In the ruptured group, 9 (69.2%) were male and 4 (30.8%) were female. Within the total group, hypertension was present in 65 (94%) patients. Cardiac symptoms such as angina, prior myocardial infarction or history of congestive heart failure were noted in 63 (91%) patients. One (2%) of these elective patients had severe asymptomatic carotid stenosis and had uneventful endarterectomy before aneurysm repair. Five (9%) other patients in the elective group were found to have asymptomatic moderate internal carotid artery stenosis. Lower extremity vascular disease ranging from mild claudication to prior major amputation was present in 30 (43%) patients. As expected, previous or active smokers comprised 84% (58 patients) of the group and the incidence of chronic obstructive pulmonary disease was 65% (45 patients).

Routine work-up for elective aneurysm repair included carotid duplex ultrasonography and noninvasive cardiac evaluation utilizing dobutamine stress echocardiography, exercise treadmill testing or adenosine thallium scanning. A positive cardiac stress test lead to preoperative coronary angiography in 7 (12.5%) patients. Two (3.6%) of these patients had coronary bypass before aneurysm repair. Otherwise, patients being evaluated for back, flank or ill-defined abdominal pain and a pulsatile abdominal mass without cardiovascular instability were assessed with CT scan and operated on once the diagnosis was established. Patients with ruptured aneurysms and hemodynamic instability were immediately resuscitated in the operating room in preparation for emergent repair. Operative characteristics of both groups are listed in Table 10.1.

In both the nonruptured and ruptured aneurysm groups, nonfatal postoperative complications commonly involve cardiac, respiratory and renal systems. However, the incidence of complications was significantly higher in the ruptured group compared to the nonruptured group (77% versus 23%, respectively; p = 0.001). Cardiac dysrhythmias requiring treatment occurred in 4 patients (3 in nonruptured group and 1 in ruptured group). Two patients with ruptured aneurysms developed congestive heart failure and one patient had a postoperative myocardial infarction. Pneumonia complicated aneurysm repair in 5 patients (4 in nonruptured group and 1 in ruptured group). Transient renal failure, not requiring dialysis, occurred in 6 patients with elective aneurysm repair and one patient with ruptured repair. Two other patients in the ruptured group with renal failure required transient hemodialysis. Significant postoperative bleeding necessitating re-exploration also complicated two ruptured aneurysm cases.

Mean intensive care unit and hospital days in the ruptured aneurysm group were significantly longer than the nonruptured group (p = 0.001). Mean ICU days were 15.7 (range 0-49 days) and 6.4 (range 1-45 days), respectively and mean hospital days were 22.8 (range 1-49 days) and 11.1 (range 4-49 days), respectively. There was no significant difference in patient discharge disposition between the two groups (p = 0.15). In the nonruptured group, hospital discharges were to home in 46 (92%) patients and to extended care facilities in 4 (8%) patients. Four (66.6%) patients in the ruptured group were discharged to home and two (33.3%) were discharged to extended care facilities.

Perioperative mortality rate was 10.7% (6 patients) in the nonruptured aneurysm group and 53.8% (7 patients) in the ruptured aneurysm group (p < 0.00001). Metastatic carcinoma in 5 patients (4 in nonruptured group and 1 in ruptured group) and myocardial infarction in 1 patient (nonruptured group) were the causes of late death. Cumulative survival rates as demonstrated in Figure 10.1. for the nonruptured group were 83.7%, 68.6% and 54.9 at 1, 4 and 8 years, respectively and 27.8% at one year for the ruptured group. Mean cumulative survival was 8.6 years in the nonruptured group and 1.1 years in the ruptured group (p = 0.0001, log rank analysis). No preoperative variable was found to be a significant predictor of survival by uni- or multivariate regression analysis in either group (all p values > 0.05).

These and other data demonstrate that elective repair of aneurysms in patients over age 80 has morbidity and mortality similar to younger patients. In fact, overall survival after elective aneurysm repair in the very elderly is similar to that of age-matched controls in the general population. Mean age was 83 years in our experience. At this age, a patient will live another 7.04 years on average based on U.S. census data. This survival data compares quite favorably with survival data following elective aneurysm repair in our experience. In addition, the discharge disposition data offers indirect evidence that an independent lifestyle can be maintained in these elderly patients. Clearly, elective aneurysm repair did not shorten life-expectancy. However, life expectancy in the very elderly after ruptured aneurysm repair is severely compromised and we were unable to identify any preoperative signs or symptoms that predicted survival in this group.

Therefore, these data clearly support the conclusion that nonemergent aneurysm repair in octa- and nonagenarians is safe and effective in prolonging rupture-free survival. Delayed, or no treatment, for elective aneurysmal disease in the very elderly is not supported by these data. It is apparent that the same standards set in younger patients for elective aneurysm repair should be applied to the very elderly. Most patients in our experience were able to resume their preoperative life-style following aortic reconstruction.

We strongly feel that appropriate patient selection in this very elderly age-group plays a significant role in eventual outcome. Management of significant coexistent vascular disease requires careful consideration. In our practice, very elderly patients presenting with ruptured aneurysm, cardiovascular collapse and no urine output are not offered surgical intervention. Likewise, patients with debilitating mental disorders are not felt to be candidates for any elective aortic reconstruction. However, elective aortic reconstruction for aneurysmal or occlusive disease can be expected to improve lifestyle without negatively impacting life expectancy.

Selected Readings

1. Bunt TJ, Ballard JL. A rational approach to the sequence of operations in the elderly. Chapter 7. In: Aronow WS, Stemmer EA, Wilson SE, eds. Vascular Diseases in the Elderly. New York: Futura Publishing Company, Inc. 1997:105-122.
   This ambitious book with 36 contributors covers topics ranging from principles of geriatric medicine, aging of the vascular system, epidemiology of vascular disease, vascular surgery and anesthetic management in the elderly. The above chapter details the sequence of operations in the elderly with an exhaustive review of the literature on the subject.

2. O'Hara PJ, Hertzer NR, Krajewski LP et al. Ten-year experience with abdominal aortic aneurysm repair in octogenarians: Early results and late outcome. J Vasc Surg 1995; 21:830-838.
   One hundred fourteen octogenarians (mean age 83) had abdominal aortic aneurysm repair at the Cleveland Clinic from 1984 to 1993. The 30-day operative mortality rate for the entire series was 14%, but it declined from 23% during the first five years of the study to 8% in the last five years! The authors emphasize the importance of proper patient selection for safe and durable repair of aortic aneurysms in this age group.

3. Dean RH, Woody JD, Enarson CE, Hansen KJ, Plonk GW Jr. Operative treatment of abdominal aortic aneurysms in octogenarians: When is it too much too late? Ann Surg 1993; 217:721-728.

10

From a total experience of 548 aneurysm repairs over a 7-1/2 year period, 34 octogenarians were extracted for review. In this subgroup, 18 had elective repair, 5 had urgent repair and 11 had ruptured AAA repair. Operative mortality was 5.6%, 40% and 91%, respectively. These data are striking and confirm the fact that elective repair of AAA's in octogenarians is reasonable. However, observation is probably the most prudent course of action to take for octogenarians presenting with severe hemodynamic instability and ruptured AAA.

4. Wong DT, Ballard JL, Killeen JD. Carotid endarterectomy and abdominal aortic aneurysm repair: are these reasonable treatments for patients over age 80? Am Surg 1998; 64:998-1001.

    This manuscript was summarized in the preceding chapter.

5. Plecha FR, Bertin VS, Plecha ES et al. The early results of vascular surgery in patients 75 years of age and older: an analysis of 3529 cases. J Vasc Surg 1985; 2:6:769-75.

    From a computerized registry of the Cleveland Vascular Society, 19,990 vascular procedures were divided into two groups based on age greater or less than 75 years old. For all categories of vascular procedures (aortic reconstruction, femoropopliteal reconstruction, lower extremity thromboendarterectomy and amputation), operative mortality was statistically significantly higher in the older age group (all P values <0.01). This data demonstrate the challenge that confronts all vascular surgeons as the US population continues to age.

6. Hertzer NR, Loop FD, Beven EG et al. Surgical staging for simultaneous coronary and carotid disease: A study including prospective randomization. J Vasc Surg 1989; 9:455-64.

    Simultaneous carotid disease was documented in 275 of 9714 patients scheduled for CABG including 80 with symptomatic lesions and 195 with asymptomatic stenoses. Within this group, 129 patients with unilateral, asymptomatic carotid lesions and unstable cardiac disease were randomized to receive combined operations (71 patients) or CABG first then delayed CEA (58 patients). The composite stroke risk for the later group (14%) exceeded that of the combined group (2.8%) suggesting that simultaneous operations were safer than staged procedures during the same hospitalization.

7. Brener BJ, Brief BK, Alpert J et al. A four-year experience with preoperative noninvasive carotid evaluation of 2026 patients undergoing cardiac surgery. J Vasc Surg 1984; 1:326-38.

    A group of 2026 patients scheduled to have CABG had a battery of preoperative noninvasive carotid tests. The incidence of ipsilateral neurological events following cardiac surgery in 47 patients with documented carotid disease was 15% whereas this incidence was only 2% in patients with no evidence of significant carotid disease. Data such as these are the reason that we favor combined CEA/CABG for appropriately selected patients.

8. Barnes RW, Nix MC, Sansonetti D et al. Late outcome of untreated asymptomatic carotid disease following cardiovascular operations. J Vasc Surg 1985; 2:843-849.

    This article reviews the late (2 to 61 months, mean 35 months) postoperative outcome of 67 patients with >50% asymptomatic carotid stenosis who had previous uneventful coronary or peripheral arterial reconstruction. Ipsilateral transient ischemic attacks occurred in 6% of patients after an average interval of 31 months and 4.5% of patients suffered a stroke. These data underscore the fact that patients with >50% asymptomatic carotid stenosis can undergo successful coronary or peripheral arterial reconstruction but they require careful follow-up for disease progression.

9. Coyle KA, Smith RB III, Salam AA et al. Carotid endarterectomy in the octoge-narian. Ann Vasc Surg 1994; 8:417-420.

    This article reviews the outcome of seventy-nine patients over age 80 who had CEA from 1983 to 1992 at Emory University School of Medicine. Combined 30-day stroke and death rate was 1.3% (one patient)! Furthermore, there were no ipsilateral strokes noted after an average follow-up of 35 months. CEA in octogenarians is safe and durable.

10. Favre JP, Guy JM, Frering V et al. Carotid surgery in the octogenarian. Ann Vasc Surg 1994; 8:421-426.

    The records of 52 octogenarians who had 56 carotid artery reconstructions were ana-lyzed retrospectively. Combined 30-day stroke and death rate was 8%. This rate includes one lethal and three nonfatal strokes. Two-year actuarial survival was 76% for the surviving 49 patients (two were lost to follow-up) who were followed for a mean of 24 months. Although operative stroke and death rate is higher than that of the preceding series, this study demonstrates that life expectancy is reasonable after carotid reconstruc-tion in octogenarians.

11. Katz DA, Littenberg B, Cronenwett JL. Management of small abdominal aortic aneurysms. Early surgery vs watchful waiting. JAMA 1992; 268:19:2678-86.

    This carefully analyzed study compares two clinical strategies for the management of small (<5 cm in diameter) abdominal aortic aneurysms: early surgery versus watchful waiting until AAA reaches 5 cm in size. Interestingly, in the majority of scenarios stud-ied, early surgery predicted improved survival; however, this benefit decreased with advancing age. Therefore, watchful waiting is prudent for the octogenarian with a small abdominal aortic aneurysm.

12. Seiwert AJ, Elmore JR, Youkey JR et al. Ruptured abdominal aortic aneurysm repair: The financial analysis. Am J Surg 1995; 170:91-96.

    This retrospective clinical and financial chart review focused on 119 patients who had ruptured AAA repair from 1986-1993. Overall in-hospital mortality was 45%. Unfortunately no clinical or physiologic parameter was able to predict poor outcome. These compelling data are one of the reasons that we do not repair ruptured aneurysms in patients over age 80 who have severe hemodynamic instability.

10

CHAPTER 11

Aortic Reconstruction for Occlusive Disease

Thomas F. Rehring and David C. Brewster

The aortic bifurcation and iliac arteries are among the most common sites of chronic obliterative atherosclerosis in patients with symptomatic vascular disease of the lower extremities. As atherosclerosis is a generalized process, aortoiliac disease frequently coexists with stenoses or occlusions below the inguinal ligament. Despite this prevalence of "multi-level" disease, successful inflow reconstruction generally provides highly satisfactory clinical relief of ischemic symptoms. As such, restoration of arterial inflow as a first step in arterial reconstruction is well recognized as a basic tenet in vascular surgery.

It has been nearly one half of a century since the initial attempts at aortoiliac reconstruction. Since that time, improvements in graft material, surgical technique, anesthesia and critical care have decreased associated morbidity and allowed for superb long-term results. This chapter will focus on direct reconstruction of aortoiliac occlusive disease as extra-anatomic bypass and novel endovascular strategies are discussed elsewhere in this book.

Evaluation

A careful history and physical examination will frequently provide the clinician with considerable information. In general, risk factors for aortoiliac occlusive disease parallel those seen for other atherosclerotic lesions (elderly, male, diabetes, hypertension, tobacco abuse). In contrast, however, nearly half of all patients with limited, localized aortoiliac disease are women. Women patients tend to have more focal disease, are active smokers and present at a younger age than their male counterparts. Male patients are somewhat older and tend to have diffuse atherosclerotic disease. Patients with localized, segmental disease typically present with varying degrees of claudication. Frequently, this may involve the proximal thigh, buttock or hip. The classic Leriche syndrome describes the patient with thigh or buttock claudication associated with impotence, wasting of the thigh musculature and diminution of the femoral pulses. However, as mentioned previously, many of these patients have multilevel disease and may present only with calf claudication. Absent or weakened femoral pulses are found frequently. Auscultatable bruits may be noted over the lower abdomen or femoral vessels.

Occasionally, patients present with classic symptoms but normal pedal pulses at rest despite hemodynamically significant aortoiliac stenoses. These can often be elicited by exercise-induced diminution in ankle-brachial indices or pulse volume

Aortic Surgery, edited by Jeffrey L. Ballard. ©2000 Landes Bioscience.

recordings in the vascular laboratory. The noninvasive vascular laboratory not only improves diagnostic accuracy but also provides physiologic quantification of the severity of the disease process. In addition, these studies provide a baseline for comparison to postintervention results.

Contrast angiography provides structural and anatomic information to the surgeon. Its use is reserved for planning of an intervention, be it catheter-based or open. Hemodynamic information may also be obtained through the use of pressure gradient measurements. Stenoses are thought significant if the resting gradient is at least 10 mmHg or a 15% drop occurs in response to reactive hyperemia or pharmacological vasodilatation. Newer modalities, such as magnetic resonance arteriography and CT-angiography are also becoming increasingly utilized as their technology improves.

Indications for an intervention include disabling or lifestyle-limiting claudication, rest pain or ischemia-induced tissue loss. Ischemia at rest or gangrene almost always occurs in patients with accompanying femoropopliteal occlusive disease. Rarely, isolated aortoiliac disease may provide a nidus for atheroemboli resulting in focal pedal ischemic lesions—the so-called "blue toe syndrome".

Reconstruction

Aortoiliac Endarterectomy

Aortoiliac endarterectomy was introduced in 1947 by J. C. dos Santos and popularized prior to the modern era of prosthetic bypass conduits. Its advantage lies in the avoidance of prosthetic material and their innate shortcomings (dilatation, infection, anastomotic aneurysm). It is indicated for focal disease of the distal aorta, aortic bifurcation and common iliac arteries. Long-term patency is equivalent to that of bypass grafting for this indication. Such localized disease, however, is relatively unusual, comprising only 5-10% of patients requiring aortoiliac reconstruction. Furthermore, endovascular techniques such as angioplasty and stenting have limited the requirement for this type of intervention. Contraindications to endarterectomy include any degree of local aneurysmal degeneration, aortic occlusion or extension of the atherosclerotic disease process into the external iliac or distal vessels. The utilization of aortoiliac endarterectomy is quite uncommon in our practice. One can imagine a circumstance for endarterectomy, albeit rare, where a graft is to be avoided at all costs and the disease process is quite focal yet not amenable to angioplasty/stenting.

Direct Reconstruction

As mentioned previously, direct aortoiliac reconstruction with aortofemoral bypass provides excellent clinical results. While retroperitoneal, endovascular and laparoscopic approaches have been described; we prefer to use a transabdominal, midline incision. The proximal anastomosis may be constructed end-to-end or end-to-side, but should be placed relatively close to the renal arteries. Potential benefits of the end-to-end anastomosis include better flow dynamics, decreased competitive flow with patent iliac arteries, decreased incidence of dislodging intramural thrombus (by avoidance of a side-biting clamp) and decreased incidence of aortoenteric fistula formation. Relative indications for the end-to-side anastomosis include the desire to preserve a large aberrant renal artery or inferior mesenteric artery. More importantly, if the pattern of occlusive disease involves mainly the external iliac arteries, an end-to-end anastomosis may interrupt flow to patent internal iliac arteries, potentially increasing the risk of erectile dysfunction and buttock claudication or more serious sequelae such as colonic ischemia or paraplegia.

Distal Anastomosis

While selection of the external iliac artery for the distal anastomosis may on occasion seem appealing, long-term results of this approach have not been optimal. When compared to aortofemoral grafts, aorto-external iliac grafts have an increased late failure rate and a higher requirement for repeat interventions as a result of progression of atherosclerotic disease at, or just distal to the anastomosis. Furthermore, carrying the graft to the femoral artery level allows for outflow assessment and augmentation with such techniques as profundaplasty. As such, the aortobifemoral bypass has become the procedure of choice for direct reconstruction of aortoiliac occlusive disease.

Unilateral Iliac Occlusion

Options for the treatment for unilateral iliac occlusion include aortobifemoral bypass, iliac lysis/angioplasty/stent, femorofemoral bypass, iliofemoral bypass, iliac endarterectomy or unilateral axillofemoral bypass. No single choice amongst these options will be uniformly correct. Advantages of catheter-based techniques and extra-anatomic bypass are covered elsewhere in this text. Suffice it to say that each has its merit and usefulness in the armamentarium of the vascular surgeon. It should be kept in mind, however, that 10 to 15% of these patients will develop symptomatic atherosclerotic occlusive disease in the uninvolved iliac artery which may influence operative strategy toward aortofemoral bypass in select patients.

Complications

In addition to standard cardiac and pulmonary morbidities associated with aortic surgery, early complications of direct aortofemoral reconstruction may include hemorrhage, limb ischemia, renal failure, intestinal ischemia, spinal cord ischemia and ureteral injury. Postoperative limb ischemia may be secondary to intimal flaps, dissection, graft kinking or thromboembolic debris and requires surgical re-exploration and/or revision. The incidence of renal failure varies from 1-8% in most reports and occurs as a result of hypoperfusion, embolic debris, radiographic contrast or myoglobinuria from ischemic limbs. Intestinal ischemia occurs in approximately 2% of cases, and usually involves the rectosigmoid. It is heralded by the onset of diarrhea, sepsis and metabolic acidosis. Spinal cord ischemia resulting in devastating lower extremity weakness or paralysis occurs in approximately 0.25% of patients and is thought secondary to interruption of flow from the great radicular artery of Adamkiewicz. The ureter is prone to injury during aortofemoral reconstruction in its anatomic position draped over the iliac artery. Careful dissection and attention to its location are keys to the avoidance of this complication.

If followed for 20 years, secondary operations for late complications of direct aortofemoral reconstruction will be necessary in up to 21% of patients. The most frequent late complication is graft limb occlusion occurring in 5-10% of patients over the first five years after operation and as many as 15-30% if followed for 10 years or more. Anastomotic false aneurysm formation occurs in 1-5% of patients and is generally seen at the femoral anastomosis. The incidence of iatrogenic impotence or retrograde ejaculation approaches 25% in men undergoing direct aortofemoral reconstruction. Retrograde ejaculation is thought to be secondary to interruption of autonomic nerve fibers coursing over the left common iliac artery just beyond the bifurcation. True impotence may be secondary to inadequate preservation of hypogastric circulation; however, the functional, psychological and pharmacological etiologies of erectile dysfunction must also be addressed. Graft infection occurs in approximately one percent of patients. Perhaps the most feared complication of aortofemoral reconstruction is aortoenteric fistula with its attendant formidable morbidity and mortality rates. This may present as a "herald" bleed, and is the most significant diagnosis of exclusion in all patients with gastrointestinal hemorrhage and a history of aortic reconstruction.

Results

In general, excellent early and late results of direct aortofemoral reconstructions can be expected with low mortality and acceptable morbidity. The long-term results of aortofemoral reconstruction are largely dependent on outflow. Multiple studies confirm 85-90% five-year patency and 70-75% ten-year patency of aortofemoral reconstruction. Perioperative mortality rates are generally under 3%. Thus, direct reconstruction for aortoiliac occlusive disease provides distinctly satisfying results.

11

Selected Readings

1. Brewster DC. Direct reconstruction for aortoiliac occlusive disease. In: Rutherford RB, ed. Vascular Surgery, 5th ed. Philadelphia: WB Saunders 2000; 943-972.
   A comprehensive overview of this subject, extensively referenced.
2. Brewster DC. Current controversies in the management of aortoiliac occlusive disease. J Vasc Surg 1997;25:365-79.
   Specifically addresses options in management of aortoiliac occlusive disease.
3. Weinstein ES, Langsfeld M. Aortoiliac endarterectomy. Semin Vasc Surg 1994;7:28-34.
   A thorough review of historical and technical aspects of aortoiliac endarterectomy.

CHAPTER 12

Extra-Anatomic Bypass for Aortoiliac Occlusive Disease

John Karwowski and Ronald L. Dalman

Extra-anatomic bypass refers to the tunneling of vascular grafts in configurations that do not follow normal anatomic planes. Unlike "anatomically" tunneled grafts, extra-anatomic grafts are not placed directly adjacent to or in line with the diseased or occluded native artery. For example, femoro-femoral bypass grafts are tunneled in a suprapubic subcutaneous plane and axillo-femoral grafts are tunneled subcutaneously along the thorax and abdomen. These procedures are well established and are useful alternatives to more direct reconstruction procedures such as aortofemoral bypass grafting or iliac artery angioplasty and stenting. Extra-anatomic procedures are particularly useful whenever patient comorbidities or anatomic variables make in-line revascularization impractical or impossible. Although there are many different extra-anatomic graft configurations, this chapter will consider only procedures relevant to the treatment of occlusive and aneurysmal disease of the abdominal aorta and iliac arteries.

Axillofemoral Bypass

The first axillofemoral bypass (AxFB) was performed emergently following cardiac arrest during anesthetic induction prior to planned aortofemoral bypass (AFB) grafting.[1] Although that procedure was ultimately successful (the patient survived with a patent graft), early reports describing results of AxFB grafting did not compare well with concurrently performed in-line anatomic aortic reconstruction. For this reason AxFB never gained prominence as a primary revascularization option for aortoiliac occlusive disease. Subsequent use has continued to be limited to high-risk patients with unfavorable anatomic or comorbid conditions, especially those with an infected aortic prosthesis.[2]

Indications for Axillofemoral bypass

Most surgeons consider AxFB procedures to incorporate both an axillo-femoral limb and a femoro-femoral limb, although axillo-unifemoral bypass is a durable and important surgical option.[3] Since most patients who are candidates for axillofemoral bypass need bilateral lower extremity revascularization, this distinction is often moot. Furthermore, overall reported results comparing axillo-unifemoral and axillobifemoral procedures suggest that bilateral lower extremity runoff may improve overall long-term graft patency.[4-5]

Aortic Surgery, edited by Jeffrey L. Ballard. ©2000 Landes Bioscience.

As originally proposed by Blaisdell, the most widely acknowledged indication for AxFB remains management of aortic graft infection and, less commonly, primary aortic infection.[2,6] Recently, new options for management of infected aortic prostheses have been considered such as resection, debridement and in-situ replacement with autogenous superficial femoral vein, cryopreserved homograft or a second prosthetic graft. However, complete graft excision, wide local debridement, aortic stump closure and lower extremity revascularization via AxFB remains the benchmark. Modern results of graft extirpation and extra-anatomic bypass were recently summarized by Ricotta and associates.[7] These data compare favorably with current results from the various in-situ management paradigms.[8]

In addition to aortic sepsis, other generally accepted indications for AxFB are:

1. excessive operative risk (usually cardiac or pulmonary) of temporary aortic occlusion for patients with aortoiliac occlusive disease and limb-threatening lower extremity ischemia;

2. in conjunction with aortic ligation or occluding aortic endoluminal stent grafting as alternative management of abdominal aortic aneurysms (AAA),[9,10] or;

3. as adjunctive management of penetrating injuries of the aorta or iliac arteries, especially in the setting of massive enteric abdominal contamination.

Temporary external axillo-unifemoral bypass grafts have also been constructed to support transplanted kidney function in the ipsilateral external iliac artery during complex, proximal aortic reconstructive surgery and prolonged aortic occlusion.

With experience and some technical modifications, reported results following AxFB procedures have improved over time.[4] A major advance occurred with the development of externally supported polytetrafluoroethylene (ePTFE) and polyester grafts. These grafts are resistant to external compression from clothing, furniture and dependent positioning which otherwise might cause graft occlusion. Harris and associates reported 85% 4-year actuarial primary patency following seventy-six AxFB procedures performed with externally supported ePTFE grafts.[5] Most of these procedures were performed for indications other than aortic sepsis. These included extreme aortic calcification, dense abdominal and intestinal adhesions and scarring or obliteration of anatomic planes following previous procedures. Despite their improved results, however, Harris and associates continued to prefer anatomic, inline reconstruction whenever feasible, reserving AxFB for unusual and complicated situations.[5]

Indications for Femorofemoral Bypass

Indications for Femorofemoral bypass grafting include unilateral iliac occlusive disease, adjunctive management of AAA (via aorto-uni-iliac stent grafting, contralateral common iliac exclusion and Femorofemoral bypass grafting to maintain limb perfusion of the limb opposite the stent graft, or adjunctive management of traumatic or iatrogenic iliac artery injuries.[11] Femorofemoral bypass is also useful in managing a number of urologic and orthopedic-related iliac artery injuries in the setting of urine soilage or pelvic osteomyelitis, where in situ graft replacement is generally contraindicated. Similar to AxFB grafting, however, primary patency rates of Femorofemoral bypass grafts are decreased compared to in-line, anatomic bypass grafting.[4] For this reason, as in the case of AxFB, Femorofemoral bypass is not generally considered a primary revascularization option for most patients.

This opinion is not universally held, however. Nazzal and associates from the University of Iowa recently reviewed their experience with Femorofemoral bypass versus a concurrent series of unilateral iliofemoral bypass procedures and found no significant difference in graft patency and limb salvage between the two groups.[12] What is most remarkable about this report is the fact that so many unilateral aorto- and iliofemoral bypass procedures were performed in the first place. Most vascular specialists recognize the potential for progression of contralateral iliac disease following unilateral treatment, and recommend bilateral femoral bypass grafting whenever there is evidence of contralateral moderate-to-severe contralateral iliac disease. Femorofemoral bypass grafting alone or following proximal common iliac artery angioplasty and stent deployment inevitably leverages the survival of both limbs on a single iliac inflow source.[13] Over time these grafts do not provide durability comparable to that achieved with in-line anatomic reconstruction originating from the infrarenal aorta.

More recently, technical advances in transfemoral catheter-directed procedures have improved results of endovascular interventions to the point where they are often preferentially considered as an alternative to Femorofemoral bypass grafting. This is particularly true for patients whose operative risks would otherwise contraindicate traditional in-line anatomic revascularization. No current comparison exists regarding outcome following extra-anatomic and endovascular revascularization procedures, but in our own practice we have for several years preferentially performed catheter-based endovascular procedures whenever possible. Perhaps the most significant change evident to us is the frequency with which occluded or severely diseased common iliac arteries can be recannalized using state of the art hydrophilic guidewires, high pressure, low profile balloon catheters and new generation flexible self-expanding stents. Clinical trials now underway suggest stent-graft devices may perform even better for these indications. Since most of these procedures do not require general or regional anesthesia, for truly "high-risk" patients with favorable anatomy, endovascular treatment strategies seem preferable to those based on "traditional" extra-anatomic techniques.

Technical Issues Related to AxFB and Femorofemoral Bypass Grafting

As previously noted, AxFB and Femorofemoral bypass grafts are currently performed with either ePTFE or polyester externally supported grafts and the ePTFE grafts usually have 5 or 10 cm at each end without external support. These grafts are available in 10 cm increments between 60 and 100 cm in length. Typically, 80 cm long conduits are required for the axillo-femoral limb. We prefer to use stretch ePTFE or crimped Dacron" polyester grafts as they allow for some "give" along the graft. If the inguinal region is contaminated or infected, a 100 cm graft may be required to span the distance between the axillary artery and the distal deep or superficial femoral artery. In this case, the deep femoral artery is exposed lateral to the sartorius muscle in the proximal third portion of the thigh.

During axillary-femoral tunneling, care is required to provide sufficient graft length to prevent excess tension along the conduit. Tension may increase significantly with abduction and external rotation of the shoulder or extension of the ipsilateral lower extremity. The graft tunnel begins subcutaneously in the inguinal region and extends proximally, medial to the anterior superior iliac spine, along the abdominal wall and chest. Care is taken to maintain the subcutaneous plane over the costal margin. The tunnel is then routed deep to the pectoralis major and minor muscles as it nears the clavicle. This tunneling maneuver usually can be accomplished without a counter incision. The "Oregon" tunneler is used for this purpose, as the device has sufficient length, diameter and rigidity to safely create the tunnel and pass the graft limb.

The axillary incision is made directly over the artery, beginning a fingerbreadth below the mid-clavicle and extending laterally 10-15 cm. The muscle fibers of the pectoralis major are spread longitudinally, and the pectoralis minor is usually retracted laterally. Self-retaining Weitlaner retractors are used to maintain exposure of the axillary artery, vein and cords of the brachial plexus. Careful dissection may be required to expose the axillary artery from between the surrounding nerve and venous structures. Since 1992, we have used the modification described by Bunt and Moore to reduce tension on the axillary artery at the point of anastomosis (Fig. 12.1).[14] This positioning leaves 8-10 cm of graft adjacent to the axillary artery before it extends distally to the groin. In addition, the axillary anastomosis must be completed proximal to the thoracoacromial artery to reduce tension on the artery and graft during upper extremity abduction. Failure to properly position this anastomosis in relationship to the pectoralis minor and major muscles, thoracoacromial artery and clavicle may result in catastrophic graft or anastomotic disruption days or weeks following the procedure.[15]

Curvilinear femoral incisions are used for inguinal exposure. These are modified depending on the body habitus of the patient and the degree to which femoral and deep femoral artery exposure and preparation is required. Ioban™ (3M Corporation, Minneapolis, MN) iodine impregnated adhesive drapes are placed over the operative field to prevent contact between prepped skin and graft material. During AxFB grafting, the anastomoses between the graft and the axillary and ipsilateral femoral artery are completed first using standard graft bevels and continuous running suture technique. For ePTFE grafts we use ePTFE suture; for polyester grafts we use polypropylene suture. Tunneling of the femorofemoral graft limb is performed in a suprapubic subcutaneous plane in a gentle inverted U-shaped curve. A "graftotomy" is then performed on the anteromedial aspect of the axillofemoral graft limb just proximal to the distal anastomosis, and the proximal anastomosis of the femorofemoral graft is then completed as described above.

In general, for AxFB and Femorofemoral bypass grafting, we use 8 mm diameter graft conduits. Occasionally 10 mm diameter grafts are required in larger patients. Six mm graft limbs, especially in the axillofemoral location may not provide sufficient inflow to achieve the desired clinical effect. In the absence of significant proximal

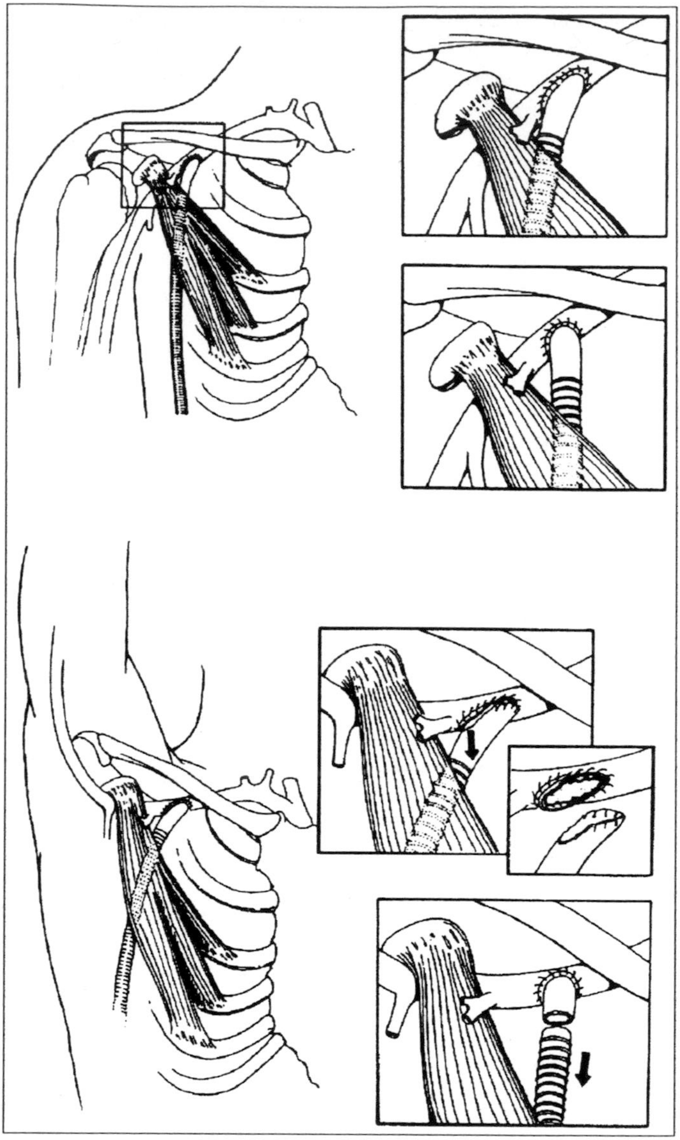

Fig. 12.1. The preferred configuration for proximal anastomosis to axillary artery is a "cobra-head." The anastomosis should be proximal to the thoracoacromial artery and the graft should parallel the axillary artery for a few centimeters before extending distally to the groin.

subclavian or innominate artery occlusive disease, an 8 mm diameter axillofemoral limb will provide sufficient inflow to both lower extremities to prevent a "steal" phenomenon from either lower limb. Similarly, it is wise to ensure that the superficial femoral artery is patent in the donor extremity. Otherwise, the donor limb may become symptomatic due to steal from the recipient limb.

Results of AxFB and Femorofemoral Bypass Procedures

As previously noted, patency following extra-anatomic bypass procedures is generally less than that expected for traditional, in-line anatomic procedures, especially when performed for treatment of occlusive disease. Table 12.1 lists the weighted average of primary patency from 10 series reporting outcome of AxFB procedures and 6 series of Femorofemoral bypass procedures. After 3 months, there is a significant difference in patency between ax-bifemoral and ax-unifemoral procedures. Cumulative patient survival from these series is listed in Table 12.2. These data reflect the general clinical bias towards reserving extra-anatomic bypass for ill patients thought unfit for more complex revascularization procedures. Table 12.3 reflects the overall utility of extra-anatomic procedures in providing lower extremity salvage in medically compromised patients, comprising the results of 11 separate series.

Table 12.4 lists the incidence of complications encountered following AxFB from 13 separate series, and Table 12.5 lists the incidence of complications encountered in 11 series of Femorofemoral bypass grafting procedures.[4] As indicated by these overall results, AxFB and Femorofemoral bypass procedures are generally safe. Procedure-related morbidity is generally limited to local wound complications, seromas and graft infections. Systemic complications for both procedures reflect the significance of underlying medical comorbidities. An example is pulmonary failure/pneumonia in patients undergoing AxFB, a revascularization procedure frequently chosen for patients with severe respiratory compromise.

Indications for Thoracofemoral Bypass

Descending thoracic aorta-to-iliofemoral bypass grafting is a well established secondary procedure used to salvage failed or infected infrarenal aortic prostheses. In general, these grafts originate from the descending thoracic aorta above the diaphragm and are tunneled through the retroperitoneum to the left external iliac or common femoral artery. In the setting of aortic infection, care is obviously taken to avoid infected or contaminated fields. Contralateral limb blood flow is provided by an additional graft limb tunneled to the opposite iliac or femoral artery.

Technical Issues Related to Thoracofemoral Bypass Grafting

Patients under consideration for grafting from the descending thoracic aorta to iliac or femoral artery need to undergo appropriate pulmonary function testing prior to the procedure, as documented severe pulmonary disease is a serious potential contraindication. As recently reviewed by Passman and associates,[16] after induction of general anesthesia via a double-lumen endotracheal tube, the left thorax is elevated 45-60° to a right lateral decubitus position. The pelvis is usually left relatively flat to facilitate bilateral groin exposure. Following standard femoral artery exposure, the left external and common iliac arteries are exposed via retroperitoneal dissection.

Table 12.1. Cumulative primary patency rates for extra anatomic bypass

	3	6	12	24	36	48	60 (mo)
Ax-fem	87	73	72	68	61	58	43
Ax-bifem	90	85	79	78	69	69	58
Ax-unifem	88	65	50	48	44	28	24
Fem-fem	94	91	89	80	74	65	65

Data expressed as percent.

Table 12.2. Cumulative patient survival after extra-anatomic bypass

	3	6	12	24	36	48	60 (mo)
Ax-fem	87	83	77	71	58	55	53
Fem-fem	96	94	89	84	71	63	51

Data expressed as percent.

Table 12.3. Limb salvage rate after extra-anatomic bypass

	3	6	12	24	36	48	60 (mo)
Ax-fem	94	91	88	85	81	81	81
Ax-bifem	94	92	92	89	88	88	84
Ax-unifem	100	90	82	82	73	73	73
Fem-fem	91	91	88	87	85	85	85

Data expressed as percent.

Table 12.4. Incidence of complications after axillofemoral bypass

Complications	%
Myocardial failure/infarction	9
Graft infection	8
Lymphocele/seroma	6
Pulmonary failure/pneumonia	4
Groin pseudoaneurysm	4
Hemorrhage/hematoma	4
Stroke	2
Axillary/brachial artery thrombosis	2
Fractured graft	1

12

Table 12.5. Incidence of complications after femorofemoral bypass

Complications	%
Lymphocele/seroma	4
Pulmonary failure/pneumonia	4
Myocardial failure/infarction	3
Graft infection	3
Wound infection	3
Hemorrhage/hematoma	3
Pseudoaneurysm	2
Stroke	1

Tunneling to the right side is accomplished in a preperitoneal plane, anterior and cephalad to the urinary bladder. In the chest, a left posterolateral muscle-sparing thoracotomy is performed through the eight or ninth intercostal space. A minimally diseased portion of the descending thoracic aorta is chosen for the proximal anastomosis. Following mobilization of the diaphragm from its posterior attachments, the retroperitoneal tunnel is extended between the left retroperitoneal space and the left hemithorax, posterior to the kidney along the psoas muscle. Standard knitted or woven polyester grafts are used for both limbs of these grafts. The anastomoses are completed using standard techniques. Suction drainage is provided to the left pleural space postoperatively via tube thoracostomy.

Results of Thoracofemoral Bypass Procedures

Passman and associates recently reported a 15-year experience with 50 such procedures performed for aortoiliac revascularization.[16] The cumulative 5-year actuarial primary and secondary patency, limb salvage and survival rates following these procedures were 79%, 84%, 93% and 67%, respectively. Based on this experience, the authors proposed that these procedures should be considered as primary therapy for lower extremity revascularization, especially for patients with severe atherosclerotic disease or occlusion of the peri-renal and suprarenal abdominal aorta.

Summary

Extra-anatomic bypass grafting, born of surgical necessity in 1963 has provided vascular surgeons with an important alternative for high-risk, reoperative aortic surgery for more than 30 years. It represents one alternative among many available for reconstruction of the aorta and iliac arteries. Advances in catheter-directed endovascular techniques and minimally invasive surgical procedures and devices have decreased the number of patients currently considered for extra-anatomic bypass in our own practice. Long-term graft patency following AxFB and Femorofemoral bypass do not equal those achieved by in-line anatomic reconstruction. Furthermore, patency rates for endovascular procedures for certain subsets of patients may be superior to those achieved following AxFB and Femorofemoral bypass. However, direct comparison between extra-anatomic bypass grafting and endovascular procedures have not been performed to date. For very select patients, such as those with prosthetic graft infections or penetrating abdominal injuries, extra-anatomic bypass remains an excellent choice for safe and reasonably effective lower extremity revascularization. The role of Femorofemoral bypass grafting as a component of endovascular aortic exclusion is a transitional one. It will probably disappear as second and third generation endovascular stent grafts become available with smaller profiles and improved delivery systems.

Selected Readings

1. Louw JH. Splenic-to-femoral and axillary-to-femoral bypass grafts in diffuse atherosclerotic occlusive disease. Lancet 1963; 1:1401-2.

2. Blaisdell WF, Hall AD. Axillary-femoral artery bypass for lower extremity ischemia Surgery 1963; 54:563-8.

3. Ascer E, Veith FJ, Gupta SK et al. Comparison of axillounifemoral and axillobifemoral bypass operations. Surgery 1985; 97:169-174.

4. Fann JI, Harris EJ Jr., Dalman RL. Basic data related to extra-anatomic bypass. Ann Vasc Surg 1993; 7:378-383.
    Meta-analysis of extra-anatomic bypass procedures. Authors examined indications, patient characteristics, operative mortality, primary and secondary patency rates, and limb salvage rates for axillo-femoral (uni or bi) as well as femorofemoral bypass procedures.

5. Harris EJ Jr., Taylor C Jr., McConnell DB et al. Clinical Results of axillofemoral bypass using externally supported polytetrafluoroethylene. J Vasc Surg 1990; 4:416-26.

6. Moneta GL, Taylor LM Jr., Yeager RA et al. Surgical treatment of infected aortic aneurysm. Am J Surg 1998; 175:396-9.

7. Ricotta JJ, Faggioli GL, Stella A et al. Total excision and extra-anatomic bypass for aortic graft infection. Am J Surg 1991; 162:145-9.

8. Henke PK, Bergamini TM, Rose SM et al. Current options in prosthetic vascular graft infection. Am Surg 1998; 64:39-45.
    Retrospective review of treatment modalities prosthetic graft infections. Data suggests that extra-anatomic bypass (vs. graft preservation or in situ replacement) is still associated with the best overall outcome. Graft preservation has no role in the setting of sepsis or bleeding. Both graft preservation and in situ replacement are most viable in the setting of early infection with indolent coagulase negative Staphylococcus.

9. Le Minh T, Motte S, Hoang AD et al. Occluding aortic endoluminal stent graft combined with extra-anatomic axillofemoral bypass as alternative management of abdominal aortic aneurysms for patients at high risk with complex anatomic features: A preliminary report. J Vasc Surg 1998; 28:651-6.

10. Pevec WC, Holcroft JW, Blaisdell FW. Ligation and extra-anatomic arterial reconstruction for the treatment of aneurysms of the abdominal aorta. J Vasc Surg 1994; 20:629-36.
    Authors reviewed 26 patients with significant comorbidities and abdominal aortic aneurysmal disease that was supra-renal in location or acute in onset. All patients underwent axillofemoral bypass with or without aortic ligation. Axillofemoral bypass without ligation did not effectively reduce the risk of aneurysm rupture. However, axillofemoral bypass with aortic ligation is an acceptable treatment for patients with severe medical problems and symptomatic, anatomically complicated, and large abdominal aortic aneurysms.

11. Carrillo EH, Sapin DA, Wilson MA et al. Alternatives in the management of penetrating injuries to the iliac vessels. J Trauma 1998; 44:1024-9.

12

12. Nazzal MM, Hoballah JJ, Jacobovicz C et al. A comparative evaluation of femorofemoral crossover bypass and iliofemoral bypass for unilateral iliac artery occlusive disease. Angiology 1998; 49:259-65.

13. Dalman RL, Porter JM. Current status of noncoronary endovascular procedures. Pers Vasc Surg 1990; 3:1-25.

14. Bunt TJ, Moore W. Optimal proximal anastomosis/tunnel for axillofemoral grafts. J Vasc Surg 1986; 3:673-6.

   Blaisdell's original description of the axillofemoral bypass in 1961 involved a "T" proximal anastomosis of the graft, where the graft followed a subpectoralis major route and was sewn to the axillary artery in a perpendicular fashion. The authors here advocate the use of a "cobra-head" proximal anastomosis to the axillary artery, with subpectoralis minor passage of the graft. Theoretical advantages of such an anastomosis include improve flow characteristics, decreased tendency to pseudoaneurysm formation due to excessive tension, and a decreased tendency to kinking (axillary artery thrombosis or brachial artery embolus).

15. Taylor LM Jr., Park TC, Edwards JM et al. Acute disruption of polytetrafluoroethylene grafts adjacent to axillary anastomoses: A complication of axillofemoral grafting. J Vasc Surg 1994; 20:520-8.

   Large series of axillofemoral bypass grafting procedures performed by the authors, with special attention paid to incidences of graft disruption at the proximal anastomosis. With improved patency rates due to the use externally supported grafts, axillobifemoral vs. axillounifemoral grafting, and the use of multilevel constructions where appropriate, increased use a primary procedure for aortic athero-occlusive disease has led to recognition of certain complications. They reported a 5% incidence of disruption, commonly found early in the postoperative course and associated with arm abduction. No difference was seen in the incidence of anastomotic disruption versus graft material (PTFE) failure. This in spite of modifications to the procedure as originally described, namely abduction of the arm to 90° intraoperatively, and redundant graft length proximally.

16. Passman MA, Farber MA, Criado E et al. Descending thoracic aorta to iliofemoral artery bypass grafting: A role for primary revascularization for aortoiliac occlusive disease? J Vasc Surg 1999; 29:249-58.

   The authors present their 15-year experience with 50 descending thoracic aorta to iliofemoral artery bypass grafts. This is first report of long term results using the technique as a primary or secondary procedure for severe claudication, rest pain, ischemic ulceration, or failed prior grafting. The authors note excellent long term patency, limb salvage, and survival rates that support a more liberal use for patients with severe atherosclerotic disease or complete occlusion of the infrarenal aorta.

12

CHAPTER 13

Stent Deployment for Aortoiliac Occlusive Disease

Frank C. Taylor and Jeffrey L. Ballard

It has been nearly a decade since metallic stents were first made available to treat failed or suboptimal angioplasty sites within the iliac arteries. Along with bypass grafting and percutaneous transluminal angioplasty (PTA) stent indications have expanded and are now an indispensable part of the armamentarium for treating aortoiliac occlusive disease. The next generation of innovations covered-stents or endovascular grafts, are just over the horizon.

The purpose of this chapter is to provide a brief overview of stenting for aortoiliac occlusive disease. General principles, indications, potential complications, expected outcomes, cost and patient/lesion selection will be highlighted. It is the author's hope that this information facilitates appropriate use of these devices, as well as an understanding of their limitations and their role in complementing other established endovascular and open surgical procedures. For more details governing specific devices and their deployment, information from the manufacturers, as well as numerous peer-reviewed articles and texts can be easily consulted.

Preprocedure Evaluation

Preparation for stenting procedures is similar to that required for diagnostic arteriography. General principles are listed below:

1. Patients referred for possible percutaneous intervention require a focused and brief problem-related history and physical.
2. Document comorbid conditions such as coronary artery disease, hypertension, diabetes, drug and other allergies, any prior contrast reaction, etc.
3. List current medications and doses.*
4. Immediate preprocedure laboratory work is not routine in our practice, however, if warranted by the history, selective testing is conducted.
5. Document preprocedure lower extremity pulses and ankle/brachial index (ABI).

---

* [Metformin (Glucophage, Bristol-Myers Squibb Co.) is a popular oral hypoglycemic. Severe lactic acidosis can occur in patients with compromised renal function on this medication who receive iodinated contrast media. This medication should be stopped in all patients at the time of the procedure and should not be restarted until 48 hours later, after renal function has been assessed. In patients with compromised renal function, metformin should be stopped 48 hours prior to receiving iodinated contrast and the patient placed on another agent until renal function has been reassessed 48 hours after the procedure.]

Aortic Surgery, edited by Jeffrey L. Ballard. ©2000 Landes Bioscience.

6. Patients are instructed to take nothing by mouth (except for medications) for at least 6 hours prior to the procedure. (Patients with diabetes are generally instructed to take only _ their morning insulin dose).
7. Intravenous hydration is started prior to the patient entering the angiography/endovascular suite.
8. Informed consent is obtained. In our practice all patients undergoing any peripheral arterial procedure are consented for PTA, stenting and thrombolysis as these techniques all may be required in treating complications that may occur during any percutaneous intervention.

Percutaneous Transluminal Angioplasty

A discussion of aortoiliac stenting and its indication first requires an understanding of percutaneous transluminal balloon angioplasty (PTA). For almost two decades, PTA of iliac stenoses has been accepted as a valid alternative to bypass grafting in selected patients. Patency data from 2,697 iliac angioplasty procedures showed an initial technical success of 92% with a two-year patency of 81% and a five-year patency of 72%.[1] Compared to aortobifemoral bypass that has a 5-year patency of at least 85% and 10 and 20 year patency of up to 75% and 55% respectively, there is plenty of room for improvement for percutaneous interventions. Careful analysis of many studies of percutaneous transluminal angioplasty have lead to the publication of guidelines regarding the use of PTA and the types of lesions to which its use may be best applied or discouraged.[2] Table 13. 1 lists the SCVIR/AHA category definitions and the description of the correlating lesions within the iliac arteries.

Most often PTA has been use to treat patients with lifestyle limiting claudication and to a lesser extent, patients with rest pain and/or tissue loss. Long-term results are better in patients with mild or disabling intermittent claudication. PTA is also more likely to be successful if stenoses rather than occlusions are treated. Patients with good infra-inguinal arterial run-off also do better than those with poor run-off.

Pertaining to iliac PTA, overall technical success of 90-95% can be anticipated with category 1 or 2 type stenoses with patency of 80-85% expected at 3-5 years. However PTA success for category 3 lesions is much less and category 4 lesions are basically contraindicated for PTA.[2]

PTA is considered clinically successful when there is complete relief or substantial improvement in symptoms. Angiographic success is conferred if the angiographic diameter stenosis is 20% or less following PTA. Primary patency is defined as ending when symptoms recur to the same degree as previous and there is angiographic or noninvasive evidence that recurrence is in the same vessel segment.[3]

Stent Devices

Only two products are officially approved by the FDA for treatment of iliac artery lesions: the Johnson & Johnson Palmaz balloon-expandable stent (BES) and the Wallstent iliac endoprosthesis which is a self-expanding stent (SES). All other stents have biliary or tracheo-bronchial FDA approval and are being used for "off-label" vascular indications. Generally, however all stents do fall into the category of

13

Table 13.1. Guidelines for peripheral percutaneous transluminal angioplasty of the abdominal aorta and lower extremity vessels

Selection criteria for percutaneous transluminal angioplasty	Categories of iliac artery occlusive disease
Category 1: Lesions for which percutaneous transluminal angioplasty alone is the procedure of choice. Treatment of these lesions will result in a high technical success rate and will generally result in complete relief of symptoms or normalization of pressure gradients.	Category 1: Stenosis is less than 3 cm in length and is concentric and noncalcified.
Category 2: Lesions that are well suited for percutaneous transluminal angioplasty. Treatment of these lesions will result in complete relief or significant improvement in symptoms, pulses or pressure gradients. This category includes lesions that will be treated by procedures to be followed by surgical bypass to treat multilevel vascular disease.	Category 2: (1) Stenosis is 3-5 cm in length or (2) calcified or eccentric and less than 3 cm in length.
Category 3: Lesions that may be treated with percutaneous therapy, but because of disease extent, location, or severity have a significantly lower chance of initial technical success or long-term benefit than if treated with surgical bypass. However, percutaneous transluminal angioplasty may be performed, generally because of patient risk factors or because of lack of suitable bypass material.	Category 3: (1) Stenosis is 5-10 cm in length or (2) occlusion is less than 5 cm in length after thrombolytic therapy with chronic symptoms.
Category 4: Extensive vascular disease, for which percutaneous therapy has a very limited role because of low technical success rate or poor long-term benefit. In very high risk patients, or in those for whom no surgical procedure is applicable, percutaneous transluminal angioplasty may have some place.	Category 4: (1) Stenosis is greater than 10 cm in length, (2) occlusion is greater than 5 cm in length. After thrombolytic therapy and with chronic symptoms, (3) there is extensive bilateral aortoiliac atherosclerotic disease, or (4) the lesion is an iliac stenosis in a patient with abdominal aortic aneurysm or another lesion requiring aortic or iliac surgery.

From: Pentecost MJ, Criqui MH, Dorros G et al. Guidelines for peripheral percutaneous transluminal angioplasty of the abdominal aorta and lower extremity vessels. Circulation 1994; Vol. 89:1.

being either a BES or SES and share certain characteristics with their approved "cousins"(Table 13.2).

The FDA approves the Palmaz stent for use following a technically successful but suboptimal balloon angioplasty in the common or external iliac artery. A sub-

Table 13.2.

Balloon expandable stents	Self expanding stents
Palmaz stent (cordis Endovascular/ Johnson&Johnson, Warren, NJ	Wallstent (Boston Scientific, Natick, MA)
Corinthian stent (Cordis Enovascular/ Johnson & Johnson	S.M.A.R.T. stent (Cordis Endovascular/ Johnson & Johnson
AVE stent (Medtronic Inc., Minneapolis, MN)	Memotherm stent (C.R. Bard, Covington, GA)
Intra-stent (Intra-Therapeutics, St. Paul, MN)	Symphony stent (Boston Scientific)
Multi-link stent (Guidant, Santa Clara, CA)	

optimal angioplasty is defined as an inadequate angiographic result characterized by an intimal dissection and/or residual stenosis > 30% or an unsatisfactory hemodynamic result (a mean pressure gradient across the treated iliac segment of > 5 mm Hg). Likewise, the contraindications for stent placement include patients with occlusion of both iliac arteries, aneurysmal dilation proximal or distal to the intended site of treatment, densely calcified lesions, lesions that cannot be fully dilated by balloon angioplasty, patients with bleeding diatheses, poor renal function or severe hypertension. Patients with impaired pain sensation, vessel perforation (characterized by contrast extravasation at the site of primary dilation), uncontrolled hypercoaguability, marked tortuosity of the iliac artery which prevents passage of the stent, stenosis of the common femoral artery and significant stenosis distal to the intended lesion to be treated are also considered contraindications on the FDA approved label. In the decade or so that has passed since its original approval, "off label" applications for the Palmaz stent and other stent devices may indeed predominate their use.

The Palmaz BES is rigid with high hoop-strength and therefore resists elastic recoil. If a long lesion is to be treated with the Palmaz stent, several overlapping stents may have to be used. Since it is rigid throughout its length it is also useful for origin stenoses. It is however subject to two-point compression and will not rebound once it is deformed. Therefore, it should never be deployed where this may be a possibility (such as across a joint). Placement of the Palmaz stent can be done very precisely as there is very little shortening of the device when the balloon expands it.

The Wallstent SES is very flexible and is available in several lengths and diameters. It is useful for covering longer lesions and is less resistant to arterial elastic recoil but it has considerably less hoop-strength than a rigid BES. Its maximal hoop strength is reached when the stent has expanded to near its maximum diameter. SES cannot be expanded beyond their built-in maximum diameter and shorten considerably during deployment. Because of this shortening, SES are somewhat more difficult to position precisely when they are released from their delivery system. The Wallstent can be recaptured or reconstrained if it has not been completely released and can be repositioned if necessary. The other SES devices cannot. The Wallstent is less subject to two-point compression and will rebound if deformed. The flexibility

13

of the Wallstent also allows it to track through tortuous iliac arteries, and when deployed will conform to the contours of the artery.

Diagnostic Angiography

When considering deployment of endovascular devices, a precise preintervention arteriogram is required. The operator should have a basic understanding of angiographic anatomy and experience with basic percutaneous needle access, catheter and guidewire skills and knowledge of fluoroscopy and radiation safety. Satisfactory equipment should be available for angiography. We recommend cardiac monitoring, pulse oximetry, continuous blood pressure monitoring during these procedures. Arterial pressure monitoring is absolutely necessary when interventions are planned. Operating room fluoroscopy C-arms are inadequate for most full-scale interventions and should be used only in a limited role. A dedicated, properly supplied and staffed angiographic/endovascular laboratory is the ideal environment.

The diagnostic arteriogram is critical for confirming the diagnosis suggested by any noninvasive study. Oblique views of the pelvis are often necessary to bring eccentric lesions into profile. Pressure gradients can be helpful in determining whether some lesions that may not appear particularly critical should be treated or not. The decision to make an ipsilateral, contralateral or an axillary approach to an iliac occlusive lesion depends upon the anticipated intervention. For example SES can more easily be used from a contralateral approach than with the more rigid BES. If very precise positioning for a lesion involving a common iliac artery origin is required; an ipsilateral approach may be preferred. The large sheaths required for placement of larger balloons or stents can occlude outflow. Therefore use of a vasodilator such as nitroglycerin, along with systemic heparinization (2000-5000 IU) is strongly suggested before intervening in these instances.

Lesion Evaluation and Selection

An arterial stenosis is considered significant if the cross-sectional area is reduced by at least 70%. If multiple projections fail to demonstrate a significant stenosis, pressure measurements across the suspected lesion should be made. Vasodilators (nitroglycerin 100 mg, tolazoline 25 mg, or papaverine 30 mg) should be given intra-arterially when a borderline gradient is measured. If after vasodilation a significant gradient (> 10 mm Hg) is measured, intervention should be considered.

Pressures are measured in a number of ways. A two-transducer technique, with a catheter in the aorta and another below the level of the lesion is one method. A single catheter pullback technique is another. If one measures a pressure through a catheter in the aorta and the distal pressure through the side port of the introducer sheath, the gradient may be accentuated due to partial occlusion of the lumen by the catheter.

It is now generally accepted that both immediate technical success, and long term success of iliac artery stenting is superior to PTA alone.[4] However, stent procedures are significantly more costly. Therefore many authors recommend a selective approach to stenting (Fig. 13.1). In other words, PTA alone will be performed on all category 1 lesions and perhaps some category 2 lesions. Following the intervention,

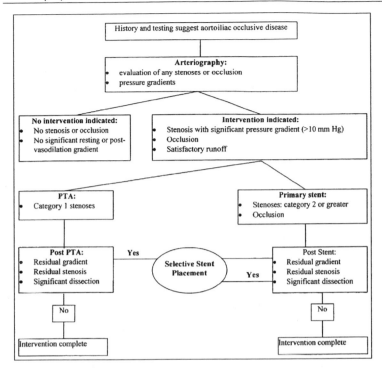

Fig. 13.1. Algorithm for selective stent deployment.

a limited arteriogram should be performed along with pressure measurements. Hemodynamics are more helpful than angiographic appearance alone when assessing the results of PTA or stenting. Hemodynamic pressure measurements will help determine whether or not further intervention (i.e., stent deployment) is indicated and to assess the results of the intervention when completed.

There is some disagreement as to how these pressure measurements should be made: peak systolic or mean, whether or not vasodilators should be used and what the threshold gradient for intervention should be. In a recent study comparing post-PTA mean pressure gradients no difference at 12 month follow up (measuring peak systolic velocities with color duplex ultrasound) was seen between those patients with a post-PTA gradient of < 5 mm Hg and those with a gradient ≥ 5 mm Hg but ≤ 10 mm Hg (5 mm Hg mean gradient is the threshold according to FDA criteria). This suggests that 5 mm Hg mean gradient may be too low. However, a 10 mm Hg threshold was not studied although this is an often-accepted value and the threshold we use.[5] There is no clear consensus as to whether a mean or peak systolic gradient is more meaningful.

13

Stent Deployment

Matching the size of the stent or balloon to a particular vessel can be accomplished in a number of ways. If film arteriography is performed a direct measurement from the image will give the appropriate size of the balloon. The film image is magnified 15-20% in most cases and this is the right amount of over-sizing one needs for successful PTA and/or stenting. When digital images are obtained, a calibrated catheter or radiopaque ruler on the patient's skin can be used. Since these images are analyzed on a video screen and there is no built-in magnification as in film angiography, one must make the correct adjustment by adding 15-20% to determine the balloon or stent size.

During balloon dilation, either during angioplasty or stent deployment, an alert and cooperative patient should experience moderate but significant discomfort that resolves when the balloon is deflated. The lack of significant discomfort suggests that there has been underdilation of the vessel. (If the pain is severe during dilation, deflate the balloon immediately and reassess the situation: monitor vital signs, perform angiography to re-evaluate the lesion if necessary, and double-check the balloon size).

As stated earlier, a SES has its greatest hoop strength when it expands close to its maximum diameter. With this in mind, a SES should be chosen that is 1-2 mm larger than the measured artery when using digital images or the same size or slightly larger than the measured artery on film images.

When positioning balloons and stents, bony landmarks and radiopaque rulers are not entirely reliable. Due to parallax of the fluoroscopic beam, the position of the lesion will change relative to bony landmarks or markers anterior or posterior to it if the patient has moved even slightly. Therefore a contrast injection through a vascular sheath immediately prior to stent deployment should be done to confirm the exact location for treatment. Some angiographic machines have features where a "live image" is superimposed upon a digitally stored "road map". This feature will also allow for precise balloon or stent positioning.

13

BES can be precisely positioned and deployed since these type of stents do not shorten significantly as they are expanded, unless they are expanded beyond their recommended maximum diameter. Although experience with deployment of SES is the best teacher, one generally should begin deployment with the distal end of the stent at least 1 cm beyond the lesion. Stent shortening should bring the end of the stent to the proper position. Although the Wallstent can be recaptured and repositioned before it is fully deployed, stents made from nitinol such as the Memotherm, S.M.A.R.T. stent, or Symphony stent cannot. The nitinol stents also have a tendency to "jump" forward if they are deployed too quickly. When SES are being used we recommend that they be deployed very slowly with back-tension on the delivery sheath and guidewire to reduce the chance of significant movement during the deployment process.

If the origin of the common iliac artery is to be stented some authors advocate a "kissing" balloon technique. By simultaneously inflating a balloon in the contralateral common iliac artery during stent placement the origin of the nonstented vessel is "protected" from plaque or thrombus being pushed over the bifurcation. In reality this complication is uncommon and we rarely "protect" the opposite iliac when treating common iliac origin stenoses. The "kissing" technique is however very useful when stents are to be placed to treat bilateral origin stenoses and/or occlusions, or a distal aortic stenosis. It is important when performing the "kissing" technique that the combined balloons and stents can be accommodated by the terminal aorta.

After deployment of a BES or a SES that has been further dilated using a balloon catheter, the balloon should be fully deflated before its removal over a guidewire. As the balloon catheter is being withdrawn it should be rotated to prevent it from catching on the stent. A guidewire should remain through the stent and across the treated lesion until it has been determined that the intervention is complete. If the follow-up arteriogram or pressure gradients require placement of an additional stent, the introducer/dilator should be reinserted into the vascular sheath and the sheath/introducer readvanced over the guidewire into the stented segment. This will prevent the additional stent from getting caught on the already deployed one while the stent is being positioned for its deployment. If a guidewire must be advanced through an already-deployed stent, a small-J guidewire should be used to avoid dissecting under the edge of the stent or passing the wire through the interstices of the stent.

When an iliac lesion requires a stent to be deployed to a large diameter (10 mm or 12 mm) the BES mounted on the optimally sized balloon may not fit through a sheath that will normally accept that same balloon without the stent. In such an instance we deploy the stent on a smaller balloon and use the correctly sized balloon to complete the dilation rather than up-size the vascular sheath.

Guidewire Traversal of Stenoses and Occlusion

Most aortoiliac stenoses are easily crossed using standard coil-spring type angiographic wires. In many cases a shaped catheter (we prefer a hockey-stick shape in most cases) can be used to "steer" through an irregular arterial stenosis. Angled-tip hydrophilic guidewires are also very popular for negotiating tortuous stenoses, but they also tend to dissect subintimally more often than other wires and therefore must be used carefully. Another alternative is to use a tapered, high torque soft-tip wire. The TAD wire (Mallinkrodt, St. Louis, Mo.) is an example of such a wire with a stiff .035" shaft that tapers distally to a .018" shapeable soft platinum tip.

Guidewire traversal is the "make it or break it" of aortoiliac interventions. If one cannot cross the affected segment, no percutaneous intervention can be performed. When dealing with an occlusion we generally take the 5 French hockey stick catheter to the edge of the occlusion. An attempt is first made to cross the lesion with a soft, straight coil-spring wire (Bentson, Cook Inc., Bloomington, IN). If this is not successful, a stiff .035 tight-J wire (Rosen wire, 1.5 mm J, Cook Inc.) supported by the catheter can sometimes "plow" through the occluded lumen. When these attempts are not successful, the angled-tip hydrophilic wire (Glidewire, Boston Scientific, Natick, MA) will be used. Although one tries to stay within the lumen, the wire may dissect under the plaque and the intima.

When subintimal dissection occurs it can be recognized by a spiral course of the wire during lesion traversal. If contrast is injected within the dissection, a smooth, crescent collection along the planes of dissection will be seen. Several options should be considered if subintimal dissection occurs. First, one must be certain that the adventitia has not been transgressed. A contrast injection should be performed. If contrast extravasates into the retroperitoneum the procedure should be terminated. The patient should be observed carefully. In virtually all cases where only guidewire perforation has occurred within the region of an occluded segment no drastic intervention is required. The procedure can be reattempted a week or so later after the dissection has had a chance to heal. If contrast injection confirms that the wire is only subintimal another option is to continue to advance the wire, along with the catheter and attempt to re-enter the true lumen on the other side of the occluded segment. If this is successful the dissected passage can be dilated and stented successfully. Some authors even propose that the "clean" subintimal path may be preferable to stenting the plaque and debris-ridden true lumen.

If the true lumen cannot be re-entered directly, a contralateral approach may be successful, with the contra-lateral wire staying within the true lumen. If the intima is dissected from the contralateral approach as well, one might consider using a 5 or 10 mm Amplatz snare (Microvena, White Bear Lake, MN) to aid in lesion traversal. The snare can be opened in the false passage and used to grasp the subintimal wire introduced from the opposite side. The wire can then be pulled out through the contralateral groin (or even an axillary or brachial access). With this "through and through" wire, balloon catheters and stents can be advanced through even very tough areas and successfully deployed.

When dealing with long segment disease (category 3 and 4 lesions) some authors have recommended predilating the lesion before stent deployment. We predilate to a sub-optimal size only to allow easier passage of sheaths or stent delivery catheters. In the case of SESs we deploy these in the sub-optimally dilated segment and then use additional balloon catheters to dilate the stent to the desired diameter.

Another option is to pretreat occluded segments with an infusion of thrombolytic drugs. The goal is to dissolve any thrombus and to possibly improve the lesion to a shorter occlusion or stenosis. Thrombolysis may also eliminate or reduce the risk of embolization during balloon dilation or stent deployment. In reality however, the risk of embolization when recanalizing occlusions is quite low (< 5%) and lytic therapy has not demonstrated a significant advantage with chronic occlusions.[6,7] The increased cost and risk of lytic therapy probably does not warrant its routine use in this application. Lytic therapy is nevertheless an important adjunct in treating acute thromboses or embolization if either should occur.

Technical Endpoints

A good technical result is important to long-term success. Although a postprocedure angiogram may look good, the use of pressure gradients to document success is critical. A gradient following stent placement can indicate a technical problem in underdeployment of the stent. If pressure gradients are not satisfactory, consider using a larger balloon to "bump" up the stent or re-treat an area of elastic recoil. Incomplete embedding of the stent structure onto the endothelial surface will allow fibrin and thrombus to deposit on the stent and slow reendothelialization. This may contribute to thrombosis of the stented segment or the development of myointimal hyperplasia.

Additional stents may be needed to extend the treated area or tack down a significant dissection. Occasionally elastic recoil prevents a Wallstent from fully expanding. In such a case a Palmaz stent may be necessary to shore up the narrowed area. A 0-mm Hg mean gradient is not always possible however this should be the goal.

Complications

The complications associated with stent placement are the same as those frequently seen with diagnostic angiography and PTA procedures. Most often they are related to arterial access. A groin hematoma is most common but continued retroperitoneal hemorrhage can also occur. Patient complaints of significant back pain following a PTA or stent procedure should be evaluated carefully and a CT scan should be considered to rule out hemorrhage.

Acute tubular necrosis can sometimes occur, as the amount of contrast used during complicated stent procedures can be very high. To prevent this, patients should be well hydrated before and after the procedure.

Stenting of aortoiliac occlusive lesions is not easy, although the literature supports an expectation of a high degree of initial technical success. Major complications, requiring significant departure from the treatment plan, occur in approximately 6% of cases with less than 2% requiring surgical intervention.[8] Mortality of aortoiliac stent placement is < 0.5%.[8] However when complications are recorded strictly, based on "intent to treat" the complication rate can approach 20% even in the hands of experienced operators.[9] This complication rate is derived from the fact that many times a lesion that is intended to be treated with a single stent or angioplasty requires placement of additional stents due to extensive intimal dissection, an unsatisfactory pressure gradient or unsatisfactory positioning of the original stent. Acute thrombosis or embolization rarely occur but can frequently be treated successfully with thrombolytic therapy. These additional maneuvers can salvage the procedure most of the time.

The incidence of intraprocedural complications is increased if patients have pedal gangrene, if more than one stent is deployed, if the patient is female or if there is poor runoff (i.e., occluded superficial femoral artery). This increased complication rate in these situations may be due to an association of more severe and diffuse disease, or in the case of female patients, generally smaller arteries. This translates to the likelihood of more access problems, difficult guidewire passage with an increased risk of intimal dissection. Likewise with the placement of additional stents there are more maneuvers required and therefore more risk for complications.

Other rare but potentially disastrous complications include loss of the stent prior to satisfactory deployment, stent infection and arterial rupture. If a balloon expandable stent slides off its balloon before it has been inflated it can be recaptured. If it is still over the wire a smaller sized balloon catheter can in some instances be reinserted and the stent can be repositioned or deployed in another segment of the iliac artery. A wire snare can be used to grasp the loose stent and possibly remove it. Stent infection is a potentially life- or limb-threatening complication. Although this complication has been rarely reported we have seen two cases in our experience: one patient required removal of the affected arterial segment and above-knee amputation, the other patient with a chronic infection developed a large pseudoaneurysm that was successfully treated by embolization and aggressive antibiotic therapy. Because infection of a stented artery is so devastating we now give prophylactic antibiotics to all our stent patients at the time of the procedure. (Broad-spectrum first or second-generation cephalosporins are considered adequate when prosthetic grafts are placed).

Arterial rupture is very rare but potentially disastrous. It is usually accompanied by pain that does not resolve when the dilating balloon is deflated. The blood pressure will also immediately drop. In addition to fluid administration, the rupture should be treated by inflation of a balloon catheter across the rent in the artery in order to tamponade it until emergency surgery can be performed. Another alternative is to deploy a Wallstent across the ruptured segment and balloon tamponade it for 20-30 minutes. This has been successful on two occasions and surgery was not required to stop the hemorrhage.[9] We believe that balloon tamponade allows the periarterial hemorrhage to thrombose and that the stent compresses any intimal flap and provides a low resistance conduit, preventing pseudoaneurysm formation.

Patient Selection

Patient selection is paramount to a successful endovascular procedure. Several studies have been conducted in which patient gender, pattern of disease, postprocedure pressure gradients, ankle/brachial indices, and numerous risk factors (diabetes, coronary artery diseases, hypertension, continued smoking, etc.) have been considered. Although there is some disagreement between these studies, generally poor outflow defined as an occluded superficial femoral artery or a severely diseased and stenotic superficial femoral artery is the only distal disease pattern that reduces the likelihood of long-term stent patency. Unlike PTA, some studies have demonstrated that stenting the external iliac artery does not affect long-term patency. Female gender, possibly due to generally smaller arteries not only portends a higher complication rate but also a less successful outcome overall. Other risk factors such as those listed above do not ultimately affect patency of the stented iliac artery. The ideal stent candidate is most likely a male with patent infrainguinal runoff and a category 1 or 2 lesion.

Long-Term Results

Aortoiliac stenting has emerged as a means to not only improve upon suboptimal PTA results but also to treat lesions that had previously been considered unsuitable for PTA alone (category 3 and 4). Initial technical success in treating iliac artery stenoses is well over 90% in most published series. Statistical review of over 800 stent patients from 8 different studies demonstrates primary patency rates at 4 years of 77% for stenoses and 53% for occlusions in patients with claudication and 67% for stenoses and 53% for occlusions in patients with critical ischemia.[4] In consideration of these results, one must bear in mind that patency has not been consistently defined in the literature. Standard definitions for reporting patency rates are listed in Table 13.3. A technical success of 81% was reported in a series dealing with chronic occlusions with primary patency of 87% at one year, 83% at two years, and 78% at four years. Secondary patency was 94% at one year, 90% at two years, and 88% at four years.[7] A similar study dealing with both complex stenoses and occlusions had a technical success of 91% and primary patency of 78% at one year and 53% at two years. Secondary patency was 86% at one year and 82% at 32 months.[6]

Ultimate long-term success of aortoiliac stent deployment depends on some factors previously mentioned. One of those is outflow. If there is severe ipsilateral superficial femoral artery stenosis or occlusion distal to a newly deployed iliac artery stent, one should probably consider adjunctive femoral-popliteal bypass grafting or additional endovascular treatment of any significant stenoses. Likewise, patients with small artery caliber, such as females, should be carefully followed so that reintervention can be instituted in a timely manner. It is important to state, however that clinical benefit may be maintained despite the loss of patency according to traditional reporting standards.[3,8] Reintervention should not be instituted unless the patient has recurrence of symptoms. When symptoms do recur, numerous procedures exist for improving or restoring patency. Assisted primary patency and secondary patency rates for treating restenosis are quite high and should be considered prior to attempting surgical bypass.[8]

Restenosis

Thrombosis and/or restenosis within the stented artery are the primary threat to long-term patency. Generally the more severe the lesion treated the greater the likelihood of thrombosis and decreased long-term stent patency. Most frequently, restenosis occurs at the ends of the stent rather mid-stent. Regardless, this build up of myointima within or at the ends of the stent can cause a return of symptoms or stent occlusion. Although angioplasty within the stented segment and/or placement of additional stents can successfully treat these restenoses, the problem may still recur. The build up of myointima may cause a relatively more rapid narrowing of the lumen in patients with smaller vessels. When secondary maneuvers designed to assist patency before reocclusion or to restore patency fail, a bypass procedure should be considered.

Pharmacologic agents that prevent platelet adhesion (abciximab, ReoPro‰: Centocor, Malvern, PA) and myointimal proliferation and even local radiation therapy or radioactive stents are currently being studied as means to prevent intra-stent restenosis.

Cost

In the current environment of health-care cost cutting it is important to understand the economic ramifications of these procedures. Very few studies have been done to compare costs of treatment of like lesions by surgical bypass or PTA or stenting. In one paper making such a comparison, direct costs were not significantly different (total mean hospital cost $8626 for the stent group, $9383 for the surgery group), although hospital stay (mean stay 10 days for the surgery group, 2 days for the stent group) did differ significantly.[10]

Table 13.3. Definitions of patency

Primary patency	Uninterrupted patency with no additional procedure performed on or at the margins of the treated segment. Progressive disease treated in an adjacent vessel does not alter this definition.
Assisted primary patency	An otherwise still patent previously treated arterial segment that required a second procedure to prevent failure or thrombosis.
Secondary patency	Restored flow through a previously patent but now thrombosed treated segment by a secondary procedure

Postprocedure Care

All patients should be observed at bed rest for a few hours. Appropriately trained personnel should monitor blood pressure and vital signs. The extremity and pulses distal to the arterial puncture site and the site of intervention should also be observed and monitored. Initial ambulation should also be supervised and stability of the puncture site checked prior to patient discharge.

Recently a few puncture site hemostasis devices have been made available. These devices consist of collagen plugs or percutaneously placed sutures and are intended to allow for early ambulation and discharge of the patient. Whether one chooses to utilize such a device or not is entirely up to the preference of the practitioner and the particular practice setting.

Prior to discharge a follow-up visit should be arranged (1-2 weeks). The patient should be given instructions regarding care of the puncture site and signs of hematoma formation. The patient is also advised to take 1 aspirin (325 mg) daily as an antiplatelet agent. The treating physician or his/her designate should be available to answer questions or concerns the patient may have in the early postprocedure follow-up period. After the initial follow-up visit, the patient should be seen regularly (every 6 months) over 2 years. During this time period when intimal hyperplasia and restenosis are most likely to occur, reintervention may be required to maintain stent patency. After 2 years, if the patient is doing well they should be advised to return to clinic if symptoms recur.

Conclusion

Successful stenting for both immediate and long-term outcome depends upon the technical expertise of the operator, selection of the lesion and patient and an understanding of potential complications. Experience is ultimately the best teacher of these skills and techniques. The medical literature connected with endovascular devices and procedures is still in evolution and there are only a few clear concensuses. For this reason the current literature needs to be reviewed frequently and analytically.

Selected Readings

1. Becker GJ, Katzen BT, Dake MD. Noncoronary angioplasty. Radiology 1989; 170:921-940.
    Principles of noncoronary angioplasty including balloon catheter and guidewire terminology, use of pharmacological adjuncts, indications, contraindications, general technical principles, complications and limitations.

2. Pentecost MJ, Criqui MH, Dorros G et al. Guidelines for peripheral percutaneous transluminal angioplasty of the abdominal aorta and lower extremity vessels. Circulation 1994; Vol 89:No. 1.
    Reviews classifications of claudication, limb ischemia and grading of clinical improvement following intervention. Outcome criteria and definitions of categories of lesions amenable to angioplasty. Standards of care, comparisons to vascular surgery, results of iliac angioplasty, etc.
    See also: Spies JB, Bakal CB, Burke DR et al. Standards of practice committee of the society of cardiovascular and interventional radiology. Guidelines for percutaneous transluminal angioplasty. Radiology 1990; 177:619-626.

3. Rutherford RB, Becker GJ. Standards for evaluating and reporting the results of surgical and percutaneous therapy for peripheral arterial disease. Radiology 1991; 181:277-281.
    Definitions of primary patency, primary assisted patency and secondary patency. These standards provide a means to report patency data following surgical or percutaneous intervention. They attempt to take into account the patient's clinical condition both before and after the intervention. Objective means for determining patency are described including the use of the ankle/brachial index (ABI) and the thigh/brachial index (TBI).

4. Bosch JL, Hunink MGM. Meta-analysis of the results of percutaneous transluminal angioplasty and stent placement for aortoiliac occlusive disease. Radiology 1997; 204:87-96.
    A meta-analysis of 1,300 PTA patients in 6 studies and 816 stent patients in 8 studies were statistically analyzed. Complication rates for PTA and stenting was similar however technical success and long-term success was superior with stenting.

5. Kamphius AGA, van Engelen AD, Tetteroo E et al. Impact of different hemodynamic criteria for stent placement after suboptimal iliac angioplasty. JVIR 1999; 10:741-746.
    Few publications are available that address the issue of selective stenting. This article discusses the various published thresholds for stenting and addresses specifically the 5 mm Hg FDA approved threshold.

6. Murphy TP, Webb MS, Lambiase RE et al. Percutaneous revascularization of complex iliac artery stenoses and occlusions with use of Wallstents: Three-year experience. JVIR 1996; 7:21-27.

7. Vorwerk D, Guenther RW, Schurmann K et al. Primary stent placement for chronic iliac artery occlusion: Follow-up results in 103 patients. Radiology 1995; 194:745-749.
    These two articles (Ref. 6 and 7) describe stenting for complex iliac lesions (stenoses and occlusions). Both demonstrate high technical success and few complications. One of the principle differences in these two papers is that thrombolysis was used to pretreat chronic occlusions (Murphy et al) but no preliminary thrombolysis was used in the cases described by Vorwerk et al. This would support the hypothesis that thrombolysis is not advantageous as part of a primary approach to treating chronic iliac occlusions.

13

8. Murphy TP, Khwaja AA, Webb MS. Aortoiliac stent placement in patients treated for intermittent claudication. JVIR 1998; 9:421-428.

    Iliac stenting for patients with category 2 and 3 lesions and claudication (no rest pain or tissue loss) was reviewed. Cumulative patency was 77%, 71%, 62%, 62% at 1, 2, 3, 4 years, respectively. Clinical improvement was present in 80%, 80%, 73%, 73% at 1, 2, 3, 4 years, respectively. The authors suggest that the mismatch between clinical benefit and current reporting standards for patency (Rutherford criteria, see ref 3) may indicate a need to revise the reporting criteria.

9. Ballard JL, Sparks SR, Taylor FC et al. Complications of iliac artery stent deployment. J Vasc Surg 1996; 24:545-55.

    Procedure-related complications occurred in 19.4% of treated limbs. In spite of this, additional intraprocedural maneuvers were able to salvage most of the procedures and yield a technical success of 96.7%.

10. Ballard JL, Bergan JJ, Singh P et al. Aortoiliac stent deployment versus surgical reconstruction: Analysis of outcome and cost. J Vasc Surg 1998; 28:94-103.

    Comparison of complication rates, primary patency, and cost of stenting versus surgical reconstruction for the treatment of aortoiliac occlusive disease. Both groups were similar in demographics and presenting symptoms. Incidence of complications was also similar. Although hospital stays were significantly shorter for the stent group (2 days vs. 10 days), cost was not (total hospital and professional costs: stent group—$9161, surgery group $10,585). Primary patency of bypass grafts was superior to stenting (at 18 months: surgery group 93%, stent group 77%; at 42 months: surgery group 93%, stent group 68%).

13

CHAPTER 14

Infrarenal Aortic Aneurysm Repair

E. John Harris, Jr.

The treatment of abdominal aortic aneurysms began with the historic procedure reported by Dubost in 1951, resection of the aneurysm and replacement with an aortic homograft. Within a short time period multiple surgeons throughout the world were duplicating and subsequently modifying Dubost's procedure with the use of various prosthetic grafts, establishing aortic reconstruction with prosthetic grafts as the treatment of choice for abdominal aortic aneurysms. Since that time, further development and improvement of prosthetic grafts, refinements in operative technique, and improvements in perioperative intensive care and monitoring have established direct graft replacement of infrarenal abdominal aortic aneurysms as the standard of care.

Natural History Versus Treatment

The natural history of aortic aneurysms is to enlarge and rupture. The average rate of aneurysm enlargement is 0.5 cm/year and the risk of rupture increases exponentially with increasing aneurysm size. From several clinical series it appears that the risk of rupture/year for aneurysms less than 4 cm is small, on the order of 2%. Data for aneurysms 4-5 cm in diameter is less secure as many of these patients go on to repair, but 5-year rupture rates for these moderate sized aneurysms have been reported between 3-12 %. For large aneurysms, those greater than 5 cm in diameter, 25-41% will go on to rupture within 5 years. It is estimated that as many as 50% of patients with aortic aneurysms who do not undergo operative repair will die of a ruptured aneurysm. The mortality rate for ruptured aortic aneurysm approaches 90% if one includes the deaths of those who do not reach the hospital alive. Operative mortality rates for ruptured aneurysms range from 30-80%, averaging approximately 50% in most clinical series. This sobering statistic has not changed over the 40 plus year history of aortic aneurysm surgery.

Despite control of hypertension and major efforts directed toward controlling risk factors of atherosclerosis, the prevalence of abdominal aortic aneurysms is increasing, as much as 300% over the past 40 years. Whether this represents an increased prevalence of aneurysms in our ever-aging population, or an increase in detection by the frequent use of abdominal imaging studies remains uncertain. Over this same 40-year period, while deaths from heart attacks and strokes have decreased 25%, mortality from aortic aneurysms is increasing. Therefore, medical therapy for aneurysms must be judged to be totally ineffective in preventing the risk of rupture.

Aortic Surgery, edited by Jeffrey L. Ballard. ©2000 Landes Bioscience.

Surgical therapy has, on the other hand, been very successful in eliminating the risk of death from rupture of aortic aneurysms. Aneurysmorrhaphy with interposition prosthetic grafts attached to nonaneurysmal aorta and/or iliac arteries has proven to be a safe and durable procedure. Surgical aneurysmorrhaphy is effective both for simple and complex aneurysm morphologies and can correct coexistent occlusive disease of adjacent arterial segments and branches. The procedure can be adjusted to repair supra or pararenal aneurysms, renal artery stenoses, mesenteric artery stenoses, iliac artery stenoses or aneurysms or common femoral artery stenoses or aneurysms. In the 40 years since the original aneurysm repair, careful follow-up of patients undergoing aneurysmorrhaphy with prosthetic graft replacement has proven this procedure as durable. Thus, the issue regarding aneurysmorrhaphy is not whether this surgical therapy is effective and durable compared to the natural history of untreated aortic aneurysms, it is. The issue revolves around the risks and complications associated with a major surgical procedure. The expected outcome of surgical therapy of aneurysms must take into consideration the medical risk of the patient and the morphology of the aneurysm, as well as any associated occlusive disease, all of which may significantly influence results.

Defining Perioperative Risk

It is well established that pre-existing medical conditions can greatly influence the morbidity and mortality of elective abdominal aortic aneurysm repair. Some medical conditions increase risk not only for direct operative morbidity and mortality rates, but also for late survival rates. Coronary artery disease is such a condition, and it remains the major cause of both early postoperative death and long-term death following major vascular surgery. Significant underlying coronary artery disease in patients with abdominal aortic aneurysms has been documented both invasively and noninvasively. Many surgeons have recommended extensive preoperative cardiac risk assessment and intervention prior to elective noncardiac vascular surgery. Others have noted the occurrence of ischemic cardiac events predominantly in patients with clinical and ECG evidence of coronary disease, and suggest that extensive routine preoperative cardiac screening is of little value. Reduction of cardiac morbidity and mortality rates have been documented in patients undergoing noncardiac vascular surgery when these procedures are preceded by coronary artery bypass grafting, or performed at the same time as coronary artery bypass grafting. In spite of these improved perioperative cardiac morbidity and mortality rates, long term survival following coronary artery bypass grafting in patients with peripheral vascular occlusive disease has not been improved.

In 1992, the SVS/ISCVS joint council convened a panel of experts to review and define the medical risk for elective aortic aneurysm repair. This panel identified age, cardiac function, pulmonary function and renal function as the primary predictors of operative risk. Predicted operative mortality rates for low risk patients under the age of 75 with normal cardiac, pulmonary, and renal function was less than 1% whereas operative mortality for patients over the age of 90 with unstable angina, COPD requiring home oxygen and on chronic hemodialysis could exceed 30% (Table 14.1.). As with the assessment of cardiac risks, the true influence of multiple

Table 14.1. ISCVS/SVS joint council subcommittee medical risk categorization: Elective aneurysm repair

	Level 0 low risk	Level I minimal risk	Level II moderate risk	Level III high risk
Age	< 75	75-80	85-90	> 90
Cardiac	No CAD	CAD—Mild stable angina or remote MI, negative coronary angio, normal cardiac stress test, LVEF < 50% but > 30%.	CAD—Stable angina or remote MI, mild to moderate lesions on coronary angio. small reperfusion defects on radionuclide scan, LVEF < 30% by > 20%.	CAD—Unstable angina, significant areas of myocardium at risk based on coronary angio or radionuclide scans, LVEF < 20%, recent CHF
Pulmonary	Normal pulmonary function	COPD—able to carry out normal activities of daily life	COPD—moderate to severe pulmonary dysfunction	COPD—requiring home oxygen, Fe < 25-75 < 20% predicted
Renal	Normal renal function	Mild renal dysfunction, creatinine < 2 mg/dl	Renal dysfunction, creatinine 2-3.5 mg/dl	Chronic dialysis, creatinine > 3.5 mg/dl
Predicted mortality rate	0-1%	1-3%	3 8%	8-30%

Reprinted with permission from J Endovasc Surg 1997; 4:232-41.

comorbid conditions on perioperative morbidity and mortality rates remains incompletely defined. Nonetheless, in studies reporting the results of treatment of aneurysms, the risk classification of patients undergoing treatment should be clearly defined.

14

Defining Aneurysm Morphology Risk

The influence of aneurysm morphology on perioperative morbidity and mortality is not clearly defined in the literature. Inflammatory aneurysms are perceived as more difficult to repair operatively than typical atherosclerotic aneurysms, yet this perception is not supported by increased morbidity and mortality rates. Clinical series reporting results with suprarenal or pararenal aneurysm repairs requiring suprarenal aortic cross clamping have documented increased intraoperative blood loss and an increased incidence of postoperative renal dysfunction, yet postoperative mortality has not increased. Aneurysms extending into the ilio-femoral systems require more complex repairs. Although generally perceived as increasing operative morbidity and mortality, again there is no conclusive data suggesting that simultaneous repair of iliac and femoral aneurysms increases perioperative morbidity and mortality. There may be a slight increase in the incidence of wound infection and graft limb thrombosis when the graft is extended to the femoral region.

Treatment of concomitant atherosclerotic occlusive disease during aneurysmorrhaphy adds complexity to the repair, and many believe increases morbidity and mortality. A recent review of 722 elective aortic reconstructions, 61% for aneurysmal disease and 39% for occlusive disease, identified an operative mortality rate of 4.9% which increased to 8.9% with simultaneous renal revascularization and 15.8% with simultaneous lower extremity vascular procedures. This latter mortality rate is somewhat misleading in that 36% of the lower extremity vascular procedures were performed unexpectedly for acute ischemia, suggesting technical problems or poor preoperative planning as the cause for this increased risk. Well conceived elective plans for simultaneous aortic aneurysm repair and lower limb revascularization can be completed safely, as evidenced by our own recently reported small series of aneurysm repairs. In this group of 73 consecutive aneurysm repairs, 29% had simultaneous lower extremity or renal revascularization, with no operative mortality for the series. The operative mortality associated with simultaneous aortic reconstruction and renal artery revascularization of previously reported series has ranged from 3-10%. Advocates suggest all renal artery stenoses, even asymptomatic stenoses, should be repaired at the same time as the aneurysm repair, based on these low mortality rates. The natural history of asymptomatic concomitant renal artery stenoses is incompletely defined, but may be more benign than these advocates for revascularization suggest. Simultaneous renal artery revascularization and aortic aneurysm repair is best reserved for those surgeons with an established experience in renal artery revascularization.

High Risk Patients

Recognizing that patients with high-risk pre-existing medical conditions have an increased morbidity and mortality for operative aneurysm repair has led to the development of alternative methods of aneurysm exclusion and revascularization. From the first report of a two-stage ligation of the iliac arteries and axillofemoral bypass for treatment of aortic aneurysm in a high-risk patient, through the early 1980s, nonresective therapy for high-risk aortic aneurysms enjoyed a small group of advocates. Operative mortality was 8%, but aneurysm related postoperative mortality was 10%. Late fatal rupture led the innovator of this procedure to add aortic ligation to the iliac artery ligations, a procedural modification now not unlike aortic replacement as far as physiologic stress. In a recently updated series of 26 high risk AAA patients treated with ligation (62% included aortic ligation) and axillofemoral bypass, operative mortality was 8% and 12% died of ruptured aneurysms postoperatively. Although these results are improved over the natural history data, these results compare unfavorably with two recent series of high-risk AAA patients who had conventional aneurysm resection and replacement with operative mortality rates of 5-6%, and no postoperative aneurysm related mortality. Currently, all but a few surgeons have abandoned these nonresective procedures. Endoluminal stent grafts developed as a logical step in the evolution of alternative therapy for high-risk AAA patients and these continually evolving devices are likely to be far more effective than nonresective therapies.

Results of Aortic Aneurysm Repair

Results of elective abdominal aortic aneurysm repair have improved significantly over the past 40 years with significant reductions in operative mortality and complication rates. Current performance standards and expected outcomes can be determined by reviewing published reports from single authors or institutions, multicenter experiences and population based studies. The best results, of course, will be found in single center experiences from experienced surgeons with a particular interest in aneurysm repair. Most single center reports will include only vascular surgeons with formal training in vascular surgery.

Multicenter reports document the outcome from multiple centers within a region or health care system. Multicenter reports will include a broader representative sample of surgeons performing aneurysm repair, such as general surgeons, vascular surgeons and some cardiac surgeons, and probably best represent the standard of care for operative repair of abdominal aortic aneurysms at the current time. These reports may include patients with symptomatic but nonruptured aneurysms, juxtarenal aneurysms and associated aortic branch vessel disease. However, the majority of cases would represent straightforward, infrarenal aortic aneurysm repair. Results from multicenter reports will usually be inferior to those reported in single center experiences.

Population based studies provide mortality data on all aneurysms repaired in a geographic region and include nonspecialized hospitals and may include surgeons with uncertain training and background to perform aneurysm repair. These reports should reflect the overall community experience and will usually have higher mortality rates than multicenter reports. Mortality rates from population based studies are usually fairly accurate, but morbidity rates are usually under-reported.

Single center experience reports during the past 10 years of more than 100 patients were reviewed and document an operative mortality rate for nonruptured aortic aneurysm of 0-3.7% as typical for such centers of excellence. Among the 7 centers reviewed, a total of 2375 patients were treated with a 30-day mortality of 49 patients for an operative mortality rate of 2.1%.

Multicenter reports during the past 10 years of more than 300 patients were reviewed and document an operative mortality rate for nonruptured aneurysm of 3.6-4.9% as typical for multicenter experiences. A broad range of multicenter reports were reviewed for this table and included all of the Canadian Aneurysm Study group, all hospitals in Paris, all hospitals in Ontario, all hospitals in Southwest Virginia, and the entire Veterans Affairs hospital system. A total of 10,366 patients were treated with 439 deaths in 30 days for an operative mortality of 4.2%.

A review of population based surveys of aneurysm repair during the past 10 years revealed an operative mortality of 6-7.3% as typical for this type of report. Statewide experiences from Kentucky, New York, and Michigan of all patients treated for nonruptured abdominal aortic aneurysms, identified by discharge data abstracts and ICD-9 and CPT codes, were reviewed to identify 9681 patients with a 30 day

14

mortality of 704 patients for an operative mortality rate of 7.3%. These reports rely heavily on the accuracy of both CPT and ICD-9 coding.

The differences among single center reports, multicenter reports and population-based experiences are shown in Table 14.2. It appears that specialized centers performing frequent abdominal aortic aneurysm repair can expect better results than centers performing occasional aneurysm repair. Although this concept is supported by the Veterans Affairs study of 3419 aneurysms treated electively in 116 VA medical centers, with centers performing more than 16 aneurysm repairs per year enjoying more favorable operative mortality rates, some low volume centers also had excellent results.

Early complications reported after elective repair of abdominal aortic aneurysms approximate those of the multicenter Canadian aneurysm study, with myocardial ischemia, dysrhythmia, or congestive heart failure in up to 15%, pulmonary insufficiency in 8%, renal damage in 6%, bleeding complications in 4%, distal thromboembolism in 3%, and wound infection in 2%. Late vascular complications from aneurysm repair are infrequent. Although most patients do well after resection of infrarenal aneurysm, two small retrospective studies suggest that 3-8% of patients later develop aortic aneurysms proximal to the original graft.

This finding of para-anastomotic aneurysm formation during intermediate and late follow-up suggests the possibility that continued aortic enlargement may occur after aneurysm repair and this aortic enlargement may become an issue for endovascular repair strategies. Para-anastomotic aneurysms are more frequently encountered proximal to the aortic graft, are more frequently true aneurysms of residual aorta, and repair of these lesions is associated with significant morbidity and mortality, often 2-3 times that of the initial aneurysm repair. A recent population based study extending over 36 years confirms that standard surgical repair of abdominal aortic aneurysms remains free of any significant graft related complications during the patients remaining lifetime. Kaplan-Meier 5- and 10-year survival free estimates were 98% and 96% for anastomotic pseudoaneurysm, 98% and 95% for graft infection, and 98% and 97% for graft thrombosis.

Mortality rates after repair of ruptured aortic aneurysms remains high and has not changed appreciably over the past 20 years, ranging from 30-80%. Multicenter experiences during the past 10 years evaluating the outcome of surgical repair note that ruptured aortic aneurysms comprise only 14% of the total combined experience of 11,195 patients but accounted for the majority of the deaths from aortic aneurysms. The 30-day mortality rate for nonruptured aneurysms among 9577 patients was 4.2% while the 30-day mortality for 1618 ruptured aortic aneurysms was 42%. Complication rates and cost are also much higher for ruptured abdominal aortic aneurysm repairs.

Long-term survival after elective abdominal aortic aneurysm repair is less than age and sex-matched controls. In the Canadian Aneurysm trial, the 6-year survival rate of patients after elective aneurysm repair was 60.2% compared to 79.2% 6-year survival for the normal population. In a study of elective abdominal aortic aneurysm repair in 114 octogenarians, 5-year survival following repair was 48% compared to 59% for the normal control population. In both this and the Canadian

14

Table 14.2. Summary of operative mortalities

	Operative repair of nonruptured AAA Reported results—last 10 years	
	Number of patients	**Operative mortality**
Single center reports (n = 7)	2,375	2.1%
Multicenter reports (n = 5)	10,366	4.2%
Population based reports (n = 3)	9,681	7.3%

study, 5-year survival rates were closely associated with the heart-related mortality rates. In the Canadian study, the heart related 5-year mortality rate was 14.3% compared to 6.4% for age and sex matched controls. In the octogenarian study, the 5-year post aneurysm repair survival rate was 80% for operative survivors who received previous myocardial revascularization compared with 38% for those who did not.

Recommendations for Abdominal Aortic Aneurysm Repair

Aneurysms greater than 5 cm in size in good risk patients are best treated by replacement with a prosthetic graft. In centers of excellence a 30-day operative mortality of less than 3% is expected. In multicenter experiences a 30-day operative mortality less than 5% is expected. In a population based experience a 30-day operative mortality of less than 8% is expected. Excessive medical risk is infrequently encountered and more than 95% of all patients with abdominal aortic aneurysm are candidates for elective open repair. No specific risk factor alone is predictive of increased perioperative mortality risk but rather multiple risk factors together are predictive of increasing operative risk. These risk factors would include increasing age, significant cardiac occlusive or valvular disease, severe pulmonary dysfunction and severe renal insufficiency. Intra-operative risk factors not significantly influencing perioperative mortality risk include suprarenal aortic cross-clamping and graft configuration. As many as 30% of all patients with infrarenal aortic aneurysms can be successfully reconstructed with a tube graft. Placement of a tube graft is not associated with an increased incidence of late iliac artery aneurysm development or occlusive changes. Bifurcated graft configurations are predominantly utilized for aortic reconstructions of abdominal aneurysms and are expected to have 5 year graft limb patencies greater than 95% and 10 year graft limb patencies greater than 90%. Perioperative morbidity that prolongs the hospital course may be expected in as many as 10% of patients with multiple comorbid conditions and less than 3% of those with one or less comorbid conditions, and would include perioperative myocardial infarction, respiratory failure or renal failure. Minor morbidities not prolonging hospital stay may be expected in as many as 15-20% of patients, and would include wound infection, wound hematoma and urinary tract dysfunction. Long term survival following successful repair of abdominal aortic aneurysms does not approximate that expected of the control population. Actuarial 5-year survival of 65% and 8 year survival of 45% following elective repair of abdominal aortic aneurysms can be expected. Of these late deaths, the majority are cardiac related.

14

Selected Readings

1. Hallett JW, Jr., Marshall DM et al. Graft-related complications after abdominal
    aortic aneurysm repair: Reassurance from a 36-year population-based experience.
    J Vasc Surg 1997; 25(2):277-84; discussion 285-6.

    *Graft-related complications must be factored into the long-term morbidity and mortality
    rates of abdominal aortic aneurysm (AAA) repair. However, the true incidence may be
    underestimated because some patients do not return to the original surgical center when
    a problem arises. To minimize referral bias and loss to follow-up, all patients who
    underwent AAA repair between 1957 and 1990 in a geographically defined community
    where all AAA operations were performed and followed by a single surgical practice are
    reported. All patients who remained alive were asked to have their aortic grafts imaged.
    Among 307 patients who underwent AAA repair, 9.4% had a graft-related complication.
    At a mean follow-up of 5.8 years (range, 30 days to 36 years), the most common com-
    plication was anastomotic pseudoaneurysm (3.0%), followed by graft thrombosis (2.0%),
    graft-enteric erosion/fistula (1.6%), graft infection (1.3%), anastomotic hemorrhage
    (1.3%), colon ischemia (0.7%) and atheroembolism (0.3%). Complications were
    recognized within 30 days after surgery in eight patients (2.6%) and at late follow-up
    in 21 patients (6.8%). These complications were observed at a median follow-up of 6.1
    years for anastomotic pseudoaneurysm, 4.3 years for graft-enteric erosion, and 0.15
    years for graft infection. Kaplan-Meier 5- and 10-year survival free estimates were
    98% and 96% for anastomotic pseudoaneurysm, 98% and 95% for combined graft-
    enteric erosion/infection, and 98% and 97% for graft thrombosis. CONCLUSIONS:
    This 36-year population-based study confirms that the vast majority of patients who
    undergo standard surgical repair of an abdominal aortic aneurysm remain free of any
    significant graft-related complication during their remaining lifetime.*

2. Hallett JW, Jr., Naessens JM et al. Early and late outcome of surgical repair for
    small abdominal aortic aneurysms: A population-based analysis. J Vasc Surg 1993;
    18(4):684-91.

    *Whether small (≤ to 5 cm in diameter) abdominal aortic aneurysms (AAAs) should be
    repaired early to enhance late survival remains controversial. To examine an entire
    community experience with small AAAs, a population-based analysis of the recogni-
    tion, reasons for operation, perioperative mortality rates and late survival in Olmsted
    County, Minnesota was performed. The incidence of recognized small AAAs increased
    30-fold during a 30-year period. The propensity to repair small AAAs also increased
    during the same period. Eventually one third of small AAAs were repaired. The results
    of this population-based analysis indicate that early operative results for elective repair
    of small AAAs are excellent, but late survival remains significantly impaired by coro-
    nary heart disease. Consequently, the data question whether early repair of small AAAs
    will enhance late survival.*

3. Johnston KW. Multicenter prospective study of nonruptured abdominal aortic
    aneurysm. Part II. Variables predicting morbidity and mortality. J Vasc Surg 1989;
    9(3):437-47.

    *A previous article (Part I) described the patient population and operative management
    of 666 patients who had surgery for nonruptured abdominal aortic aneurysms. This
    article details perioperative complications and, by chi-square and logistic regression
    analysis, identifies variables that are associated with each complication. This excellent
    report carefully details risk factors associated with perioperative complications for the
    Canadian Society for Vascular Surgery Aneurysm Study Group. These results can be
    extrapolated to a benchmark for morbidity for aortic aneurysm repair.*

14

4. Johnston KW. Nonruptured abdominal aortic aneurysm: Six-year follow-up results from the multicenter prospective Canadian aneurysm study. Canadian Society for Vascular Surgery Aneurysm Study Group. J Vasc Surg 1994; 20(2):163-70.

Based on the prospective analysis of data on 680 patients undergoing surgery for nonruptured abdominal aortic aneurysm (AAA) and recorded in the Canadian Society for Vascular Surgery Aneurysm Registry, this study determines the late survival rate by comparison to an age- and sex-matched population, the causes of late death, the effect of heart-related death on late survival and the prognostic variables that are associated with late survival. Early survival rates were excellent, but the late survival rate of patients with AAA is significantly less than the age- and sex-matched normal population . The calculated 5-year heart-related mortality rate was 14.3%. This is higher than the heart-related mortality rate for the age- and sex-matched population, which was 6.4%. Hence, the risk of heart-related death for patients who have undergone AAA repair is increased by 1.6% per year. Because cardiac complications accounted for 68.8% of the 4.7% in-hospital mortality rate, a strategy to reduce the cardiac operative risk by identifying and treating patients at high risk before operation was recommended.

5. Johnston KW, Scobie TK. Multicenter prospective study of nonruptured abdominal aortic aneurysms. I. Population and operative management. J Vasc Surg 1988; 7(1):69-81.

This article describes the patient population and operative management of 666 patients with nonruptured aneurysms of the abdominal aorta. The chi-square test and logistic regression analysis determined statistical significance of variables. There were no statistically significant differences (p>0.05) in mortality rate for abdominal aortic aneurysm (AAA) on the basis of indication for surgery. Characteristics of the 72 participating surgeons did not influence the operative mortality rate. A family history of AAA was documented in 6.1% of cases. Patients without clinical evidence of coronary artery disease had a 0.8% mortality rate from cardiac disease compared with 6.2% if any stigmata of coronary disease was present. Prior aortocoronary bypass surgery did not reduce the incidence of postoperative cardiac events or operative mortality rate. The 6.8% of patients requiring suprarenal aortic cross clamping had a higher incidence of postoperative renal dysfunction and intraoperative blood loss, but cardiac events were not more frequent. Patients having an intra-abdominal graft (tube, 38.5% and bi-iliac, 30.7%) had fewer wound infections and graft thromboses than the patients with a femoral anastomosis. After renal artery bypass in 2.1%, the mortality rate was not increased, but the incidence of transient renal dysfunction was increased.

6. Kazmers A, Jacobs L et al. Abdominal aortic aneurysm repair in Veterans Affairs medical centers. J Vasc Surg 1996; 23(2):191-200.

This study was performed to define outcomes after abdominal aortic aneurysm (AAA) repair in Veterans Affairs (VA) medical centers during fiscal years 1991 through 1993. In the categories of repair of nonruptured and ruptured AAA, mortality and postoperative complication rates were defined for patients who underwent AAA repair in VA medical centers during the 3-year study period. Hospital mortality rates were 4.86% (166 of 3419) after repair of nonruptured AAA and 47.0% (126 of 268) after repair of ruptured AAA.

CONCLUSIONS: Mortality rates after AAA repairs in VA hospitals were comparable with those previously reported in other large series. Outcomes for veterans with AAA may improve by referring patients eligible for elective repair to VA medical centers with a greater operative volume or to lower-volume centers that have had excellent results.

14

7.   Limet R, Sakalihassan N et al. Determination of the expansion rate and incidence
      of rupture of abdominal aortic aneurysms. J Vasc Surg 1991; 14(4):540-8.
      *Expansion rate and incidence of rupture of abdominal aortic aneurysms in relation to
      their size is a source of debate. A study of 114 patients was performed (out of a cohort of
      752 consecutive patients admitted with abdominal aortic aneurysms) who were denied
      any immediate operation because of patient's refusal, high surgical risk, or small trans-
      verse diameter as assessed by CT scanning and ultrasonography. All patients not oper-
      ated on underwent from two to six repeated examinations during an average follow-up
      period of 26.8 months (range, 3 to 132). Forty-seven patients (41.2%) were subsequently
      operated on electively because of marked increase of transverse diameter of the aneurysm
      (n = 44) or for other reasons (n = 3), with a death rate of 0%. Eighteen other patients
      underwent emergency operation for leaking or ruptured aneurysms, and there were five
      deaths. The incidence of rupture was clearly related to the final diameter value, rising
      from 0% in aneurysms less than 40 mm to 22% in large size aneurysms (≥ to 50 mm).
      Among the 49 patients not operated on, one died of rupture before operation and five of
      causes unrelated to the disease. Using individual serial measurements, a linear expansion
      rate of the aneurysm was determined, which proved to be related to initial diameter
      values: 5.3 mm/year for diameters less than 40 mm, 6.9 mm/year in the 40-49 mm
      group , and 7.4 mm/year for diameters of 50 mm or more.*

8.   Nevitt MP, Ballard DJ et al. Prognosis of abdominal aortic aneurysms. A popula-
      tion-based study [see comments]. N Engl J Med 1989; 321(15):1009-14.
      *Information is incomplete about the rate of expansion of abdominal aortic aneurysms
      and the risk of rupture in relation to their size. To address these questions, a population-
      based study was performed. Of the 370 residents of Rochester, MN, with an aneurysm
      initially diagnosed from 1951 through 1984, 181 had the aneurysm documented by
      ultrasound examination. Among the 103 patients who underwent more than one
      ultrasound study, the diameter of the aneurysm increased by a median of 0.21 cm per
      year. Only 24 percent had a rate of expansion of 0.4 cm or more per year. Among the
      176 patients who had an unruptured aneurysm at the time of the initial ultrasound
      study, the cumulative incidence of rupture was 6 percent after 5 years and 8 percent
      after 10 years. However, the risk of rupture over five years was 0 percent for the 130
      patients with an aneurysm less than 5 cm in diameter and 25 percent for the 46 patients
      with an aneurysm 5 cm or more in diameter. All 16 patients who had ruptures had
      aneurysms that were 5 cm or more in diameter at the time of the rupture. These popu-
      lation-based data challenge the clinical perception that aneurysms typically expand at a
      rate of 0.4 to 0.5 cm per year. Our data also suggest that for aneurysms less than 5 cm
      in diameter the risk of rupture is considerably lower than has been reported previously.
      However, the risk of rupture is substantial for aneurysms 5 cm or more in diameter.*

9.   Plate G, Hollier LA et al. Recurrent aneurysms and late vascular complications
      following repair of abdominal aortic aneurysms. Arch Surg 1985; 120(5):590-4.
      *Between 1970 and 1976, 1,112 patients underwent abdominal aortic aneurysm repair.
      Follow-up, ranging from six to 12 years, was complete in 1,087 patients (97.7%). The
      most frequent cause of late death was coronary artery disease (45.6%), but significant
      morbidity related to the peripheral vascular system had developed in some patients and
      led to 8.4% of all late deaths. Forty-nine true, 14 anastomotic and five proximal aortic
      dissections were detected in 59 patients (5.4%) a mean of 5.2 +/- 3.1 years after the
      initial aneurysm repair. These aneurysms were located in the thoracic (24),
      thoracoabdominal (five) or abdominal aorta (11), and in the iliac (six), femoral (17),*

14

popliteal (four) and renal arteries (one). Only one of 26 patients presenting with a rupture of one of these secondary aneurysms survived. There was a significant association between preoperative hypertension and recurrent aneurysm. These findings suggest that subsequent vascular disease, including recurrent aneurysms and graft complications, cause significant late morbidity and mortality after repair of abdominal aortic aneurysm. Careful follow-up and adequate control of hypertension may allow reduction in morbidity and an improvement in late survival.

10. Zarins CK, Harris EJ, Jr. Operative repair for aortic aneurysms: The gold standard. J Endovasc Surg 1997; 4(3):232-41.

Surgical treatment of abdominal aortic aneurysm (AAA) is being challenged by newer, minimally invasive therapies. Such new treatment strategies will need to prove themselves against concurrent results of standard operative AAA repair, within defined medical risk and aneurysm morphological categories. This study reviews the natural history of AAAs, the medical risk levels for elective AAA repair, aneurysm morphology and its impact on operative mortality, the issue of high-risk patient treatment, and the current standard of care for AAAs based on single- center, multicenter, and population-based statistics. In good-risk patients, aneurysms > 5 cm in diameter are best treated by replacement with a prosthetic graft. Operative mortality should be < 5% and one-year survival > 90%. Aortic endograft techniques must meet or exceed these standards if they are to supplant standard surgical repair.

14

CHAPTER 15

Suprarenal Aortic Aneurysm Repair

David Han and Peter Gloviczki

Surgical repair of abdominal aortic aneurysms (AAAs) that involve the renal arteries are more challenging than infrarenal AAA repairs. Morbidity is increased due to a longer operation, more extensive dissection and an increased risk of bleeding. In addition, there is a distinct risk of renal, visceral or, occasionally, spinal cord ischemia. Suprarenal or superceliac aortic cross-clamping results in increased afterload. Therefore, cardiac complications are more frequent in these cases than after infrarenal aortic reconstructions. Although endovascular techniques with stent grafts have already been used to treat AAA's that extend up to the renal arteries, most suprarenal aneurysms require an open surgical approach. In this chapter, we review the different types of suprarenal aneurysms, discuss preoperative evaluation, surgical indications, techniques and current surgical results.

Classification

Aortic aneurysms involving the abdominal aorta at or above the level of the renal arteries have been called suprarenal aortic aneurysms (Fig. 15.1A-C). Depending on the extent of the AAA and the level of renal artery involvement, three different suprarenal aneurysms are distinguished. The term juxtarenal aortic aneurysms is reserved for AAAs without a neck distal to at least one main renal artery orifice, preventing safe infrarenal aortic clamping during surgical repair (Fig. 15.1A). The more proximal pararenal aneurysms involve the orifices of the renal arteries, but do not extend up to the origin of the superior mesenteric artery (Fig. 15.1B.). Finally, the term paravisceral aneurysm usually is reserved for those high abdominal aneurysms that involve the orifices of all visceral and renal arteries (Fig. 15.1C.). The infrarenal aorta may not be involved at all. These are essentially Type IV thoracoabdominal aortic aneurysms, using Crawford classification, since they usually require repair through a low thoracoabdominal approach with clamping of the descending thoracic aorta at or just above the level of the diaphragm.

Clinical Evaluation and Imaging Studies

While the reliability of physical examination in the detection of abdominal aortic aneurysms is notoriously variable, it continues to play an important role in the detection of asymptomatic lesions. Aortic calcification may be noted on plain abdominal radiographs, or an aneurysm may be identified on imaging studies undertaken to delineate other intraabdominal pathology. A wide neck of an infrarenal AAA on abdominal ultrasound examination raises suspicion for suprarenal aneurysm.

Aortic Surgery, edited by Jeffrey L. Ballard. ©2000 Landes Bioscience.

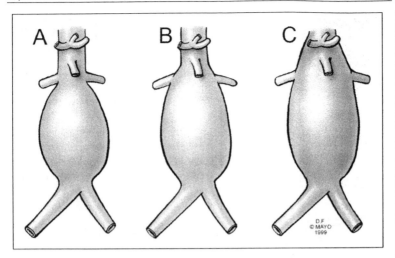

Fig. 15.1. Suprarenal aortic aneurysms. A) Juxtarenal aneurysm, B) Pararenal aneurysm, C) Paravisceral aneurysm or Type IV thoracoabdominal aortic aneurysm.

Contrast-enhanced computed tomography (CT) scanning is necessary to image the suprarenal aorta, and it is required to identify the extent of the aneurysm and its relationship to the visceral vessels (Fig. 15.2A). CT scan also delineates any venous or renal anomaly. Characteristic findings on CT such as lack of aortic calcification, saccular or irregular shape may suggest mycotic aneurysm. Computed tomography will also identify contained rupture or aortic dissection.

Patients with suprarenal aneurysms undergo contrast or magnetic resonance arteriography to delineate the visceral and renal arteries and aneurysmal or occlusive changes of the aortoiliac vessels (Fig. 15.2B). Biplane aortography is helpful in assessing ostial stenoses of the celiac trunk or the superior mesenteric artery; it also helps to define the proximal extent of the aneurysm and to select a suitable proximal clamp site. In patients with significant renal dysfunction precluding the use of intravenous contrast, magnetic resonance imaging (MRI) and angiography (MRA) have been useful diagnostic tools. The information they provide is frequently similar to that obtained with CT scan or contrast aortography. We use MRA with gadolinium enhancement with increasing frequency. Once a suprarenal aneurysm is identified, indications for repair and preoperative evaluation must be individualized.

Surgical Indications

While patients with infrarenal AAAs usually have surgical consultation when the aneurysm is between 4 and 5 cm and usually undergo repair when the antero-posterior or lateral diameter reaches 5 cm, the risks of surgical repair of a suprarenal AAA is generally higher than that of infrarenal AAA repair. Therefore, in our practice asymptomatic degenerative suprarenal aneurysms are considered for surgical treatment when the diameter is above 5.5-6 cm. Smaller, saccular aneurysms (Fig. 15.2B)

15

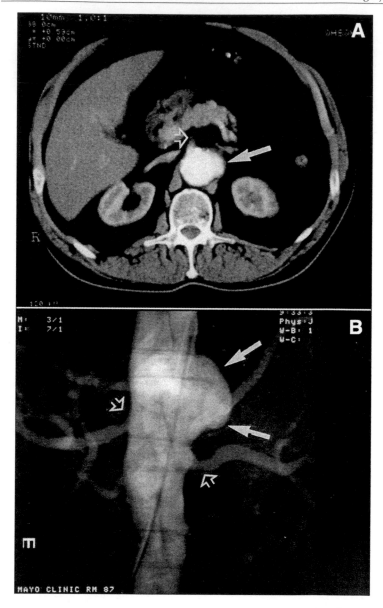

Fig. 15.2.A. 5 cm suprarenal saccular aneurysm in a 65-year-old male patient. Arrow indicates aneurysm. Arrowhead indicates the superior mesenteric artery. B. Aortography reveals a lobulated suprarenal aneurysm at the level of the origin of the celiac and superior mesenteric artery. Arrow indicates the aneurysm. The right renal artery had moderate, the left renal artery had high-grade stenosis (arrowhead).

are repaired if mycotic aneurysm cannot be excluded. Smaller aneurysms are also considered for repair, if they are symptomatic, if they are false aneurysms or if the aneurysm is ruptured.

Preoperative Cardiac and Pulmonary Evaluation

Preoperative cardiac evaluation is essential in all elective patients because of the increased risk of myocardial dysfunction. We prefer functional evaluation with exercise or pharmacological stress imaging, such as dipyridamole-thallium scanning, or dobutamine stress echocardiography. Patients with positive tests are considered for coronary angiography to identify those who may benefit from preoperative coronary revascularization. The timing of such interventions, while controversial, again needs to be individualized. In patients with symptomatic or very large aneurysms, repair may be undertaken during the same hospitalization as myocardial revascularization. Otherwise, a recuperative period of 6-8 weeks can be allowed prior to aneurysm repair.

Pulmonary evaluation in patients with chronic obstructive pulmonary disease includes chest x-ray, spirometry and baseline arterial blood gases. Patients with significant pulmonary insufficiency such as an $FEV_1 < 50\%$, may benefit from preoperative bronchodilator therapy, or a short course of steroids prior to surgery.

Preparation for Surgery

Admission on the morning of surgery is becoming customary, although patients with high serum creatinine benefit from overnight preoperative intravenous hydration. Mechanical cleansing of the colon is undertaken the night before using magnesium citrate, and the patients are instructed in the use of incentive spirometry. When possible, family members as well as the patient are given a tour of the intensive care unit to help alleviate anxiety. Cardiac medications including beta-blockers and aspirin are continued, given with a sip of water on the morning of surgery. For antibiotic prophylaxis we use a first generation cephalosporin before the operation and continue at least three doses afterwards.

Close communication with the anesthesiologist and operating room personnel helps to ensure the safety and success of complex aortic reconstruction. As with infrarenal AAA repair, large bore intravenous access, and arterial pressure monitoring, usually through a radial arterial line, is standard. Hemodynamic monitoring requires the use of a pulmonary artery flow-directed catheter, in order to optimize volume management as well as vasodilator and vasopressor pharmacotherapy. An epidural catheter greatly facilitates postoperative pain management, and this is used routinely unless previous spine surgery, preoperative hemodynamic instability or need for anticoagulation prevent its use. Patients with Type IV thoracoabdominal aneurysms undergo spinal fluid drainage and pressure monitoring. In these patients epidural catheter is placed only, if epidural cooling of the perispinal space is performed. During the operation brisk diuresis is ensured with the use of both low dose dopamine (2-3 mcg/kg/min) and mannitol (12.5 gms), given before aortic cross-clamping.

15

Surgical Technique

Juxtarenal Aneurysm Repair

Most juxtarenal aneurysms in the senior author's experience have been repaired through a midline incision, using a transperitoneal approach. This allows full exploration of the abdomen, and excellent exposure of the abdominal aorta and both iliac bifurcations. To improve access to the juxtarenal aorta, the fourth portion of the duodenum is mobilized and the ligament of Treitz is transected. The inferior mesenteric vein is divided but the renal vein is preserved. Division of the adrenal, gonadal and lumbar tributaries of the left renal vein allows easy mobilization of this vessel without need for division. These patients require suprarenal cross-clamping, which can be done distal to the pancreas, either between the renal and superior mesenteric arteries or between the superior mesenteric artery and the celiac trunk. An alternative clamp site is the supraceliac aorta, which is exposed through the lesser sac, after incising the gastrohepatic ligament. When the clamp sites have been selected, systemic anticoagulation is achieved with 5000 U of intravenous heparin. If the renal arteries originate at different levels, suprarenal clamping on one side and infrarenal clamping on the other side can also be accomplished.

Embolization of the renal arteries should be avoided during clamp placement. If thrombus is present in the juxtarenal aorta, a higher clamp site is selected. The best technique is to place fine bulldog clamps on the renal artery before suprarenal aortic cross-clamping. Clamps are applied proximally and then distally and the aneurysm is entered sharply. Renal ischemia is usually less than 30 minutes, unless concomitant renal revascularization has to be performed. In these patients, we use intermittent cold perfusion of the renal arteries with iced Lactated Ringers solution. As soon as the proximal aortic anastomosis is completed, the clamp is placed distal to the renal arteries, on the aortic graft, to allow renal perfusion. The operation than continues as in patients with infrarenal aneurysm repair, by performing the distal aortic or the iliac anastomoses.

Juxtarenal aneurysms can also be exposed using a left retroperitoneal approach. This exposure is especially useful for patients with severe chronic obstructive pulmonary disease, extensive abdominal adhesions or those with a horseshoe kidney. Some authors use retroperitoneal repair routinely for all abdominal aneurysms. It is important to remember, however, that supraceliac clamping in some patients needs extension of the retroperitoneal incision into the chest. Also, access to the right renal artery and to the right distal common or external iliac artery through left retroperitoneal approach is frequently difficult.

15

Pararenal Aneurysms

Since these aneurysms do not involve the aorta above the superior mesenteric artery, aortic cross-clamp through a midline incision, distal to the pancreas, between the celiac and superior mesenteric artery or proximal to the pancreas, above the celiac artery is performed. Complete medial visceral rotation, mobilizing the pancreas and the spleen is usually not needed. The aorta at the level of the origin of the renal arteries is aneurysmal and the graft at least in part has to be sutured to the suprarenal aorta. One option is to perform a fish-mouth anastomosis (Fig. 15.3) or to do unilateral or bilateral renal artery reconstruction, by reimplanting the renal orifice into the graft with a small aortic Carrel patch, or using a saphenous or polyethylene Dacron aortorenal interposition graft (Fig. 15.4A-C).

Paravisceral Aneurysms

Repair of aneurysms that involves the orifice of the superior mesenteric artery and proximal clamping above the celiac artery is required, are best approached retroperitoneally, through a low thoracoabdominal incision. The patient is positioned in a semi-right lateral decubitus position, with the chest turned 45-60°. The left arm is placed over the right in a padded "over-arm" board, with an axillary roll under the right axilla. The hips are rotated back so that the buttocks lay flat against the operating table. The skin overlying the entire chest, abdomen, pelvis, and thighs is prepared, and a left oblique abdominal incision is made from the midline, halfway between the umbilicus and the pubis towards the tip of the 9th rib. The chest is entered through the 9th intercostal space and the diaphragm is incised but spared, leaving at least 2/3rd intact to avoid transection of the phrenic nerve and decrease postoperative pulmonary complications.

The abdominal muscles are transected and the retroperitoneum is exposed. At this point one must decide whether or not the left kidney will be mobilized. In most patients we mobilize the kidney and retract it medially with the peritoneal sac, paying careful attention to avoid splenic injury. If the kidney is not mobilized, a plane has to be developed between Gerota's fascia and the pancreas and the latter will be rotated medially with the spleen. Care should be taken not to devascularize the left ureter during dissection.

The superior mesenteric artery and the celiac trunk are identified although they are not dissected. The left crus of the diaphragm is sharply divided and the diaphragm is encircled on a red rubber catheter to allow easy mobilization during clamp placement.

Since reestablishment of visceral circulation is accomplished usually within 30 minutes, we do not use partial bypass for paravisceral aneurysms. The celiac, superior mesenteric and right renal arteries are frequently incorporated into the proximal anastomosis, while the left renal artery is either included into the anastomosis or reimplanted separately with a Carrel patch or a polyethylene interposition graft (Fig. 15.5A-B). Occasionally, the proximal anastomosis is performed with the aorta and the visceral vessels are reimplanted into the graft as a separate Carrel patch. Low intercostal arteries at the level of the diaphragm are preserved and incorporated into the proximal anastomosis. Bleeding from the visceral vessels are controlled with No. 4 Fogarty catheters, while the kidneys are protected by perfusing intermittently or continuously with iced Lactated Ringers, with diluted heparin solution (1000U of heparin in 1000 ml of Lactated Ringers).

Results

Published figures on morbidity and mortality are generally between those reported following infrarenal and thoracoabdominal aortic aneurysm repair. In a collected

15

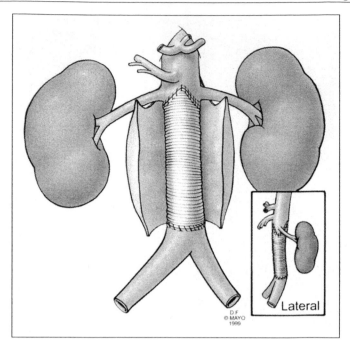

Fig. 15.3. Pararenal aortic aneurysm reconstructed with a fish-mouth proximal anastomosis, using a polyethylene aortic graft.

review of 518 Type IV thoracoabdominal aneurysm repairs, published in 5 large series, Panneton and Hollier reported an average mortality of 7%, ranging from 0-28%. Mortality in more recent selected series, reviewed at the end of this chapter, has ranged from 1.5-11%. Significant complications occurred in 20-35% of patients, even in the best series. Myocardial infarction and multisystem organ failure are the most frequent causes of death, but prolonged mechanical ventilation is the most frequent cause of major morbidity. Renal insufficiency occurs in 12-31% of these patients. In the Washington University, St. Louis experience with 65 operations, 2 patients required temporary dialysis. Multivariate analysis in that study identified elevated preoperative creatinine (1.88 ± 0.33 mg/dl) as an independent predictor of decreased renal function one week after the operation. These authors emphasized the need for cold renal perfusion to protect the kidneys from ischemia and reperfusion injury and advocated the need for renal reconstruction in patients with concomitant high-grade renal artery stenoses. We concur with these recommendations and prefer revascularization of the left renal artery usually with a separate polyethylene interposition graft to optimize renal perfusion (Fig. 15.5B). Although the incidence of renal failure requiring dialysis in 64 patients was 6%, none of the 4 patients had renal protection with cold perfusion. Our data support the findings of others, that

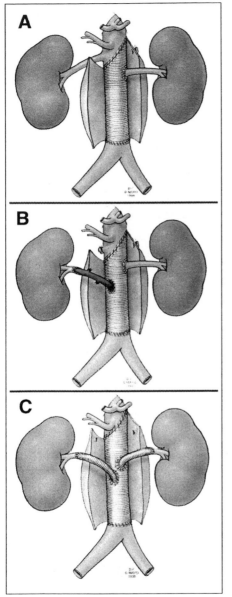

Fig. 15.4. Techniques to revascularize the renal arteries in patients with suprarenal aortic aneurysms. A) Reimplantation of left renal artery into the graft using a small Carrel aortic patch, B) Saphenous vein interposition graft (right renal artery) and reimplantation (left renal artery), C) polyethylene aortorenal grafts (end-to-end)

15

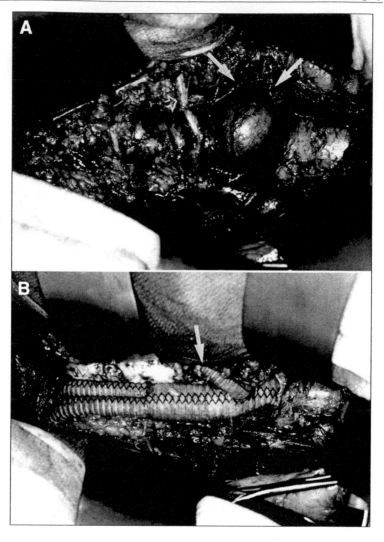

Fig. 15.5A. Intraoperative photograph of the suprarenal saccular aneurysm of the patient presented in Figure 15.2., when the aneurysm was exposed through a low thoracoabdominal retroperitoneal incision. Arrow indicates the saccular aneurysm. Arrowhead indicates the left renal artery that had a high-grade stenosis. B. Reconstruction of the aneurysm with a gelatin-coated zero porosity polyethylene graft from the level of the celiac artery to both common iliac arteries. The left renal artery stenosis was reconstructed with a 6-mm interposition polyethylene graft from the common limb of the bifurcated graft to the left renal artery. Arrow indicates the graft renal artery anastomosis (end-to-end).

preexisting renal failure, suprarenal aortic cross-clamp time above 60 minutes and renal artery occlusive disease are predictors of postoperative renal insufficiency.

While spinal cord injury is rare, we use spinal fluid drainage and spinal fluid pressure monitoring during and 24 hours after these operations. Epidural cooling of the cord was used previously in a series of patients, but it's utility in Type IV thoracoabdominal aneurysms has not been proven and we no longer use it during repair of paravisceral aneurysms.

In patients with mycotic aneurysms, excision and thorough debridement is done, and repair is performed with gelatin coated polyethylene aortic graft, soaked for 15 minutes in 500 mg of Rifampin solution before implantation. There is experimental evidence, that such grafts maintain antibiotic activity for several days after implantation. Current data using cryopreserved homografts for such indication are also promising, although long term results in this location are still unknown.

Long-term survival in patients with suprarenal and low thoracoabdominal aneurysm in the Cleveland Clinic study was 71% at 3 years and 50% at 10 years. The need for postoperative dialysis significantly shortened late survival and only 13% of these patients lived longer than 5 years.

Conclusions

Open repair of suprarenal aneurysms can be performed with low mortality and acceptable morbidity, usually through a low thoracoabdominal approach. Renal protection is essential, since renal failure increases both early and late mortality. Ischemic renal complications can be diminished by careful planning of the operation, minimizing the risk of renal embolization and shortening aortic cross-clamp time. Cold perfusion of the renal arteries with iced Lactated Ringers is beneficial and revascularization of renal arteries with associated occlusive disease should also be done to optimize renal perfusion. Long term results of open repair of suprarenal aortic aneurysms are satisfactory in most patients.

Selected Readings

1. Qvarfordt PG, Stoney RJ, Reilly LM et al. Management of pararenal aneurysms of the abdominal aorta. J Vasc Surg 1986; 3:84-93.

   This remarkable series of 77 suprarenal aneurysms had a perioperative mortality of 1.8% and a morbidity of 28%, consisting primarily of renal dysfunction (23%). Renal morbidity was adversely related to preoperative renal function, extent of renal artery disease and the need for renal revascularization. Aggressive intraoperative monitoring minimized cardiac complications. A landmark paper on this topic.

2. Allen BT, Anderson CB, Rubin BG et al. Preservation of renal function in juxtarenal and suprarenal abdominal aortic aneurysm repair. J Vasc Surg 1993; 17:948-59.

   Thirty-five percent of 65 patients, who underwent repair of suprarenal aneurysms, developed significant complications in this series, but mortality was low (1.5%) and only two patients required temporary dialysis. The authors emphasize the advantages of retroperitoneal approach, renal hypothermia and the need for renal revascularization in patients with associated renal artery occlusive disease.

3. Green RM, Ricotta JJ, Ouriel K et al. Results of supraceliac aortic clamping in the difficult elective resection of infrarenal aortic aneurysms. J Vasc Surg 1989; 9:125-34.

15

This important paper calls attention to the advantages of suprarenal aortic clamping performed in 30 patients with aortic aneurysms. When hazardous aortic cuff dissection at the renal artery level is expected, supraceliac aortic clamping offers safer control without added complications.

4.   Breckwoldt WL, Mackie WC, O'Donnell, TF, Jr. The effect of suprarenal cross-clamping on abdominal aortic aneurysm repair. Arch Surg 1992; 127:520-524.
The authors analyzed results of 205 operations for elective abdominal aortic aneurysm repairs. Outcome in a group of 166 patients who underwent infrarenal cross-clamping alone was compared to those of 39 patients who underwent suprarenal cross-clamping. Mortality was comparable between groups (1.2% vs. 2.6%), but transient renal insufficiency was more frequent following suprarenal cross-clamping (10% vs 28%). Dialysis rates were similar (2% vs. 3%). These authors suggest retroperitoneal approach to obtain better access to the suprarenal aorta.

5.   Gloviczki P. Bower TC. Visceral and spinal cord protection during thoracoabdominal aortic reconstructions. Sem Vasc Surg; 1992; 5:163-173.
This review from the Mayo Clinic analyzed results of 181 thoracoabdominal aortic aneurysm repairs, that included 61 patients with Type IV aneurysms. Forty-four percent of the 61 patients had postoperative serum creatinine above 2 mg/dl and 6% required dialysis. One patient developed spinal cord injury. The authors discuss etiology of ischemic complications and review current techniques of protection.

6.   Panneton JM, Hollier LH. Nondissecting thoracoabdominal aortic aneurysms. Part I. Ann Vasc Surg 1995; 9:503-514.
A useful review of the literature on epidemiology, etiology, classification, natural history and clinical presentation of thoracoabdominal aortic aneurysms. The authors also summarize the morbidity and mortality of published cases of nondissecting thoracoabdominal aortic aneurysms.

7.   Safi HJ, Harlin SA, Miller CC et al. Predictive factors for acute renal failure in thoracic and thoracoabdominal aortic aneurysm surgery. J Vasc Surg 1996; 24:338-45.
This classic study of 234 patients who underwent thoracoabdominal aortic aneurysm or descending thoracic aortic replacement included 26 patients with type IV thoracoabdominal (suprarenal) aneurysms. The authors found that postoperative acute renal failure was associated with elevated preoperative serum creatinine levels, the use of visceral perfusion during repair, renal artery reattachment and the use of a simple cross-clamp technique.

8.   Martin GH, O'Hara PJ, Hertzer NR et al. Surgical repair of aneurysms involving the suprarenal, visceral and lower thoracic aortic segments: Early results and late outcome. J Vasc Surg 2000; in press.
The Cleveland Clinic experience with 57 suprarenal and 108 thoracoabdominal aneurysm repairs analyzed perioperative complications, mortality and late survival. Suprarenal aneurysms had a 1.8% mortality and no evidence of spinal cord injury. The risk of mortality and paraplegia increased with more proximal aortic clamping and with aortic dissection.

15

CHAPTER 16

Inflammatory Abdominal Aortic Aneurysms

Aravind B. Sankar and Glenn C. Hunter

Inflammatory aneurysms are usually an incidental finding during surgical repair of atherosclerotic abdominal aortic aneurysms (AAA) or are detected with either computed tomography (CT) or magnetic resonance imaging (MRI) in symptomatic patients with aneurysms. First described by Walker et al, the characteristic shiny white fibrotic reaction involving predominantly the antero-lateral aspect of AAAs, occurs in 2.5-15% of patients undergoing aneurysm repair.

A clear understanding of the clinical presentation, diagnosis, and management of inflammatory abdominal aortic aneurysm (IAAA) is essential in view of the greater frequency of symptoms associated with these aneurysms and the potential technical hazards that may be encountered at surgery.

These features as well as the etiologic factors implicated in the pathogenesis of IAAA will be discussed below.

Clinical Presentation

Inflammatory abdominal aortic aneurysms occur predominantly in males in the 5th and 6th decades of life. The male to female ratio ranges from 15-6.5:1. Risk factors for atherosclerosis and the association with coronary artery (46-55%) and peripheral vascular disease (24%) occur with the same frequency as in patients with noninflammatory aneurysms. Nitecki et al has reported that patients with IAAA were more likely (17% versus 1.5%) to have a family history of aneurysms and currently be smoking cigarettes.

The clinical triad of chronic abdominal pain, weight loss, and an elevated erythrocyte sedimentation rate (ESR) in a patient with an abdominal aortic aneurysm is highly suggestive of an inflammatory aneurysm. Abdominal, flank, or back pain is present in up to 83% of patients with no ruptured IAAA compared to 14% of patients with noninflammatory aneurysms. Anorexia and weight loss occurs in 10-41% of patients with IAAA compared to 7-10% of those with AAA. The erythrocyte sedimentation rate is elevated in 40-88% of patients. The occurrence of fever and leukocytosis is quite variable (Table 16.1).

The most consistent finding on physical examination is the presence of a tender pulsatile mass. However, detection of a pulsatile mass is dependent on the size of the aneurysm as well as patient body habitus.

Table 16.1. Comparison of the frequency of symptoms between patients with IAAA and AAA

	IAAA	AAA
Incidence of Symptoms	65-93%	8-18%
Abdominal Pain	60-83%	14%
Back Pain	55%	
Palpable Aneurysm	84-100%	70%
Weight Loss	10-41%	7-10%
Elevated ESR	44-89%	11-33%
Ureteral Involvement	13-53%	0-20%

Diagnostic Tests

Inflammatory aneurysms are diagnosed preoperatively in only 13-33% of cases. Excretory urography, abdominal ultrasound (AUS), computed tomography and magnetic resonance imaging are the most frequently used imaging modalities used to evaluate patients with IAAA. Of these, abdominal CT is the most frequently used, cost effective, and reliable.

Plain abdominal radiographs may show blurring of the psoas margins due to the inflammatory reaction. The classic features of IAAA on excretory urography include delayed renal excretion with unilateral (20%) or bilateral hydronephrosis, medial deviation of the middle third, or narrowing of the ureters at L4, L5. Medial deviation of the ureters may be present in up to 20% of normal individuals.

The characteristic feature of an IAAA on AUS is a sonolucent halo outside of the rim of intimal calcification. On abdominal CT, a soft tissue mass surrounding the antero-lateral aspect of the aneurysm wall often sparing the posterior aspect of the aorta is usually evident (Fig. 16.1). The soft tissue mass enhances with contrast, but less so than the underlying AAA. It is located outside of the wall of the aneurysm, which can usually be distinguished by the presence of calcifications. This feature is helpful in distinguishing it from thrombus within the aneurysm wall. The differential diagnosis of IAAA on CT scans includes retroperitoneal fibrosis, hematoma, lymphoma, carcinomatous desmoplasia, metastatic lymphadenopathy, and primary sarcomas. Although IAAA is sometimes associated with retroperitoneal fibrosis, the relationship between these disease processes remains unclear. Hematomas do not enhance on abdominal CT and have characteristic features on MRI. Lymphomas are not usually associated with aneurysms, tend to be more nodular in appearance, and displace the aorta. Sarcomas are unlikely to be symmetrically centered around the aorta.

Gadolinium enhanced MRI is the preferred imaging modality in patients with impaired renal function or who have other contraindications to the administration of contrast agents. It is particularly useful in delineating the periaortic inflammatory mantle and aortic lumen. The inflammatory mass surrounding the aorta has a typical MRI appearance consisting of three or four high signal intensity concentric layers symmetrically surrounding the anterior aspect of the aortic lumen.

16

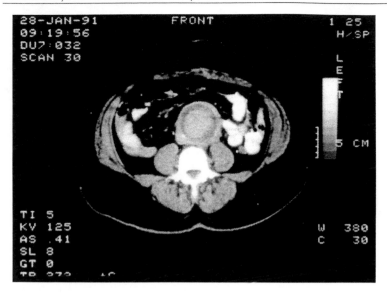

Fig. 16.1. CT scan of an inflammatory aortic aneurysm showing a soft tissue mass surrounding the aneurysmal aortic wall.

Medical Management

The role of steroid therapy in the management of IAAA is controversial. There are isolated case reports of the management of patients with IAAA deemed inoperable at laparotomy with steroid therapy. Corticosteroids have also been used preoperatively in an attempt to reduce the extent of the inflammatory process. It seems unlikely that corticosteroids will alter the long term development of IAAA and may predispose to rupture.

Operative Management

Although the incidence of rupture of IAAA appears to be lower than that of noninflammatory aneurysms, the natural history of these lesions appears to be continued enlargement and ultimately rupture, as in the case of all AAA.

Repair of inflammatory aneurysms can be undertaken using either the midline or retroperitoneal approach. The retroperitoneal approach offers some advantages if the diagnosis of IAAA is made preoperatively: first, the inflammatory reaction is not as intense posteriorly and second, it permits mobilization of the left renal vein if it is involved in the inflammatory process. Most often, the inflammatory component of the aneurysm is discovered incidentally during routine repair using a midline incision. In this instance, the duodenum is left adherent to the aneurysm wall and the aorta occluded above. If the renal vein is incorporated into the inflammatory process, occlusion of the aorta at the diaphragm until the proximal anastomosis is completed is a safe option. Division of the left renal vein may be required in order to obtain proximal control.

16

At laparotomy, the inflammatory process is usually first recognized by the presence of the shiny white fibrotic reaction and adherence of the duodenum to the anterior wall of the aorta. No attempt should be made to dissect the involved portion of duodenum off the aorta. Other structures that may be involved in the inflammatory process include the inferior vena cava, left renal vein, ureters, small bowel or sigmoid colon. The underlying principle of repair of IAAA is minimal dissection of surrounding structures to permit resection and repair of the aneurysm.

Following systemic heparinization, the aorta is occluded and opened on the left side avoiding the duodenum. Any bleeding from the lumbar arteries is controlled with suture ligatures. The inflammatory process and the degree of aneurysmal dilatation of the iliac arteries determine the extent of distal control. In the absence of aneurysmal dilatation or extension of the inflammatory process on to the iliac arteries these vessels may be occluded with either vascular clamps or occlusion balloon catheters just below the aortic bifurcation. If the inflammatory process or aneurysmal dilatation extends on to the iliac arteries, occlusion at the iliac bifurcation allows one to stay well below the inflammatory reaction. Following completion of the anastomoses, the aortic wall is approximated over the graft.

The fate of the surrounding inflammatory reaction following repair remains controversial. Regression of the surrounding inflammation occurs in over half of IAAA patients undergoing repair and in the remaining patients, the inflammatory changes rarely cause clinically significant problems. Therefore we do not recommend ureterolysis at the time of aneurysm repair. In cases where ureteral dilatation is recognized preoperatively, stents may be placed.

Incidence of Rupture

Most authors report a lower incidence of rupture in patients with IAAA compared to AAA. Pennell et al reported only one patient of 126 with acute rupture. Walker et al reported a 15% incidence of rupture in patients with inflammatory aneurysms compared to 40% in those with noninflammatory lesions. When inflammatory aneurysms do rupture, they tend to rupture posteriorly in a region of the aorta uninvolved in the inflammatory process.

The operative mortality rate ranges from 3-7.9%. Long-term survival appears to be comparable to patients with noninflammatory lesions. Crawford et al found that 67% of their patients were alive up to 9 years following surgery. Lequest et al reported 5 and 10 year survival rates of 68% and 47%, respectively.

Histologic Features

16

The characteristic histologic features of atherosclerotic aneurysms including, intimal atherosclerosis, surface thrombus accompanied by loss of medial smooth muscle cells, and fragmentation and loss of medial elastic tissue are present in all cases. The adventitia is markedly thickened (0.5-3.0 cm) due to fibrosis. A chronic inflammatory cell infiltrate consisting of macrophages, T and B lymphocytes, plasma cells, fibroblasts and extracellular matrix is uniformly present. Adventitial vasculitis, fibrosis, and perineural infiltrates are also present.

Large irregular deposits of, IgG and IgM, are present within the fibrous component of the aneurysm wall. The presence of proliferating inflammatory cells, IgG, IgM, and complement C3c supports the theory of an immune etiology due to local antigenic stimulation. Macrophages are distributed haphazardly throughout the lymphoid aggregates (Fig. 16.2).

Etiology of Inflammatory Abdominal Aortic Aneurysms

Although a number of theories have been proposed, the etiology of IAAA remains obscure. Initially, it was thought that the periaortic fibrosis was the result of repeated small bouts of hemorrhage. Although the absence of significant numbers of hemosiderin containing macrophages makes this theory less likely, there have been no reports in which systematic dissection of the entire inflammatory process was performed. In support of this theory, the finding of chronic contained rupture in approximately 20% of patients with IAAA which may represent an unusual inflammatory response to chronic retroperitoneal hematoma.

Rose and Dent were among the first to suggest that inflammatory aneurysms were merely an accentuation of the chronic inflammation and fibrosis seen in association with atherosclerotic aneurysms. The antigens responsible for initiating the inflammatory response remain undetermined. An infectious etiology due to bacteria, fungi, or syphilis appears unlikely as bacteriologic studies have been consistently negative. More recently, other microorganisms including the herpes viridae and chlamydia pneumonia have been implicated in the pathogenesis of atherosclerosis. Obstruction or disruption of lymphatic vessels by expansion of the aneurysm as well as ischemia of the aortic wall due to atheroembolism of the vaso vasorum may further contribute to degenerative changes in the aortic wall. An immune response to the structural components of the aortic wall, such as elastin, collagen fibrillar, and the lipid components of atherosclerotic plaque could possibly incite a fibrotic inflammatory reaction.

The Relationship Between Retroperitoneal Fibrosis and IAAA

The dense fibrous plaque-like lesions of retroperitoneal fibrosis involve the retroperitoneum from the hilum of the kidney superiorly to the brim of the pelvis inferiorly. The fibrosis extends laterally to involve the vena cava, ureters and psoas muscle. Less frequently, the fibrosis involves the celiac and superior mesenteric arteries. A chronic inflammatory cell infiltrate consisting of lymphocytes, plasma cells and macrophages interspersed in a connective tissue matrix is usually present early in the course of the disease. In later stages, the inflammatory response is replaced by relatively avascular fibrous tissue. CT scans in these patients show severe atherosclerosis of the underlying aorta (Fig. 16.3). Histologically, idiopathic retroperitoneal fibrosis may be associated with the extrusion of atherosclerotic debris into the adventitia. Retroperitoneal fibrosis may also be associated with a number of immune mediated diseases including Wegener's granulomatosis, ankylosing spondylitis, polyarteritis nodosa, systemic lupus erythematosus, and Raynaud's disease. Further evidence implicating an immune response is the association between retroperitoneal fibrosis

16

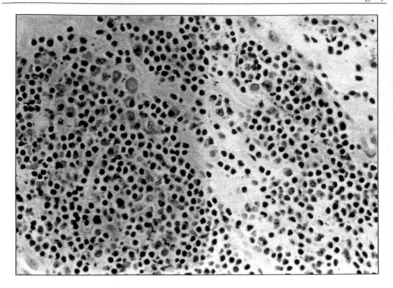

Fig. 16.2. CT scan of retroperitoneal fibrosis showing inflammatory tissue surrounding a nonaneurysmal aorta.

and HLA-B27. One percent of patients taking methysergide for migraine headaches develops retroperitoneal fibrosis, which usually regresses following withdrawal of the drug.

Retroperitoneal fibrosis should be distinguished from the desmoplastic response to metastatic tumor deposits in the retroperitoneum. The neoplasms most commonly associated with retroperitoneal desmoplasia include Hodgkin's disease, non-Hodgkin's lymphoma, retroperitoneal sarcomas and numerous carcinomas of which prostate is the most common. A desmoplastic response to neoplasm can usually be distinguished by displacement of the aorta form the spine, lateral displacement of the ureters, erosion of the vertebra, as well as the presence of visceral metastases. Furthermore, whereas retroperitoneal fibrosis is usually a relatively benign condition, the life expectancy of patients with malignant retroperitoneal fibrosis is usually 3-6 months.

Although there appears to be many similarities between retroperitoneal fibrosis and inflammatory aortic aneurysms, the relationship between these two conditions remains the subject of debate. In fact, the only real difference between the two conditions may be the degree of aortic enlargement.

Management of Ureteral Entrapment

CT scans demonstrate ureteral involvement in the periaortic fibrosis in up to 53% of patients and approximately 10-20% of patients present with obstructive uropathy and impaired renal function. These patients should undergo preoperative ureteral stent placement to relieve the obstruction. Obstruction of the ureter usually

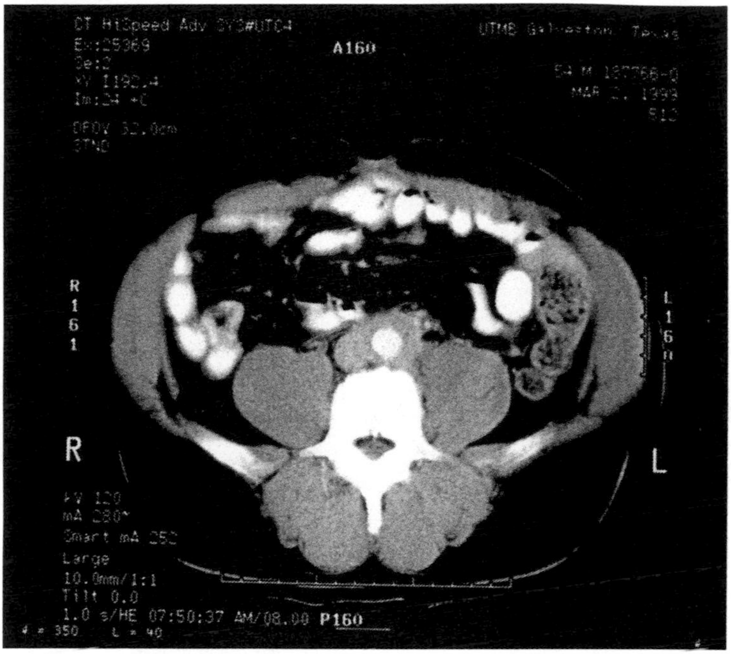

Fig. 16.3. Histologic section showing the chronic inflammatory cell infiltrate in an inflammatory aortic aneurysm.

regresses following aneurysm repair and therefore we do not recommend routine ureterolysis. Ureterolysis undertaken routinely may be associated with ureteric leaks, infection of the graft requiring nephrectomy, and possible removal of the graft.

Summary

Inflammatory aortic aneurysms are a variant of noninflammatory aneurysms and represent 2.5-15% of such lesions. The triad of chronic abdominal pain, weight loss and an elevated ESR in a patient with a known AAA is suggestive of the diagnosis.

The diagnosis is made preoperatively on abdominal CT scan in approximately 50% of patients. The treatment of IAAA is resection and grafting. Ureterolysis is fraught with danger and seldom indicated. The operative mortality and long-term survival approaches that of patients with noninflammatory aneurysms. The role of preoperative and postoperative steroid therapy remains controversial.

Selected Readings

1. Walker DI, Bloor K, Williams G et al. Inflammatory aneurysms of the abdominal aorta. Br J Surg 1972; 59(8):609-614.
    Classic article from the Manchester Royal Infirmary where the entity of IAAA is first described.

16

2. Pennell RC, Hollier LH, Lie JT et al. Inflammatory abdominal aortic aneurysms: A thirty year review. J Vasc Surg 1985; 2:859-869.
    A vast review of the key features of IAAA from the Mayo Clinic.

3. Crawford JL, Stowe CL, Safi HJ et al. Inflammatory aneurysms of the aorta. J Vasc Surg 1985; 2(1):113-124.
    A nice discussion of the symptomatic nature of IAAA and features that help the surgeon make the diagnosis preoperatively.

4. Goldstone J, Malone JM, Moore WS. Inflammatory aneurysms of the abdominal aorta. Surgery 1978; 83:425-430.
    First to emphasize that operative maneuvers in aneurysmorrhaphy should be modified in that no effort should be made to mobilize the adherent duodenum from the aorta.

5. Sterpetti AV, Hunter WJ, Feldhaus RJ et al. Inflammatory aneurysms of the abdominal aorta: incidence, pathologic, and etiologic considerations. J Vasc Surg 1989; 9:643-650.
    Proposes the concept of chronic contained rupture for the etiology of IAAA.

6. Nitecki SS, Hallett JW, Jr., Stanson AW et al. Inflammatory abdominal aortic aneurysms: New clinical implications from a case control study. J Vasc Surg 1996; 23:860-869.
    This case control study provides some evidence of the familial nature of IAAA and the key role of current smoking in the inflammatory response.

7. Rose AG, Dent DM. Inflammatory variant of abdominal aortic atherosclerotic aneurysm. Arch Pathol Lab Med 1981; 105:409-413.
    First to recognize that an inflammatory response of varying intensity is present in the aneurysm wall in all specimens.

8. Laquet JP, Lacroix H et al. Inflammatory abdominal aortic aneurysms. A retrospective study of 110 cases. Acta Chir Belg 1997; 97:286-292.
    A review of a largest European experience with special focus on the problem of ureteral obstruction.

9. Tennant WG, Hatnell GG et al. Radiologic investigation of abdominal aortic aneurysm disease: Comparison of three modalities in staging and the detection of inflammatory change. J Vasc Surg 1993; 17:703-709.
    Discussion of the role of ultrasound, CT and MRI in the diagnosis of IAAA.

10. Stotter AT, Grigg MJ et al. The response of perianeurysmal fibrosis—the "inflammatory" aneurysm—to surgery and steroid therapy. Eur J Vasc Surg 1990; 14:201-205.
    Discussion of the role of steroid therapy in IAAA.

16

CHAPTER 17

Ruptured Abdominal Aortic Aneurysm

Kaj Johansen

Abdominal aortic aneurysm (AAA) is a degenerative atherosclerotic condition characterized by progressive dilation of the abdominal aorta. In one-third to one-half of patients it expands and leads ultimately, if not managed appropriately, to rupture and exsanguination. The characteristic patient with an AAA is an elderly male with a smoking history; such patients commonly are afflicted with coronary, cerebrovascular and other peripheral manifestations of atherosclerosis as well.[1] All but 2% of such aortic aneurysms begin below the origins of the renal arteries. Therefore, the subsequent discussion will be restricted to aneurysmal dilatation of the infrarenal abdominal aorta as well as the common iliac arteries (an anatomically distinct but clinically identical condition).

A condition with which ruptured AAA is frequently confused is aortic dissection (sometimes mistakenly termed "dissecting aneurysm"). While pain and cardiovascular collapse are commonly present in patients with aortic dissection, just as in ruptured AAA patients, those with aortic dissection are commonly younger and the pain they note is usually in the upper mid back or in the chest, rather than in the lower abdomen or lower back as seen in ruptured AAA. Patients with aortic dissection are normo- or even hypertensive. Dissection is not a component of the natural history of AAA; however, approximately 30% of patients with a history of type B (descending thoracic aortic) dissection may develop aneurysmal dilatation of their dissection channels. If not detected and electively managed these aneurysmal dissections may continue to expand and may ultimately rupture.

Pathophysiology of Aneurysm Expansion and Rupture

The risk of aneurysm rupture clearly increases with AAA diameter, and it has long been taught that AAA rupture occurs in concert with the law of Laplace:

$$t \sim Pr$$

where t is circumferential wall tension, P is intraluminal pressure and r is aneurysm radius. From this it has been presumed that size is the only clinically useful predictor of AAA rupture. However, small AAAs do indeed rupture.[2] More contemporary observations have suggested that other aspects of AAA morphology such as aortic "blebs" or "blisters" or other alterations of AAAs usual fusiform shape may also be relevant to aneurysmal expansion and rupture.

Patients with AAAs demonstrate elevated levels of serum protease levels, and those whose aneurysms are expanding rapidly appear to have higher levels of such enzymes, including elastase and collagenase. Diabetic patients with AAA may be at

Aortic Surgery, edited by Jeffrey L. Ballard. ©2000 Landes Bioscience.

increased risk of aneurysmal rupture, as well as patients with chronic obstructive pulmonary disease; precise reasons for this concordance is unclear.

Hypertension appears to be present in most patients with AAA, supporting the longstanding pathogenetic role of the law of Laplace in aneurysmal expansion and rupture. Patients whose hypertension or heart disease is being managed with beta blocker medications have a slower rate of expansion of their aneurysm, possibly because of such medications' reduction in left ventricular (and thus aortic systolic) dV/dt.[3] Administration of beta-blocking medications thus may offer the first effective nonsurgical therapy for AAA: trials testing this hypothesis are under way.

Diagnosis of Ruptured AAA

The classic triad of abdominal pain, cardiovascular collapse and a pulsatile abdominal mass may often be present in patients with ruptured AAA. However, while the specificity of this diagnostic triad is high, its sensitivity is low because such patients are often so hypotensive that pulsations of the abdominal mass cannot be appreciated. Almost twenty years ago at our institution we proposed the use of emergency abdominal ultrasound in patients thought potentially to harbor a ruptured AAA. While such studies, performed in an emergency circumstance in an unprepped patient, are rarely useful for demonstrating actual extra-aortic blood, they are highly sensitive and specific for the presence of an AAA. This information, in combination with the clinical scenario, is commonly sufficient for making the decision to perform an immediate laparotomy or not. Only in unusual circumstances, and only in hemodynamically stable patients, is the performance of more detailed imaging studies such as computed tomography warranted or necessary.

Several other conditions occasionally masquerade as ruptured AAA. Acute myocardial infarction is one such condition. In addition, perforated peptic ulcer or other such intraabdominal condition, ureteral colic, or herniated disk may mimic ruptured AAA but these are rarely associated with sustained cardiovascular collapse.

Preoperative Volume Resuscitation

Lamentably, a number of patients who have suffered rupture of an AAA are transferred by ambulance technicians or paramedics after having been volume-resuscitated aggressively to a "normal" blood pressure. Too often these patients then suffer a second and now refractory collapse, in fact actually "rerupturing" their aneurysmal leak. Bickell and colleagues in Houston, evaluating hypovolemic shock in a variety of trauma and emergency vascular patients, have advanced the thesis that partial volume resuscitation is more harmful than none at all.[4] These assertions remain controversial but we attempt to control volume resuscitation in the prehospital setting to result in a systolic blood pressure of no more than 90 mm Hg.

Operative Management

Without successful surgical repair all patients with ruptured AAA will die from exsanguination. Once the diagnosis of ruptured AAA is made, the patient should be transferred directly to the operating room. Surgical repair is then undertaken by a team with as much vascular surgical expertise as possible and in a setting where perioperative care of what can be anticipated to be a critically ill patient can be carried out. Studies have suggested that surgical outcomes for ruptured AAA are optimal when carried out by certified vascular surgeons. It would also reasonably be expected that outcomes would be best in major trauma/emergency hospitals commonly accustomed to dealing with critically ill patients, large volumes of blood transfusion and prolonged ventilator support. However, this notion remains controversial because the success of surgical repair for ruptured AAA correlates directly with the rapidity with which control of bleeding takes place. It may be that the benefits of transferring a patient with a ruptured AAA to a vascular center may be neutralized by the consequences of the extra time required to do so.[5]

At Harborview Medical Center in Seattle we have long believed that the safest place for a patient with a putative ruptured AAA is in the operating room. Indeed, in our 1991 publication describing 186 ruptured AAA patients managed over the previous decade, the mean time in the emergency room was 12 minutes.[6] This, we believe, is due to an always-available operating room and anesthesia team characteristic of a Level I trauma center. Here, as for both prehospital care and the emergency room, fluids (crystalloid and blood) are administered at a rate to keep the systolic blood pressure no more than 90 mm Hg.

The rate at which operation for ruptured AAA commences is governed by the patient's hemodynamic stability. For the occasional completely unstable patient with an unrecordable blood pressure, our practice has been to carry out endotracheal intubation (if not already performed) and then immediate laparotomy for proximal abdominal aortic clamping, without waiting for insertion of further lines, monitoring catheters or even the administration of general anesthesia.

However, in most circumstances the patient is still awake and at least "metastable." There usually is time to insert large-bore peripheral intravenous lines, a central venous introducer sheath and an arterial line. In general, the time required for proper insertion of a pulmonary artery catheter is unwarranted and unnecessary. Because of the sudden sharp increase in blood pressure that may accompany insertion of a bladder catheter in the awake patient, we prefer to wait on this important monitoring "line" until after the patient is anesthetized. Because of the crucial importance of maintaining normothermia in critically ill surgical patients, time spent installing various heating devices is well spent, in our opinion.

In that majority of patients in whom a relatively measured preparation for operation has been possible it is our preference that the patient be prepped and draped, and the operating team be gowned, gloved and ready to operate, prior to the induction of general anesthesia. In this way we have found that the hemodynamic consequences of the blood pressure lability often accompanying the induction of anesthesia can be minimized to as short a time as possible.

Midline vertical laparotomy, from xiphoid to well below the umbilicus, is our favored operative incision for management of ruptured AAA. This is primarily because of the rapidity with which the peritoneal cavity can be entered to gain clamp (or at least manual) control of the proximal aorta. Others have advanced a left flank extraperitoneal approach to the aorta, an approach which has theoretical merit.

17

However, concerned about the potentially excessive time required to gain access to the aneurysm neck and the risk of directly exposing the site of aneurysm rupture prior to gaining aortic control via an extraperitoneal approach, we have continued to teach a standard celiotomy approach.

Once the intestines have been packed to the right side of the abdomen and the transverse colon has been transposed upward, the surgeon is confronted by a large nonpulsatile retroperitoneal hematoma elevating the duodenum and the pancreas. Entry into the retroperineum and blunt dissection of the hematoma may reveal the outlines of the AAA itself, with the initial findings that the tough fibrofatty tissue that ordinarily overlies the infrarenal aorta and the neck of the AAA has been elevated up off the aorta itself. This sometimes permits digital dissection of the infrarenal aorta in a fashion permitting direct application of an appropriate clamp at the aneurysm neck. Because of the hematoma and, upon occasion, active bleeding from the rupture site, visibility is frequently poor and clamp application may necessarily be "blind". The risk of damage to the renal arteries or especially the left renal vein as it crosses over the neck of the aneurysm must be weighed against the necessity for rapid aortic cross-clamp control.

An important anatomic variation associated with aortic aneurysms is relevant to emergency clamping of the aneurysmal neck. The aneurysmal aorta becomes ectatic (i.e., uncoils) in a fashion which commonly causes the aorta to be directed anteriorly rather than in its usual orientation parallel to the spinal column. Orientation of the blades of the clamp may thus necessarily be in a cephalad-caudad fashion, rather than in the usual ventral-dorsal orientation.

Several alternative approaches to gaining proximal aortic control must be kept in mind if rapid initial clamp placement at the aneurysmal neck cannot be assured. The most effective approach is to gain clamp or even manual pressure control of the proximal abdominal aorta near the diaphragm. This is best done by bluntly dissecting through the lesser omentum, retracting the left lobe of the liver rightward and obtaining control of the aorta below and just to the right of the distalmost esophagus as it meets the stomach. An absolutely accurate application of the clamp requires division of the crura of the diaphragm. This exposure may take extra time but at least it is not generally obscured by hematoma from the more distally ruptured aorta. Alternatively, the aorta can simply be compressed against the spinal column manually, with an aortic compressor device or even the end of a large hand-held retractor.

In extreme cases, where clamp control of the proximal abdominal aorta cannot be obtained, two other strategies should be kept in mind. The first is to perform a left lateral thoracotomy, thereby quickly enabling clamp control of the distal thoracic aorta. Alternatively, the aneurysm can be opened directly and the operating surgeon's thumb or fingers inserted up into the neck of the aneurysm from inside. This approach is assisted by even temporary manual compression of the aorta at the diaphragmatic hiatus. Once inside the more normal infrarenal aortic lumen, vascular control can be obtained by clamp placement externally over the digits inside the aorta. Alternatively, an adult Foley catheter can be inserted into the aorta and inflated.

It has been a consistent observation of ours that, once the AAA is opened, backbleeding is minimal to nonexistent and that distal control of the iliac arteries is often unnecessary in these severely hypovolemic patients. Because damage to nearby venous structures during blind clamping of the aorta or the iliac arteries is a leading cause of ongoing intraoperative hemorrhage and death in ruptured AAA patients we commonly avoid extensive dissection of the iliac arteries. Alternatively, placement of pediatric Foley catheters or intraluminal balloon occlusion catheters may suffice for the purpose of control of distal iliac artery backbleeding.

After proximal (and, if necessary distal) vascular control has been obtained, further conduct of the aortic graft replacement procedure is little different from that confronted in the elective circumstance. Mural thrombus is removed, backbleeding lumbar artery and inferior mesenteric arteries are oversewn and the proximal aorta is prepared for suture anastomosis of an appropriately sized graft.

One important distinction from the elective aortic graft circumstance in the ruptured AAA setting is the importance of limiting the aortic reconstructive procedure as much possible. The author strongly believes that this is not the time to deal with small iliac aneurysms, renal artery stenosis or anything but the most impenetrable distal aortic or iliac atherosclerosis. It should be kept in mind that the goal of the operative exercise in ruptured AAA is to provide rapid and effective control of aortic aneurysmal bleeding. Accordingly, it should be extremely unusual to perform anything other than aortic tube graft repair. Use of an aortic bifurcation graft is part of our operative strategy in much less than 10% of all ruptured AAA cases.

It is commonplace, at the end of graft insertion, for the ruptured AAA patient to be hypotensive, hypothermic, acidotic and coagulopathic. The bowel is frequently massively distended. What such patients need most of all is rapid abdominal closure and transfer to the intensive care unit (ICU) for warming, volume resuscitation with blood and crystalloid and coagulation factor replacement. In this regard several strategies found useful in the trauma setting have been successfully adapted to the care of the ruptured AAA patient.

Diffuse coagulopathic bleeding complicates the management of patients who have suffered ruptured AAA. Even when graft insertion has been successful, such bleeding, resulting from the morbid consequences of hypothermia, acidosis and autotransfuser-conditioned platelet malfunction on the normal clotting cascade, often eventuates in exsanguination. However, in a recent report such patients, previously doomed to an almost certain early demise in the first 24 hours in the ICU, had placement of intraabdominal laparotomy packs applied to bleeding sites, in the fashion described for uncontrollable bleeding from liver trauma. Forty percent of these patients, who later underwent elective removal of the packs, survived ruptured AAA repair.[7]

Massive retroperitoneal and intestinal edema markedly complicate abdominal closure even when repair of a ruptured AAA has been successful and intraoperative hemorrhage has been halted. In this setting, we have described the use of temporary mesh closure of the abdominal incision.[8] This approach, which was translated from the trauma setting, permits a tension-free temporary wound closure which avoids the imposition of intraabdominal and intrathoracic hypertension. This technique

17

minimizes "abdominal compartment syndrome," which may attend any attempt at primary laparotomy closure in these patients.

Immediate Postoperative Care

Patients who have survived initial operative repair of ruptured AAA are critically ill. In fact, in most large recent series most such patients have died in the ICU rather than in the operating room. This is unsurprising in view of the fact that they are elderly patients, frequently with histories of chronic cardiac, pulmonary or renal dysfunction. In addition, they have endured hypovolemic shock, an emergency operation and massive transfusion. Postoperative evidence for congestive heart failure, myocardial infarction, renal failure and pulmonary insufficiency requiring prolonged ventilatory support all are common and increase the likelihood of post operative mortality. Numerous studies have demonstrated that preexisting chronic renal insufficiency, in particular, predicts the development of postoperative acute renal failure. The mortality rate associated with such acute-on-chronic renal failure exceeds 90% and appears unaffected by the utilization of early "prophylactic" hemodialysis.

Other conditions may be relatively unique to the post operative ruptured AAA patient. For example, such patients have a substantial risk (25-60%) of developing symptoms and signs of colonic ischemia. This complication correlates most specifically with low intra- and postoperative cardiac output and the perioperative administration of alpha-agonist vasoconstrictor agents to maintain perioperative blood pressure.[9] Vigilance against this condition, which is associated with an 80% mortality, is crucial following ruptured AAA. It is our practice to perform routine flexible sigmoidoscopy within the first 12 hours after ruptured AAA repair in all such patients. Endoscopic evidence of mucosal ischemia or perforation warrants immediate laparotomy. Transmural colon infarction necessitates emergency colon resection.

Outcome

The in-hospital mortality for ruptured AAA remains approximately at 50%, a toll which has not changed significantly in three decades. Prior studies in jurisdictions in which all deaths result in a post mortem examination appear to suggest that the community mortality rate of ruptured AAA is even higher, approaching 90%. This is due to the fact that the cause of death for many elderly patients found dead at home is often assigned uncritically to coronary artery disease in the absence of routine post mortem examinations. In the near future, outcome improvement from this common and lethal condition will more probably result from prehospital changes such as augmented paramedic resuscitation and prehospital transport and resuscitation systems, as well as designation of "emergency vascular centers" which will centralize the care of such critically-ill and high-risk patients. In truth, however, the only truly significant change in the toll exacted by this condition will likely be the introduction of well-conducted screening programs for populations at risk. This will permit identification of AAA patients who can be considered for elective repair prior to aneurysmal rupture.[10]

17

Selected Readings

1. Tilson MD, Stansel HC. Differences in results for aneurysms vs. occlusive disease after bifurcation grafts: results of 100 elective grafts. Arch Surg 1980; 115:1173-1175.

   Tilson and Stansel evaluate clinical outcomes in 50 consecutive patients with abdominal aortic aneurysm (AAA) and 50 consecutive patients with aortic iliac occlusive disease (AIOD), with the demonstration that AAA patients are significantly (P < 0.05) more likely to be male, elderly, tall, to have large aortas even when normalized by body surface area and size of artery. AIOD patients are significantly more likely to be female, middle-aged, smokers, and likely to undergo arterial reconstructions elsewhere.

2. Nicholls SC, Gardner JB, Meissner MH et al. Rupture in small abdominal aortic aneurysms. J Vasc Surg 1998; 28:884-888.

   In this survey of a large number of emergency abdominal ultrasound examinations performed for ruptured aortic aneurysm, 7% of all those proven operatively to have extra-aortic blood had aneurysms measuring less than 5.0 cm in diameter. Aneurysms measured exactly 5.0 cm or less in 10% of this patient population. Other interesting findings from this study were that advanced pulmonary insufficiency, usually from heavy cigarette smoking, and diabetes appear to be predictors of small AAA rupture.

3. Leach SD, Toole AL, Stern H et al. Effect of beta-blockade on the growth rate of abdominal aortic aneurysm. Arch Surg 1988; 123:606-609.

   It has been observed that AAA patients treated with B-blockers show aneurysm expansion, and certain experimental studies appear to document that the lower blood pressure and aortic dv/dt associated with such therapy are the relevant issues.

4. Bickel WH, Wall MJ, Pepe PE et al. Immediate versus delayed fluid resuscitation for hypotensive patients with penetrating torso injuries. N Engl J Med 331; 194:1105-1109.

   Recent work from this group at Ben Taub General Hospital in Houston has suggested that the high-volume crystalloid resuscitation adopted in trauma patients and other victims of acute hypovolemia may in fact be injurious to these patients. Because such resuscitation rarely completely reverses tissue hypoperfusion, such resuscitation risks the generation of toxic oxygen radicals which predispose the patient to subsequent ARDS and other forms of multiple system organ failure. The ruptured AAA patient may also be potentially negatively impacted because too-exuberant volume resuscitation of such patients may raise the blood pressure high enough to rerupture a tamponaded leak site in the retroperitoneum.

5. Meyer AA, Ahlquist RE, Trunhey DD. Mortality from ruptured abdominal aortic aneurysms. A comparison of two series. Am J Surg 1986; 152:27-33.

   AAA in several different urban and rural settings suggests that, "playing it where it lies," carrying out emergency AAA repair at the first hospital to which the patient is taken may be optimal.

6. Johansen K, Kohler TR, Nicholls S et al. Ruptured abdominal aortic aneurysm: The Harborview experience. J Vasc Surg 1991; 13:240-247.

   This is a study of 186 proven ruptured AAA patients arriving alive at Harborview Medical Center in Seattle during the decade 1980-1989. Virtually all patients in this series had a recorded blood pressure of less than 90 mm Hg prior to operation. Mortality rate in this series was 70%. Most patients survived operative repair of the ruptured AAA only to expire from persistent bleeding or multiple system organ failure in the ICU. Mortality was greater than 90% in several different subsets of patients (women,

17

those aged greater than 80, patients with persistent hypotension or marked hemorrhage). This paper engendered substantial controversy because of its authors' suggestion that such discouraging outcomes suggest that operative repair is futile in certain ruptured AAA patient subgroups.

7. Van Herwaarden T, VanVroonhoven T. Abdominal packing for surgically uncontrollable hemorrhage in ruptured abdominal aortic aneurysm repair. J Vasc Surg, in press. AUTHOR: Please update this reference.

    Ruptured AAA patients who manifests the "lethal triad" of hypothermia, metabolic acidosis and coagulopathy commonly expire either in the operating room or early in the postoperative period in the ICU. In this study, the authors placed laparotomy packs at areas of diffuse coagulopathic bleeding in ruptured AAA patients, then closed the incisions and swiftly transported patients to the ICU for warming and volume resuscitation. Such management is akin to that used for patients with large bleeding stellate liver lacerations following abdominal trauma. The ruptured AAA patients were then returned semi-electively to the operating room for pack removal and final abdominal closure. Forty percent of patients so treated survived. As for temporary mesh laparotomy closure, its use in the ruptured AAA population of a technique validated in trauma patients appears safe, rational and effective.

8. Oelschlager BK, Boyle EM, Meissner M et al. Delayed abdominal closure in the management of ruptured aortic aneurysms. Am J Surg 1997; 172:411-415.

    A major contributing factor to morbidity and mortality following massive volume resuscitation is development of the "abdominal compartment syndrome." This syndrome results from massive perioperative swelling of the intestine and retroperitoneum. This paper suggests that temporary mesh closure of the midline fascia with a later semi-elective return to the operating room for secondary laparotomy closure after edema has resolved can be lifesaving.

9. Meissner M, Johansen K. Colon infarction after ruptured aortic aneurysm. Arch Surg 1992; 127:979-985.

    The proposed etiology of colonic ischemia, which occurs in up to 60% of patients surviving ruptured AAA, has been unclear. Perioperative inferior mesenteric artery (IMA) embolization, IMA ligation, compression of colonic blood supply by hematoma or by retractors at the time of operation or hypoperfusion or splanchnic vasoconstriction due to shock have all been hypothesized. Each of these can likely play a factor in colonic ischemia. However, this paper demonstrates in case-control fashion that only two factors, diminished cardiac output and the use of alpha adrenergic vasoconstrictor agents in the perioperative period, correlated in a statistically significant fashion with the development of colonic ischemia.

10. Scott RA, Wilson NM, Ashton HA et al. Influence of screening on the incidence of ruptured abdominal aortic aneurysm: 5-year results of a randomized controlled study. Br J Surg 1995; 82:1066-1070.

    These authors' randomized screening trial, in which AAAs discovered by screening were operated upon electively if certain criteria were met, reduced the incidence of ruptured AAA by 55% in this medical center's catchment area.

CHAPTER 18

Combined Aortic and Renal Artery Reconstruction

James M. Wong and Kimberley J. Hansen

Management of renal artery disease discovered incidentally during angiographic study of the abdominal aorta is controversial. In this setting, the surgeon must address the need for additional diagnostic study and the decision of whether to perform combined aortic and renal artery reconstruction. Data pertaining to this latter decision may be obtained from a review of the natural history of atherosclerotic renal artery disease compared with the results of combined repair. This information then helps to form a therapeutic plan appropriate to the individual patient. In the following discussion, combined management of aortic and renal artery disease will be considered as either a prophylactic or empiric procedure.

Prophylactic Renal Artery Repair

The term prophylactic repair indicates that renal revascularization is performed prior to any pathologic or clinical sequelae related to the lesion. By definition, therefore, the patient considered for prophylactic renal artery repair has neither hypertension nor reduced renal function. Correction of the renal artery lesion in this setting assumes that a significant percentage of these asymptomatic patients will survive to the point that the renal lesion will cause hypertension or renal dysfunction and that preemptive correction is necessary to prevent a clinically adverse event for which the patient cannot be treated. To test this assumption, review of available data regarding the natural history of renovascular disease will address: 1) the rate at which asymptomatic lesions not associated with hypertension or renal dysfunction progress to clinical significance, and 2) the rate at which clinically significant lesions progress to occlusion.

Data regarding the frequency of anatomic progression of renovascular disease are summarized in Table 18.1. In patients with hypertension, ipsilateral progression of renal artery lesions occurred in 44% and progression to occlusion during medical management occurred in 12%. However, among our reported patients, only one (3%) had loss of a previously reconstructable renal artery.[1] In the absence of hypertension, one must assume that the renal artery lesion must progress anatomically to become functionally significant (i.e., produce hypertension). Based on the preceding data, progression of a renal artery lesion to produce renovascular hypertension (RVH) could be expected in approximately 44% of normotensive patients. If one also assumes that the subsequent development of RVH is managed medically, then the next consideration is the frequency of decline in renal function.

Aortic Surgery, edited by Jeffrey L. Ballard. ©2000 Landes Bioscience.

Table 18.1. Angiographic progression of renal artery atherosclerosis

Mean follow-up (mo)	No.	Ipsilateral lesions		Contralateral lesions
		Percent exhibiting progression	Percent progressing to occlusion	Percent exhibiting progression
29-35*	85	44	16	–
28†	35	–	12	17

*Refs: Wollenweber J, Sheps SG, Davis GD. Clinical course of atherosclerotic renovascular disease. Am J Cardiol 1968; 21:60-71.
Schreiber MJ, Phol MA, Novick AC. The natural history of atherosclerotic fibrous renal artery disease. Urol Clin North Am 1984;11:383-92.
†Ref: Dean RH, Kieffer RW, Smith BM et al. Renovascular hypertension: Anatomic and renal function changes during drug therapy. Arch Surg 1981; 166:1408-15.

Among 30 patients with renovascular hypertension (i.e., renal artery lesions with severe hypertension and lateralizing functional studies) randomized to medical management, significant loss of renal function manifest by at least a 25% decrease in glomerular filtration rate (GFR) occurred in 40% of patients during a 15-24 month follow-up period.[1] These patients were considered failures of medical management and submitted to operative renal artery repair. However, 13% of those patients who were subsequently submitted to operation continued to exhibit progressive deterioration in renal function. Therefore, of the patients with RVH randomized to medical management only 36% had the potentially preventable loss of renal function by means of an earlier operation. Of these patients who demonstrated decline in kidney function during medical management, Novick et al[2] have reported that 67% of properly selected patients will have renal function restored by renal artery repair.

The pertinence of these issues as they relate to prophylactic renal revascularization can be demonstrated by considering 100 theoretical patients without hypertension who have an unsuspected renal artery lesion detected by angiography prior to aortic repair (Table 18.2). If the renal artery lesion is not repaired prophylactically, forty-four patients will subsequently develop RVH. Sixteen (36%) of these 44 patients will experience a preventable reduction in renal function during follow-up. However, delayed operation will restore function in 11 (67%) of these 16 patients. In theory, therefore, only five of the 100 patients receive unique benefit from prophylactic intervention.

This unique benefit should be considered in terms of the associated morbidity and mortality, of combined aortorenal repair. The operative mortality associated with the surgical treatment of isolated renal artery disease at our institution is approximately 1%; however, combined aortorenal reconstruction is associated with a 5-6% perioperative mortality.[3] If direct aortorenal methods of reconstruction are employed in conjunction with intraoperative completion duplex sonography, the

Table 18.2. Comparison of risk to benefit of prophylactic renal revascularization in 100 hypothetical normotensive patients

Benefit/Risk	No. of patients
Benefit	
Progression to RVH (44/100 or 44%)	44
RVH patients who lose renal function (16/44 or 36%)	16
Renal function restored by later operation (11/16 or 67%)	11
Renal function not restored by later operation (5/16 or 33%)	5
	—
UNIQUE BENEFIT	5
Risk	
Operative mortality (5.5%)	5
Early technical failure (0.5%)	1
Late failure of revascularization (4.0%)	4
	—
ADVERSE OUTCOME	10

early technical failure rate is approximately 0.5%. In all, early and late failures of reconstruction can be expected in 4-5% of renal artery repairs.[4] Therefore, adverse results could be expected in 9 or 10 of these 100 patients after combined aortorenal repair.

Theoretically then, prophylactic renal artery surgery combined with aortic repair could prevent irreversible adverse outcomes in only five patients but could produce an adverse outcome in 10 patients. Based on available data, we find no justification for prophylactic renal artery surgery either as an independent procedure or as a procedure performed in combination with aortic repair. These conclusions are supported by the recent reported experience of Williamson et al[5]

Empiric Renal Artery Repair

In contrast to prophylactic renal revascularization, empiric renal artery repair is appropriate under select circumstances. The term empiric repair implies that hypertension, renal dysfunction, or both are present, although a causal relationship between the renal artery lesion and these clinical sequelae has not been established. The specific circumstances in which empiric renal artery repair may be performed are summarized in the following discussion.

Repair of unilateral renal artery disease may be appropriate as an independent or combined procedure in the presence of negative functional studies (i.e., nonlateralizing renal vein renin assays) when

1. hypertension remains severe and uncontrollable with maximal drug therapy,
2. the patient is relatively young and without significant risk factors for operation, and
3. the probability of technical success is greater than 95%.

18

In these circumstances correction of a renal artery lesion may be justified in order to eliminate all possible causes of hypertension before assigning a patient to increased life-long risk of adverse cardiovascular events. However, because the probability of blood pressure benefit is low in such a patient, morbidity from the procedure must also be predictably low. Although we have undertaken unilateral renal artery repair in patients with renal insufficiency who have not had positive functional tests, such procedures have been performed as a part of a clinical research study on ischemic nephropathy. We do not recommend this as a clinically proven therapeutic intervention. Although we frequently correct bilateral renal artery disease without prior functional assessment in patients with severe hypertension, renal insufficiency, or both, we do not proceed with empiric renal artery repair as an independent procedure when the hypertension is mild and when renal insufficiency is not present.

When a patient has bilateral renal artery stenoses and hypertension, the decision to combine renal artery repair with correction of the aortic disease is based on severity of hypertension and renovascular lesions. If the renal artery lesions consist of severe disease on one side and only mild or moderate disease on the contralateral side, then the patient is treated as if only a unilateral lesion exists. If both lesions are only moderately severe (65-80% diameter-reducing stenosis), then renal revascularization is undertaken only if the hypertension is severe. In contrast, if both renal artery lesions are severe (> 80% stenosis) and the patient has drug-dependent hypertension, bilateral simultaneous renal revascularization is performed. In this instance, hypertension secondary to severe bilateral renal artery stenoses is often particularly severe and difficult to control. Furthermore, at least mild renal insufficiency is often present. Since azotemia usually parallels the severity of hypertension, a patient who presents with severe azotemia but only mild hypertension usually has renal parenchymal disease. Characteristically, renovascular hypertension associated with severe azotemia or dialysis dependence is also associated with renal artery occlusion or with very severe bilateral stenoses. When considering combined repair of incidentally identified bilateral renal artery disease with correction of aortic disease, one should evaluate the clinical status with respect to this characteristic presentation. In such situations, combined renal artery repair at the time of aortic surgery is indicated to improve excretory renal function with beneficial blood pressure response a secondary goal. Such indications appear justified in light of the observed increase in estimated survival associated with improved renal function despite the increased morbidity and mortality of a combined aortorenal procedure.

Operative Techniques

Alone or in combination with aortic repair, a variety of operative techniques have been used to correct renal artery disease. From a practical standpoint, three basic operations have been most frequently utilized: aortorenal bypass, renal artery thromboendarterectomy and renal artery reimplantation. Although each method may be useful in combined aortorenal repairs, no single approach provides optimal repair for all types of renal disease. Aortorenal bypass, preferably with thin-walled PTFE when combined with prosthetic aortic repair, is probably the most versatile technique. However, transaortic thromboendarterectomy is especially useful for orificial atherosclerosis involving multiple renal arteries. Occasionally, the renal artery will be sufficiently redundant to allow reimplantation into the aortic graft—probably the simplest technique—involving only one additional anastomosis.

Certain measures are used in almost all renal artery operations. Mannitol is administered intravenously in 12.5 gm doses early in the operation. Repeated doses are administered before and after periods of renal ischemia up to a total dose of 1 gm per kilogram patient body weight. Just prior to aortic or renal artery cross-clamping, 100 units of heparin per kilogram body weight is given intravenously and systemic anticoagulation is verified by activated clotting time. Unless required for hemostasis, protamine is not routinely administered for reversal of heparin at the completion of the operation.

Mobilization and Dissection

A xiphoid to pubis midline abdominal incision is made for operative repair of atherosclerotic renal artery disease in combination with aortic reconstruction. The last 1 or 2 cm of the proximal incision coursing to one side of the xiphoid is important in obtaining full exposure of the upper abdominal aorta and renal branches. Some form of fixed mechanical retraction is also advantageous, particularly when combined aortorenal procedures are required. Otherwise, extended flank and subcostal incisions are reserved for fibrodysplastic lesions or splanchno-renal bypass.

When the midline xiphoid-to-pubis incision is used, the posterior peritoneum overlying the aorta is incised longitudinally and the duodenum is mobilized at the ligament of Treitz. During this maneuver it is important to identify visceral collaterals which course at this level. Finally, the duodenum is reflected to the patient's right to expose the left renal artery. By extending the posterior peritoneal incision to the left along the inferior border of the pancreas, an avascular plane posterior to the pancreas can be entered (Fig. 18.1) to expose the entire renal hilum on the left. The left renal artery lies behind the left renal vein. In some cases, the vein can be retracted cephalad to expose the artery; in other cases, caudal retraction of the vein provides better access. Usually, the gonadal and adrenal veins, which enter the left renal vein, must be ligated and divided to facilitate exposure of the distal artery. Frequently a lumbar vein enters the posterior wall of the left renal vein, and it can be avulsed easily unless special care is taken while mobilizing the renal vein (Figs. 18.2A and 18.2B). The proximal portion of the right renal artery can be exposed through the base of the mesentery by ligating two or more pairs of lumbar veins and retracting the left renal vein cephalad and the vena cava to the patient's right. However, the distal portion of the right renal artery is best exposed by mobilizing the duodenum and right colon medially (Fig. 18.2C). Then, the right renal vein is mobilized and usually retracted cephalad in order to expose the artery.

Exposure of the distal right renal artery is achieved by hepatic and duodenal mobilization. With the right colon retracted medially and inferiorly, a Kocher's maneuver mobilizes the duodenum and pancreatic head to expose the inferior vena cava and right renal vein. Typically, the right renal artery is located just inferior to the accompanying vein which can be retracted superiorly to provide best exposure.

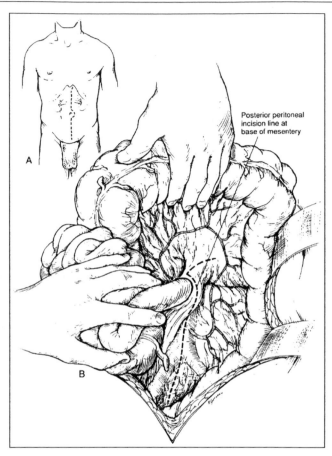

Posterior peritoneal
incision line at
base of mesentery

A

B

Fig. 18.1. Exposure of the aorta and left renal hilum through the base of the mesentery. Extension of the posterior peritoneal incision to the left, along the inferior border of the pancreas, provides entry to an avascular plane behind the pancreas. This allows excellent exposure of the entire left renal hilum as well as the proximal right renal artery. (From Techniques in Renal Artery Reconstruction: Part I, Benjamin ME and Dean RH. Ann Vasc Surg Vol. 10, No. 3, May 1996.)

Though accessory vessels may arise from the aorta or iliac vessels at any level, all arterial branches coursing anterior to the vena cava should be considered accessory renal branches and carefully preserved (Figs. 18.3A and 18.B).

When correction of bilateral lesions is combined with aortic reconstruction, these exposure techniques can be modified. Extended exposure may be provided by mobilizing the base of the small bowel mesentery to allow complete evisceration of the entire small bowel, right colon, and transverse colon. For this extended exposure, the posterior peritoneal incision begins with division of the ligament of Treitz

18

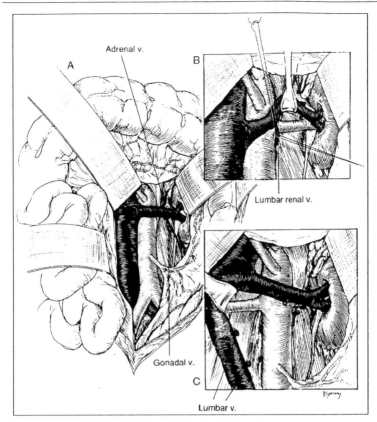

Fig. 18.2. (A) Exposure of the proximal right renal artery through the base of the mesentery. (B) Mobilization of the left renal vein by ligation and division of the adrenal, gonadal, and lumbar-renal veins allows exposure of the entire left renal artery to the hilum.(C) Two pairs of lumbar vessels have been ligated and divided to allow retraction of the vena cava to the right, revealing adequate exposure of the proximal renal artery disease. (Reprinted with permission from Techniques in Renal Artery Reconstruction: Part I, Benjamin ME and Dean RH. Ann Vasc Surg 1996; Vol. 10, No. 3.)

and proceeds along the base of the mesentery to the cecum and then up the lateral gutter to the foramen of Winslow (Fig. 18.4). The inferior border of the pancreas is fully mobilized to enter a retropancreatic plane, thereby exposing the aorta to a point above the superior mesenteric artery. Through this modified exposure, simultaneous bilateral renal endarterectomies, aortorenal grafting, or renal artery attachment to the aortic graft can be performed with wide visualization of the entire area.

We sometimes partially divide both diaphragmatic crura as they pass behind the renal arteries to their paravertebral attachment. By this partial division of the crura,

18

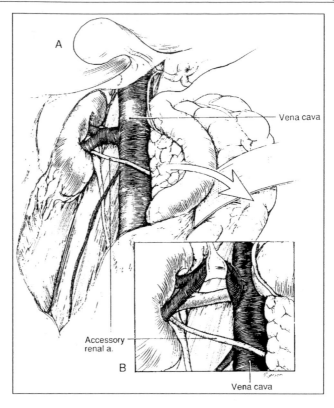

Fig. 18.3A. Not uncommonly, an accessory right renal artery arises from the anterior aorta and crosses anterior to the vena cava. B. The right renal vein is typically mobilized superiorly for exposure of the distal renal artery. (Reprinted with permission from Techniques in Renal Artery Reconstruction: Part I, Benjamin ME and Dean RH. Ann Vasc Surg 1996; Vol. 10, No. 3.)

the aorta above the superior mesenteric artery is easily visualized and can be mobilized for suprarenal cross-clamping where transaortic renal endarterectomy is performed through the divided aorta.

Aortorenal Bypass

Although three types of materials are available for aortorenal bypass (autologous saphenous vein, autologous hypogastric artery, and synthetic prosthetic), we generally prefer thin-walled 6.0 mm PTFE graft for renal reconstruction when combined with synthetic aortic replacement.

Although end-to-side distal renal anastomosis is used occasionally, end-to-end renal artery anastomosis is most commonly performed when combining aortic replacement with renal revascularization. In this circumstance, the proximal anastomosis is performed first and the distal renal anastomosis performed secondly to

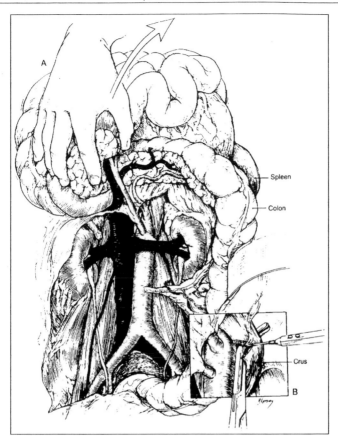

Fig. 18.4A. For complex bilateral renal artery reconstruction, wide exposure can be obtained with mobilization of the cecum and ascending colon. The entire small bowel and right colon are then mobilized to the right upper quadrant and placed on to the chest wall. B. Division of the diaphragmatic crura exposes the origin of the mesenteric vessels. (Reprinted with permission from Techniques in Renal Artery Reconstruction: Part I, Benjamin ME and Dean RH. Ann Vasc Surg 1996 ;Vol. 10, No. 3.)

limit renal ischemia. Regardless of the type of distal anastomosis, the proximal aortorenal anastomosis is best performed after excision of an ellipse of aortic graft.

Thromboendarterectomy

In some cases of bilateral atherosclerotic occlusions of the renal artery origins, simultaneous bilateral endarterectomy may be the most applicable procedure. Endarterectomy may be either transaortic or transrenal. In the latter instance, the aortotomy is made transversely and is carried across the aorta and into the renal

18

artery to a point beyond the visible disease. With this method, the distal endarterectomy can be assessed and tacked down with mattress sutures under direct vision if necessary. Following completion of the endarterectomy, the arteriotomy is closed. In most patients this closure is performed with a vein or Dacron patch to ensure that the proximal renal artery is widely patent. In most cases of combined aortic repair, the transaortic endarterectomy technique is used. The transaortic method is particularly applicable in patients with multiple renal arteries that demonstrate orificial disease. Transaortic endarterectomy is performed through the divided aorta removing a distal atherosclerotic sleeve of the aorta and renal atheroma. When using this transaortic technique, it is important to mobilize the renal arteries extensively to allow eversion of the vessel into the aorta. This allows the distal end point to be completed under direct vision.

Renal Artery Reimplantation

After the renal artery has been dissected from the surrounding retroperitoneal tissue the vessel may be somewhat redundant. When the renal artery stenosis is orificial and there is sufficient vessel length the renal artery can be transected and reimplanted into the aortic graft at a lower level. The renal artery must be spatulated and an ellipse of the aortic graft wall removed as in renal artery bypass.

Intraoperative Duplex Sonography

Provided the best method of reconstruction is chosen for combined aortorenal repair, the short course and high blood flow rates characteristic of renal reconstruction favor their patency. Consequently, flawless technical repair plays a dominant role in determining postoperative success. The negative impact of technical errors unrecognized and uncorrected at operation is implied by the fact that we have observed no late thromboses of renovascular reconstruction free of disease after one year.

The risks and the inherent limitations of completion angiography are not demonstrated by intraoperative duplex sonography.[6] Because the ultrasound probe can be placed immediately adjacent to the vascular repair, high carrying frequencies may be used which provide excellent B-scan detail sensitive to < 1 mm anatomic defects. Once imaged, defects can be viewed in a multitude of projections during conditions of uninterrupted, pulsatile blood flow. Intimal flaps not apparent during static conditions are easily imaged while avoiding the adverse effects of additional renal ischemia. In addition to excellent anatomic detail, important hemodynamic information is obtained from the spectral analysis of the Doppler-shifted signal proximal and distal to the imaged defect. Freedom from static projections, the absence of potentially nephrotoxic contrast material or additional ischemia, and the hemodynamic data provided by Doppler spectral analysis make duplex sonography a very attractive intraoperative method to assess both renovascular and mesenteric repairs.

Currently, we use a 10/5.0 mHz compact linear array probe with Doppler color flow designed specifically for intraoperative assessment. The probe is placed within a sterile sheath with a latex tip containing sterile gel. After the operative field is flooded with warm saline, B-scan images are first obtained in longitudinal projection. Care is taken to image the entire upper abdominal aorta and renal artery origins along the entire length of the repair. All defects seen in longitudinal projection are imaged in transverse projection to confirm their anatomic presence and to estimate associated luminal narrowing. Doppler samples are then obtained just proximal and distal to imaged lesions in longitudinal projection, determining their potential contribution to flow disturbance. Our criteria for major B-scan defects ($\geq$ 60% diameter-reducing stenosis or occlusion) has been validated in a canine model of graded renal artery stenosis and prospective clinical application (Table 18.3). In selecting major B-scan defects for immediate revision, we have observed 97% patency in 249 consecutive repairs with a 32 month median follow-up.

Combined Aortic and Renal Reconstruction: Results of Operation

Although simultaneous surgical management of aortic and renal artery disease causing hypertension is established as an appropriate procedure, the indication, risk, and benefit of such a procedure is debatable. To assess the management philosophy of combined repair described above, we reviewed 133 patients who had combined aortic and renovascular procedures at our center from 1/87 through 7/95.[3] Patients requiring extra-anatomic or ex vivo renal artery reconstruction, or repair combined with supraceliac, thoracic, thoracoabdominal, or extra-anatomic aortic repair were excluded, as were patients with ruptured aneurysms. These combined aortorenal procedures were compared with results from 182 consecutive patients who had isolated in situ repair for atherosclerotic renovascular disease and 562 patients who underwent isolated elective aortic reconstruction during this same period.

Ages in the "combined procedures" study group ranged from 37 to 86 years (mean: 62.5 years). There were 72 (54%) males and 61 (46%) females in the "combined group" and all patients had hypertension (range 140/90 to 300/185 mmHg; mean: 195 ± 37/103 ± 23 mmHg). Twenty-three patients had diabetes mellitus. Eighty patients (60%) had a history of heart disease. Previous coronary artery revascularization had been performed in 17 patients (12.8%). Renal insufficiency, defined as a serum creatinine of 1.3 mg/dl or greater, was present in 87 patients (65%). Forty-six patients had severe azotemia (i.e., serum creatinine of > 2.0 mg/dl) including seven patients who required hemodialysis before operation. Cerebrovascular disease, defined as the presence of transient ischemic attacks (TIAs), or a prior cerebrovascular accident (CVA) or carotid endarterectomy (CEA), was present in 21.8%. Peripheral vascular disease was present in 64.7%, and was defined as any patient with claudication due to infrainguinal occlusive disease, any prior lower extremity bypass or abnormal infrainguinal pulse examination. Only 26 patients were completely free of organ specific damage. The prevalence of clinical characteristics in the "renal surgery alone" and "aortic surgery alone" groups are compared to the combined group in Table 18.4.

Operative procedures performed in the 133 patients of the combined group are summarized in Table 18.5. Aortic procedures consisted of replacement of aortic aneurysm with either tube grafts in 38 patients or bifurcation grafts in 9 patients. Aortic occlusive disease was treated with aortofemoral bifurcation grafts in 86 patients. Renovascular procedures included renal artery thromboendarterectomy (53 vessels),

18

Table 18.3. Intraoperative doppler velocity criteria for renal artery repair

B-scan defect	Doppler criteria
Minor	
< 60% diameter-reducing stenosis	PSV from entire artery < 2.0 m/s
Major	
≥ 60% diameter-reducing stenosis	Focal PSV ≥ 2.0 m/s and distal turbulent waveform
Occlusion	No Doppler-shifted signal from renal artery B-scan image
Inadequate Study	Failure to obtain Doppler samples from entire arterial repair

Table 18.4. Prevalence of associated aortoiliac and organ-specific atherosclerosis as a function of operative procedure

	Number of patients (%)		
	Combined n=133	Isolated renal n=182	Isolated aorta n=269
Cardiac	80 (60.2%)	106 (58.2%)	
Angina	32	49	
MI	39	49	
CHF	28	40	
CABG/PTCA	17	19	
Cerebrovascular	29 (21.8%)	37 (20.3%)	
TIA	14	16	
CVA	18	25	
CEA	18	26	
Renal			
Creatinine		75 (41%)	
≥ 2.0 mg/dl	46 (35%)		
dialysis preop	7	13	1
Peripheral vascular disease	86 (64.7%)	130 (71.4%)	72 (26.8%)
AAA	47 (35.3%)	3 (1.6%)	210 (78%)
Aortic occlusive disease	86 (64.7%)	120 (65.9%)	59 (22%)
at least one manifestation present	107 (80.5%)	146 (80.2%)	151 (56.1%)

MI = myocardial infarction; CHF = congestive heart failure; CABG = coronary artery bypass graft; PTCA = percutaneous coronary angioplasty; TIA = transient ischemic attack; CVA = cerebrovascular accident; CEA = carotid endarterectomy. (Reprinted with permission from: Benjamin ME, Hansen KJ, Craven TE et al. Combined aortic and renal artery surgery: A contemporary experience. Ann Surg 1996; 233:555-567.)

Table 18.5. Summary of operative procedures for the 133 combined aortic and renal procedures

Procedure	Number	
Aortic Procedure		
Aneurysm Replacement		47
Tube Graft	38	
Y-Graft	9	
Occlusive Disease		86
Y-Graft	86	
Renal Procedure		
Aortorenal bypass		122
Vein Graft	81	
Synthetic Graft	41	
Thromboendarterectomy		53
Reimplantation		28
Contralateral Nephrectomy		11
Unilateral Repair	63 (47%)	
Bilateral Repair	70 (53%)	

(Reprinted with permission from: Benjamin ME, Hansen KJ, Craven TE et al. Combined aortic and renal artery surgery: A contemporary experience. Ann Surg 1996; 233:555-567.)

Table 18.6. Perioperative mortality compared by procedure

	No. of patients with perioperative death (%)	p-value
Combined		
n − 133	7 (5.3%)	—
Isolated renal alone		
n = 182	3 (1.6%)	p=0.145
Isolated aortic alone		
n = 269	2 (0.7%)	p=0.005

P-value is a comparison to the "combined" group
(Reprinted with permission from: Benjamin ME, Hansen KJ, Craven TE et al. Combined aortic and renal artery surgery: A contemporary experience. Ann Surg 1996; 233:555-567.)

reimplantation of 28 renal arteries, and 122 bypass grafts with either saphenous vein or synthetic material. Eleven patients had contralateral nephrectomy in conjunction with renal revascularization for unreconstructable disease to a nonfunctioning kidney. Overall, seventy patients had bilateral renal artery reconstruction. In all instances,

18

aortic grafts were attached, "end-to-end" to the proximal aorta. Similarly, most renal artery grafts were attached "end-to-end" to the distal renal artery.

Seven patients undergoing combined aortorenal procedures died within 30 days of operation producing an overall perioperative mortality of 5.3%. Four deaths occurred in patients undergoing combined repair involving aortic aneurysmal disease and 3 deaths occurred in patients undergoing the combined procedure for aortic occlusive disease. There were 4 deaths resulting from multisystem organ failure (MSOF), and 1 secondary to an acute perioperative MI. One patient died of a massive stroke and one from intraabdominal hemorrhage from a suture line disruption. Six of the seven operative deaths followed bilateral renal procedures. Table 18.6 compares the frequency of operative deaths in the combined group (5.3%) to the results in our "renal surgery alone" group (1.6%) and the "aortic procedure alone" group (0.7%). Although the "renal surgery alone" group had a lower operative mortality rate, only the "aortic procedure alone" group had a lower rate that reached statistical significance. Product-limit estimates of survival for each group are depicted in Figure 18.5.

Our operative mortality rate for "combined procedures" compares well with other contemporary experiences (Table 18.7). Review of the operative mortality rates and clinical characteristics in our current experience with "combined", "renal alone" and "aortic alone" groups suggest that operative risk is affected by the patient's stage of atherosclerosis and the complexity of the procedure. The prevalence of end organ damage such as azotemia and heart disease and the frequency of extrarenal atherosclerosis was greater in the "combined" and "renal alone" groups when compared to the "aortic alone" group. Although the operative mortality rate of the "combined" group is higher (5.3%) than that of the "renal alone" group (1.7%) the difference is not statistically significant. In contrast, it is statistically higher than the "aortic alone" operative death rate (0.7%). These two observations suggest that both stage of disease and magnitude of operation may affect operative risk.

Considering blood pressure and medication requirements at least 8 weeks after surgery among surgical survivors after combined repair, 2% were cured, 63% were considered improved, and 35% demonstrated no beneficial blood pressure response. Eighty-seven patients had preoperative ischemic nephropathy prior to combined repair. Based on at least a 20% change in serum creatinine occurring at least 4 weeks after surgery. Thirty-three percent were improved, 53% had no change, and 14% were worsened. The best renal function results were observed in the patient subgroup with the worst preoperative function—12 of 24 patients with a serum creatinine ≥ 3.0 mg/dl were improved. Compared with renal artery repair alone, there was no difference in renal function response, however, blood pressure benefit (cured/improved) was significantly different (65% versus 90%; p < 0.001).

Our experience suggests that contemporary results with combined aortic and renal procedures have improved compared to earlier reports. Nevertheless, the perioperative mortality for simultaneous reconstruction remains higher than repair of aortic disease alone. Moreover, a lower rate of favorable hypertension response was observed after combined procedures when compared with renal artery repair alone. These differences suggest that simultaneous aortic and renal artery repair

18

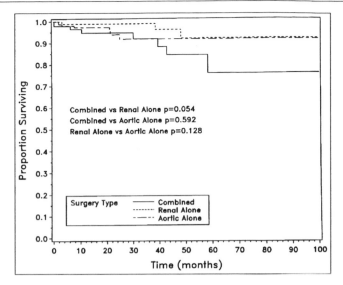

Fig. 18.5. Kaplan-Meier life table analysis of the three surgical procedure groups. (Reprinted with permission from Benjamin ME, Hansen KJ, Craven TE et al. Combined aortic and renal artery surgery: a contemporary experience. Ann Surg 1996; 233:555-567.)

Table 18.7. Comparison of major series of combined aortorenal reconstruction

Author	City	Year	Mean Age (yrs)	No. of Patients	Renal Repair Unilateral	Bilateral	HTN Response[*]	Periop Mortality
Perry	New York	1984	—	60	—	—	50%	5%
Sterpetti	Omaha	1986	61.8	39	64%	36%	65.6%	10%
Tarazi	Cleveland	1987	63	89	63%	37%	57.5%	10%
O'Mara	Jackson	1988	67	32	0	100%	90%	3%
Atnip	Hershey	1990	66	27	79	21	64%	10.3%
Allen	St. Louis	1993	66.3	102	83%	17%	86%	5%
McNeil	Mobile	1994	64	101	64%	36%	74%	1%
Huber	Gainesville	1995	—	56	—	—	—	8.9%
Brothers	Charleston	1995	63	70	59%	41%	—	16%
Cambria	Boston	1995	67.5	100	81.5%	18.5%	68%	6.5%

[*]Represents the total patients *cured and/or improved* of their hypertension.
(Adapted from: Benjamin ME, Hansen KJ, Craven TE et al. Combined aortic and renal artery surgery: A contemporary experience. Ann Surg 1996; 233:555-567.)

18

should only be performed for clinical indications. Based on these results and available natural history data, prophylactic repair of clinically silent disease is not appropriate.

Selected Readings

1. Dean RH, Kieffer RW, Smith BM et al. Renovascular hypertension: Anatomic and renal function changes during drug therapy. Arch of Surg 1981; 116:1408-1415.
    Reviews the natural history of 41 patients with atherosclerotic renovascular hypertension treated with medical therapy. Seventeen patients (41%) experienced deterioration of renal function despite acceptable blood pressure control in 15 patients.

2. Novick AC, Pohl MA, Schreiber M et al. Revascularization for preservation of renal function in patients with atherosclerotic renovascular disease. J Urol 1983; 129:907-912.
    Reviews the results of revascularization for preservation of renal function in 51 patients with atherosclerotic renovascular disease. With follow-up from 4-76 months, 67% of patients were improved, 27% unchanged and 6% worsened.

3. Benjamin ME, Hansen KJ, Craven TE et al. Combined aortic and renal artery surgery: A contemporary experience. Ann Surg 1996; 233:555-565.
    Examines the results of simultaneous aortic and renal artery repair in 133 hypertensive patients. These results were compared to those of 269 patients with aortic reconstruction alone and to 182 patients with renal artery reconstruction alone.

4. Hansen KJ, Deitch JA, Oskin TC. Renal Artery Repair: Consequence of Operative Failures. Ann Surg 1998; 227(5):678-690.
    Reviews blood pressure and renal function response in 20 patients after secondary renal revascularization following failed operative repair. These results were compared with those of 514 patients managed by primary renal revascularization.

5. Williamson WK, Abou-Zamzam AM, Moneta GL et al. Prophylactic repair of renal artery stenosis is not justified in patients who require infrarenal aortic reconstruction. J Vasc Surg 1998; 28:14-22.
    Reviews the natural history of asymptomatic renal artery stenosis in 200 patients who required aortic reconstruction. At late follow-up, patients with unrepaired high-grade asymptomatic renal artery stenosis experienced increased systolic blood pressure and required more antihypertensive medications but did not experience decreased long-term dialysis-free survival nor increased serum creatinine.

6. Hansen KJ, O'Neil EA, Reavis SW et al. Intraoperative duplex sonography during renal artery reconstruction. J Vasc Surg 1991; 14:364-374.
    Examines the results of intraoperative duplex sonography in 57 renal artery reconstructions. At a mean follow-up of 12.4 months, 48 of 49 repairs with normal B-scans or minor defects were patent and free of critical stenoses. Of 6 renal artery revisions prompted by major B-scan defects, 4 were patent while 1 stenosed and 1 occluded.

CHAPTER 19

Occlusive Disease of the Upper Abdominal Aorta

Rajabrata Sarkar and Ronald J. Stoney

Occlusive disease of the primary paired and unpaired branches of the upper abdominal aorta exhibits a wide variety of clinical presentations from silent but insidious renal failure to fatal intestinal infarction. This chapter will review the pathophysiology, clinical presentation, diagnosis and treatment of these conditions.

Acute Mesenteric Ischemia

Pathophysiology and Clinical Presentation

An embolus to the superior mesenteric artery is the most frequent (50%) cause of acute mesenteric ischemia. This sudden occlusion of a relatively normal superior mesenteric artery, usually originating in the heart, produces severe constant abdominal pain, vomiting and diarrhea as the bowel constricts with progressive ischemia. A leukocytosis then ensues. The triad of severe pain out of proportion to tenderness, elevated white blood cell count and both nausea and diarrhea should lead to the diagnosis embolic ischemia. Conditions associated with mesenteric emboli are longstanding atrial fibrillation, recent myocardial infarction and a history of other systemic arterial embolic events.

Acute mesenteric ischemia may also be due to thrombosis of severely diseased mesenteric vessels. This produces varied clinical presentations that often lead to delay in diagnosis and treatment. A history of abdominal angina is not uncommon. However, acute thrombosis is usually associated with a precipitating event, such as hypotension, dehydration or other systemic illness. Arterial occlusion occurs more slowly during thrombosis than with an embolus. Thus, symptoms of abdominal pain, nausea and vomiting often develop over the course of one to two days. If the thrombosis occurs after major surgery (e.g., post-CABG) or in a critically ill patient in the hospital, the symptoms and signs are frequently masked by postoperative pain, decreased level of consciousness and inability to communicate in the ventilated or obtunded patient. In such patients, the diagnosis is delayed and often only established at laparotomy performed for acute abdomen due to infarcted intestine.

Other less common causes of acute mesenteric ischemia are nonocclusive mesenteric ischemia and mesenteric venous thrombosis. Both of these presents with gradual onset of ischemic symptoms, although nonocclusive mesenteric ischemia due to decreased perfusion often occurs in the hypotensive ICU patient with myocardial dysfunction in whom symptoms are unreliable. Mesenteric venous

Aortic Surgery, edited by Jeffrey L. Ballard. ©2000 Landes Bioscience.

thrombosis is associated with systemic hypercoagulable states and is often confused with other gastrointestinal disorders due to the vague and initially nonspecific symptoms.

Diagnosis of Acute Mesenteric Ischemia

The diagnosis of acute mesenteric ischemia can be suspected on clinical grounds, particularly when the etiology is an acute embolus. An abdominal catastrophe in a patient with an underlying cardiac condition warrants immediate visceral angiography. Lateral aortography is necessary to visualize the visceral branch origins in profile, as they arise from the anterior surface of the upper abdominal aorta (Fig. 19.1). When symptoms are of greater duration, particularly when there are signs of peritonitis and acidosis, intestinal infarction is the likely diagnosis. In these patients immediate operation without aortography is not uncommon. However, aortography will delineate severity and distribution of visceral branch atherosclerosis (Fig. 19.2) which allows precise revascularization to restore vital blood flow to the remaining viable intestine.

There are no other reliable imaging modalities for the visceral circulation to unmistakably diagnose mesenteric occlusion. Magnetic resonance angiography (MRA) is used for screening for chronic mesenteric ischemia but cannot be used in ventilated patients and does not provide imaging detail to precisely visualize branches of the superior mesenteric artery. When clinical evidence suggests the possibility of acute mesenteric ischemia, early aortography to definitively exclude or confirm this life-threatening condition is essential.

Aortography is also a critical aid in the diagnosis and treatment of nonocclusive diseases of the mesenteric arteries. Nonocclusive mesenteric ischemia secondary to low cardiac output is an angiographic diagnosis. Treatment of nonocclusive mesenteric ischemia requires hemodynamic support for the heart to increase mesenteric blood flow and avoidance of agents that cause peripheral vasoconstriction. Selective infusion of vasodilators into the mesenteric arteries is frequently effective at relieving ischemia. Laparotomy is indicated if the patient develops signs of peritonitis or bowel infarction.

When the surgeon is presented with viable but severely ischemic bowel, revascularization before resection may improve the condition of the bowel and reduce the need for bowel resection. Although revascularization generally will not allow portions of the bowel that are already necrotic to become viable, adjacent ischemic segments will benefit. The diagnosis of acute mesenteric ischemia made at laparotomy raises the question of embolus versus thrombosis as the cause. A soft pliable pulsatile origin of the superior mesenteric artery suggests an embolus. Passage of an embolectomy catheter retrograde through a transverse arteriotomy confirms a disease-free origin and antegrade passage retrieves the embolus. Inability to pass the catheter proximally is indicative of significant visceral atherosclerotic occlusive disease and aortovisceral bypass or transaortic endarterectomy should be done as an immediate and definitive reconstruction of the diseased mesenteric circulation. Technical details of both these procedures are discussed below as treatment for chronic mesenteric ischemia.

19

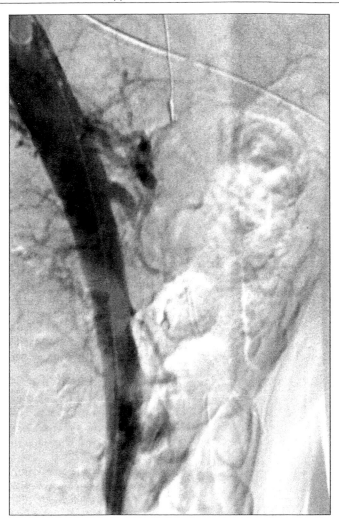

Fig. 19.1. Aortogram demonstrating embolus in superior mesenteric artery.

Treatment of Acute Mesenteric Ischemia

As soon as aortography confirms the diagnosis of mesenteric ischemia, an intravenous heparin bolus should be administered to prevent propagation of proximal and distal thrombus into vital collateral vessels. A heparin drip should also continue during surgery. A patient found to have mesenteric embolization (Fig. 19.1) should be maintained on postoperative heparin and then long-term anticoagulation to prevent further systemic embolic events.

19

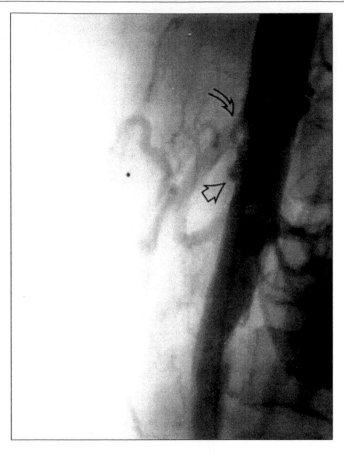

Fig. 19.2. Lateral aortogram of patient with acute thrombosis superimposed on chronic visceral occlusive disease. The occluded orifices of the celiac axis (small arrow) and superior mesenteric artery (large arrow) are indicated.

Management of acute mesenteric ischemia secondary to thrombosis of chronic mesenteric occlusive disease is considerably more challenging than a mesenteric embolus. If the preoperative angiogram demonstrates proximal occlusive disease of the celiac axis and superior mesenteric artery (Fig. 19.2), then transaortic visceral endarterectomy will remove the occlusive lesions and allow retrieval of the superimposed thrombus. Following visceral endarterectomy, the celiac axis and superior mesenteric artery are revascularized, and restoration of flow through collateral vessels to the minor visceral arteries make any additional revascularization unnecessary. Adherent distal thrombus may require an additional arteriotomy in either the celiac axis or the superior mesenteric artery to complete extraction of occlusive thrombus.

19

Transaortic endarterectomy does not require graft material. This is particularly advantageous in the face of intestinal infarction and gangrene, where contamination of the abdomen with bacteria increases the risk of infection of any prosthetic material. An alternative procedure in the patient with acute mesenteric ischemia secondary to thrombosis of a chronic occlusive lesion is reimplantation of the superior mesenteric artery into the aorta. This is done from an infracolic approach where the origin of the superior mesenteric artery is exposed at the base of the small bowel mesentery. The superior mesenteric artery is divided close to the aorta, an eversion endarterectomy is performed and the vessel is reimplanted into a soft site on the infrarenal aorta. This procedure avoids the hemodynamic stress of a supraceliac clamp in an unstable patient, but cannot address lesions of the celiac axis. Further, it is not recommended when the juxtarenal aorta has significant occlusive disease.

If the chronic atherosclerotic disease extends several centimeters into the superior mesenteric artery, then an antegrade aortovisceral bypass with prosthetic or autogenous conduits allows revascularization prior to resection of acutely ischemic bowel. The long-term patency of prosthetic aortovisceral grafts is superior to autogenous vein. [1] Consequently, aortovisceral vein grafts are recommended only in the unusual case of chronic occlusive disease too extensive for transaortic endarterectomy coupled with gross peritoneal contamination that would pose a risk of prosthetic graft infection.

After revascularization and restoration of pulses in distal mesenteric vessels, the intestine is allowed to perfuse for several minutes prior to its re-examination for viability. Limited ischemic infarction requires resection and reanastomosis. When diffuse ischemic changes persist after revascularization, resection and stomas are chosen so that further ischemia in residual bowel can be easily determined postoperatively by inspection of the mucosa by an endoscope passed through the stoma. The decision to return the patient for a second-look operation should be made at the time of the first operation and is particularly important if there has been extensive resection of the bowel. It is preferable to leave questionably viable bowel segments that may ultimately need to be resected at the second-look operation rather than to attempt a single definitive resection of all partially ischemic bowel which may result in the development of short bowel syndrome.

Treatment of mesenteric venous thrombosis consists of anticoagulation, resection of infarcted intestine and testing for a potential hypercoagulable condition. Management of nonocclusive mesenteric ischemia is largely nonoperative as discussed previously, except when advanced visceral infarction is the likely diagnosis.

Chronic Mesenteric Ischemia

Pathophysiology and Clinical Presentation

The patient with chronic mesenteric occlusive disease, unlike the typical older male patient with peripheral vascular occlusive disease, is often a woman in the fifth to sixth decade of life with a heavy smoking history. Two very characteristic symptoms are postprandial abdominal pain and profound weight loss. The abdominal angina of mesenteric ischemia is extremely reproducible in terms of both the onset

19

after meals and constant nature of the pain. Progressive atherosclerosis of the celiac axis and superior mesenteric artery is the usual lesion; unusual causes include fibromuscular dysplasia and radiation arteritis. Median arcuate ligament compression of the celiac axis alone rarely produces symptoms mimicking intestinal angina. Isolated stenoses of either vessel are compensated for by collaterals from the other mesenteric artery. Patients often have symptoms for months to years before the correct diagnosis is made with lateral aortography. It is not unusual for an exhaustive gastrointestinal evaluation, including upper and lower endoscopy, to have been performed one or more times before arriving at the correct diagnosis.

Diagnosis of Chronic Mesenteric Ischemia

The majority of these patients have undergone extensive workups for abdominal pain prior to establishment of the correct diagnosis. Cholecystectomy has often been performed to treat the postprandial pain. The best diagnostic study is contrast aortography, with lateral views necessary to visualize the orifices of the celiac and superior mesenteric arteries. Although duplex ultrasound and magnetic resonance angiography (MRA) are being used more widely for evaluation of the mesenteric circulation, these tests are not definitive. Aortography remains the most reliable and proven diagnostic modality for this diagnosis. This imaging modality also accurately defines extent of occlusive disease in the renal arteries and paravisceral and infrarenal aorta, which can alter the operative strategy used to treat the visceral atherosclerotic lesions.

Treatment of Chronic Mesenteric Ischemia

Treatment of chronic mesenteric occlusive disease centers on restoring blood flow to the celiac axis and superior mesenteric artery. Two basic strategies that have been shown to provide durable visceral reconstruction are antegrade aortovisceral bypass and transaortic thromboendarterectomy of the visceral vessels. For both techniques, a left-to-right medial visceral rotation provides unrestricted exposure of the supraceliac aorta (Fig. 19.3). We prefer the use of the Omni-Tract Self Retaining Retractor System (Omni-Tract Surgical-Minnesota Scientific, Minneapolis, MN) to completely free the first assistant.

For transaortic endarterectomy, following medial visceral rotation the dense neural tissue overlying the upper abdominal aorta is removed. The celiac axis and superior mesenteric artery are exposed circumferentially from the aorta to beyond palpable and angiographic evidence of disease. The aorta is clamped above the celiac axis and usually below the renal arteries and the four major visceral branches and posterior paired lumbar arteries are clamped to control back bleeding. A curvilinear incision is then made in the aorta which surrounds the orifices of the celiac axis and superior mesenteric artery (Fig. 19.4). Endarterectomy of the ventral aspect of the upper abdominal aorta and the visceral branches proceeds using an oscillating Halle dural elevator (Omni-Tract Surgical-Minnesota Scientific, Minneapolis, MN). The ventral aortic plaque is first separated from the underlying media and then the individual aortic branches are prolapsed toward the aortic lumen, while the elevator or extraction endarterectomy clamp continues the circumferential separation plane until

19

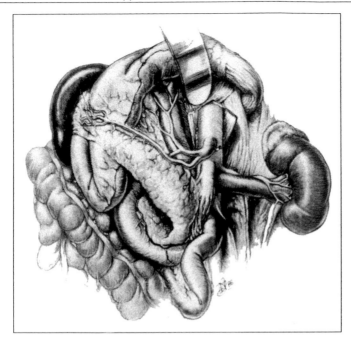

Fig. 19.3. Exposure of the upper abdominal aorta following medial visceral rotation. The Omni-Tract retractor system is in place.

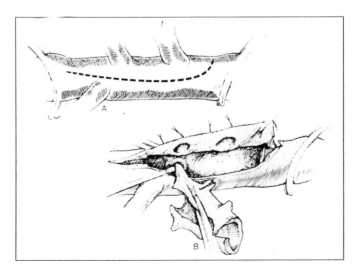

Fig. 19.4. Illustration of the position of the aortotomy and technique of combined transaortic visceral and renal endarterectomy.

19

the disease feathers and terminates. At this point, the origin plaque is removed. Backbleeding is observed from each vessel and the aortotomy is closed and blood flow restored.

Transaortic visceral endarterectomy is technically challenging and is best used for disease that is limited to the proximal several centimeters of these visceral vessels. Critical technical points in the execution of transaortic visceral endarterectomy include circumferential dissection of the vessels, establishment of the correct endarterectomy plane in the deep medial layer of the aortic wall and tapered termination of the endarterectomy under direct vision. Intraoperative duplex ultrasonography is used to confirm adequate flow and to exclude technical problems such as intimal flaps or residual stenosis. Should the superior mesenteric artery be thrombosed, distal propagation of thrombus and underlying plaque may occasionally extend beyond the technique of extraction endarterectomy through the aorta. In these cases following removal of the aortic and orifice lesions, the aortotomy is closed and blood flow restored, except in the clamped superior mesenteric artery. An additional longitudinal arteriotomy is made in the superior mesenteric artery at the termination of the disease and superimposed thrombus. The thromboendarterectomy is completed in an open manner with extraction of all distal thrombus. The superior mesenteric artery is then closed with a patch angioplasty technique.

Antegrade aortovisceral bypass offers a brief period of total or partial supraceliac occlusion to attach the proximal graft (Fig. 19.5). The supraceliac aorta is preferred for grafting since it is spared from significant atherosclerosis which continues in long-term follow-up. The short course of the antegrade prosthetic graft avoids kinking and buckling often seen with retrograde grafts originating from the infrarenal aorta. We prefer prosthetic conduits to autogenous vein for aortovisceral revascularization in elective circumstances and bifurcated grafts (12 by 6 mm or 14 by 7 mm) as opposed to any other configuration. The bifurcated graft avoids the necessity of a graft-to-graft anastomosis and the graft limbs are sewn end-to-end to the celiac axis and superior mesenteric artery beyond the occlusive disease. If possible, we revascularize both the celiac axis and the superior mesenteric artery as our long-term results demonstrate[2] that recurrent visceral ischemia occurs more commonly when visceral revascularization was limited to a single visceral branch.

For all visceral reconstructions, an angiogram is obtained prior to discharge from the hospital to document the anatomy of the revascularization. A contrast angiogram is best but magnetic resonance angiography may be indicated when impaired renal function contraindicates nephrotoxic contrast. This serves as a baseline for long-term follow-up should the patient develop recurrent visceral ischemic symptoms.

Renal Artery Occlusive Disease

Pathophysiology and Clinical Presentation

Occlusive disease of the renal arteries is most commonly due to pararenal aortic atherosclerotic plaque extending into the renal artery orifice. These lesions are often bilateral, and usually do not involve more than the proximal third of the vessel. Renal artery stenosis is particularly prevalent in older male patients with known risk

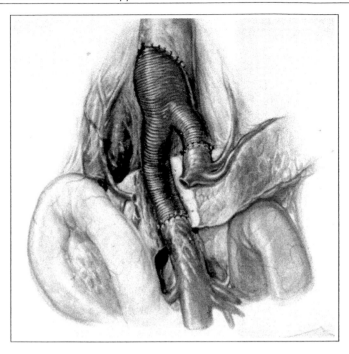

Fig. 19.5. A bifurcated antegrade aortovisceral bypass graft to the celiac axis and superior mesenteric artery. The retropancreatic position of the limb to the superior mesenteric artery is shown by the cut-away illustration of the pancreas.

factors for atherosclerosis. Most patients will have evidence of atherosclerotic occlusive disease in other vascular beds. Less common causes of renal artery occlusive disease include fibromuscular dysplasia in younger female patients and congenital or developmental stenoses in children and adolescents. These nonatherosclerotic lesions typically involve the middle and distal thirds of the main renal artery and can extend into primary and secondary renal artery branches.

Regardless of the etiology of renal artery occlusive disease, these patients are at risk to develop renovascular hypertension. This is the renin-mediated response to blood flow and pressure decrease distal to the lesion causing the juxtaglomerular apparatus of the affected kidney to release renin. Renovascular hypertension can be difficult to diagnose in older patients with generalized atherosclerosis because essential hypertension (with no defined cause of the elevated blood pressure) is quite common in this patient population. Clinical features that suggest renovascular hypertension include hypertension unresponsive to antihypertensive medications, young age or rapid onset of hypertension, lack of family history of hypertension and the presence of an abdominal bruit. Angiotensin converting enzyme (ACE) inhibitors, which inhibit the renin-angiotensin pathway, can often control renovascular hypertension but may lead to progressive renal failure particularly in patients with bilateral severe renal artery occlusive disease. Patients with severe bilateral renal artery stenosis may present with recurrent episodes of pulmonary edema, as the bilateral disease limits their ability to clear the excess plasma volume associated with their hypertension.[3] An asymptomatic but progressive decline in renal function (azotemia) in an adult patient without a history of renal parenchymal disease should alert one to the possibility of worsening bilateral renal artery occlusive disease and imaging of the renal arteries should be performed.

Diagnosis of Renal Artery Occlusive Disease

Any patient suspected of having renovascular hypertension should undergo renal artery imaging, as this is the only reliable means of establishing the presence of renal artery occlusive disease. Noninvasive studies can be helpful in suggesting the diagnosis, but confirmatory angiography is required prior to an intervention. Captopril nuclear medicine renal scans are useful in localizing renovascular hypertension to one kidney and may be helpful in more than one-half of patients in whom bilateral atherosclerotic or fibromuscular lesions are present. Duplex ultrasonography of the renal arteries requires considerable technical experience and expertise and cannot satisfactorily exclude the diagnosis. MRA of the abdominal aortic branch vessels has excellent resolution and can evaluate renal artery anatomy without radiation or contrast material. However, MRA remains imprecise in evaluating segmental stenosis or subtle patterns of disease. Therefore any patient suspected of having renovascular hypertension with an equivocal MRA should have a confirmatory contrast angiogram. This is particularly true in children, young adults and middle-aged patients, where developmental stenoses and fibromuscular disease often have a focal segmental distribution.

When a unilateral renal artery lesion has been identified, renal vein renin determination may be used to confirm the physiological significance of the lesion. While this may be helpful with an equivocal stenosis, many factors can cause erroneous results. These include the use of antihypertensive medications, patient salt intake, technical problems with catheter sampling and patient posture, as well as unreliability in the presence of bilateral disease. Therefore we rarely employ renal vein renin levels in determining the need for revascularization of renal artery occlusive disease. The presence of collateral vessels on a contrast angiogram, or of spin dephasing on MRA due to turbulent flow, suggest a hemodynamically significant lesion that is contributing to renovascular hypertension. A reduction in renal length of greater than 10% on the side of the lesion suggests ischemic nephropathy of long-standing duration and should prompt revascularization. This 10% loss of length calculates to a 1/3 volume loss of the ischemic kidney.[4]

Treatment of Renal Artery Occlusive Disease

Surgical revascularization has become the primary treatment modality for renal artery occlusive disease and has proven to provide safe and durable relief from renovascular hypertension and progressive ischemic nephropathy. Two newer interventions have altered the management of renovascular hypertension. The first, improved antihypertensive management, centers around the use of ACE inhibitors, which can effectively control the blood pressure in most patients with renovascular hypertension. The second is the evolving success of balloon angioplasty and stenting in the revascularization of atherosclerotic renal artery lesions. We believe both of these treatments complement rather than replace surgical management and extend the spectrum of disease that can be effectively managed. Although antihypertensive medications may effectively reduce blood pressure in renovascular hypertension, they do not prevent progression of the lesion and resulting ischemic nephropathy. Hunt and Strong compared medical and surgical management of renovascular hypertension and found that medical management had poorer overall survival, greater late incidence of renal failure and progression of lesions to occlusion.[5] Medical management of renovascular hypertension in patients with documented bilateral renal artery lesions, particularly when ACE inhibitors are required for pressure control, is associated with considerable risk of silent progression to renal failure. Thus, patients with renovascular hypertension most of whom have a reasonable life expectancy should be considered for renal revascularization to remove the disease and its hypertensive effects rather than blood pressure control alone.

Concomitant renal artery stenting has extended the use of balloon angioplasty in the treatment of orificial atherosclerotic lesions. Many authors have noted satisfactory technical success and relief of hypertension. It is difficult to identify comparable patient populations undergoing renal artery angioplasty and surgical revascularization, because patients with significantly less complicated renal artery lesions, most of whom would not warrant surgical revascularization, are often treated with angioplasty.[6] The durability of renal artery revascularization is well documented.[7] in most series for at least 5 years or more,[7] and comparable durability with angioplasty and stenting is unknown at this time. The use of metallic stents results in an inflammatory reaction in the renal artery and subsequent neointimal hyperplasia, causing a significant incidence of restenosis at the short (1-2 year) follow-up period. We consider using angioplasty and stenting for patients with limited life expectancy, or high operative risk.

Techniques of renal revascularization include transaortic renal endarterectomy, aortorenal bypass, various extra-anatomic bypass techniques and renal artery reimplantation. Aortorenal bypass with a saphenous vein graft originating from the infrarenal aorta was the first widely used method of renal revascularization. This technique cannot be used when significant infrarenal occlusive or aneurysmal disease is present, but is particularly useful in the presence of occlusive disease extending out to the renal hilum. The majority of atherosclerotic lesions are limited to the orifices and proximal several centimeters of the renal artery and are thus amenable to transaortic endarterectomy. This was first used at our institution in 1952 and has been our continued preference for proximal atherosclerosis of the renal arteries. This can be performed in conjunction with endarterectomy of the visceral branches (as described above), or with endarterectomy or replacement of the infrarenal aorta for either occlusive or aneurysmal disease.

The surgical approach to transaortic renal endarterectomy depends on the need for an associated mesenteric endarterectomy or infrarenal graft placement. For combined aortovisceral and renal endarterectomy left-to-right medial visceral rotation,

19

as described previously, provides excellent surgical exposure. The endarterectomy is extended from above the celiac axis to below the renal arteries (Fig. 19.4). If renal endarterectomy is performed alone or combined with reconstruction of the infrarenal aorta (without mesenteric endarterectomy) then an infracolic approach to the aorta is preferred. The inferior border of the pancreas is mobilized and gently retracted. The pararenal aorta and renal arteries are completely mobilized circumferentially and if indicated, the infrarenal aorta is exposed for reconstruction. The aorta is clamped either above the superior mesenteric artery or above the renal arteries. The proximal site depends on whether the clamp will impair access to the renal orifices.

The aorta is transected just inferior to the renal arteries when infrarenal aortic grafting is planned.[8] Transaortic endarterectomy through the transected aorta is facilitated by an oscillating endarterectomy device and extraction endarterectomy clamps. After establishing the proper medial plane a continuous separation of the circumferential aortic plaque is first achieved and the proximal end point is transected below the inferior border of the proximal clamp or orifice of the superior mesenteric artery. Now, the endarterectomy specimen is attached only by the projecting renal artery lesions. These lesions are removed by prolapsing the mobilized renal artery into the aortic lumen for direct visual inspection of the end points. If this is not possible, the extraction clamp is designed for more distal nonvisualized endpoints. Following renal artery back bleeding and flushing, the aortic graft is attached to the endarterectomized infrarenal aorta and declamping to the proximal graft ensures return of renal and mesenteric blood flow.

If reconstruction of the infrarenal aorta is not planned, the aorta is opened through an anterior midline aortotomy carried to the left above the orifice of the left renal artery. The transaortic endarterectomy proceeds as described through the transected aorta, except the visibility and exposure of the interior of the pararenal aorta is greater and the procedure is technically less demanding.

Extra-anatomic bypass of renal artery occlusive disease has usually been reserved for patients whose medical condition would not allow an aortic-based procedure. However improved perioperative care of patients with significant comorbidity allow safe conduct of aortic repair in most circumstances. Thus, there are infrequent indications for this technique today, but the durability of these extra-anatomic reconstructions has been documented by Reilly and colleagues.[9] Vein grafts are used for extra-anatomic bypass to the right kidney, and these typically originate from the common hepatic artery. The splenic artery can usually be divided distally and anastomosed end-to-end to the transected left renal artery. If the splenic artery is both calcified and tortuous, it is unsuitable for a direct renal graft but a vein graft can be used to bypass from the proximal splenic artery to the left renal artery. Rarely, the iliac vessels are used as an origin for prosthetic bypass to either renal artery because there is a high incidence of occlusive disease in the aorta that would be proximal to the graft.

Reimplantation of the renal artery into the aorta is useful for repairing developmental renal artery stenosis seen in children.[10] The anastomosis employs interrupted sutures to allow for growth of the new renal artery at its aortic orifice. The saphenous vein, which becomes aneurysmal in pediatric patients, is avoided for renal

19

reconstruction. Renal artery lesions which extend into branch vessels can be safely repaired with the ex vivo technique in which the entire kidney is removed from the patient and perfused to allow careful and meticulous repair of small renal artery branches using branched internal iliac artery autografts.[7] Regardless of the surgical technique used, excellent long-term results have been achieved with renal revascularization and this remains the standard against which new treatment modalities should be compared.

Acknowledgment

This work was supported by a grant from the Pacific Vascular Research Foundation to Dr. Sarkar.

Selected Readings

1. Cunningham CG, Reilly LM, Rapp JH et al. Chronic visceral ischemia: Three decades of progress. Ann Surg 1991; 214:276.
   This report compares outcomes in chronic visceral ischemia treated with either transaortic visceral endarterectomy or antegrade aortovisceral bypass. Complications, outcomes and durability of each of these procedures are similar in this report.

2. Schneider DB, Schneider PA, Reilly LM et al. Reoperation for recurrent chronic visceral ischemia. J Vasc Surg 1998; 27:286.
   This report focuses on the subset of patients with recurrent visceral ischemia after previous visceral revascularization. The need for an aggressive surgical approach to this difficult problem, the techniques used in the face of a prior failed reconstruction and the durability and need for subsequent procedures are well described.

3. Messina LM, Zelenock GB, Yao KA et al. Renal revascularization for recurrent pulmonary edema in patients with poorly controlled hypertension and renal insufficiency: a distinct subgroup of patients with arteriosclerotic renal artery occlusive disease. J Vasc Surg 1992; 15:73.
   This paper focuses on patients with bilateral renal artery occlusive disease who have recurrent episodes of pulmonary edema secondary to volume overload. These episodes are mistaken as cardiac failure and consequently delay surgery, but it is surgical revascularization that resolves the pulmonary edema.

4. Newman VS, Dean RH. Ischemic nephropathy as an indication for renal artery reconstruction in renovascular hypertension. Corr Opin Gen Surg 1994; 272-6.
   This review discusses renal revascularization when done for preservation of renal function rather than for treatment of renovascular hypertension. Written by the group that has defined the clinical and radiological criteria for this indication, this paper focuses on appropriately selecting patients for surgical intervention.

5. Hunt JC, Strong CG. Renovascular hypertension. Mechanisms, natural history and treatment. Am J Cardiol 1973; 32:56.
   An excellent long-term comparison of medical and surgical management of renovascular hypertension. Its current applicability is limited by the era of the study, since which time both medical and surgical management have markedly improved.

6. Rodriguez-Lopez JA, Werner A, Ray LI et al. Renal artery stenosis treated with stent deployment: Indications, technique, and outcome for 108 patients. J Vasc Surg 1999; 29:617.
   A recent report of a large series of patients treated with balloon angioplasty and stenting for renal artery occlusive disease. This experience demonstrates the safety of this procedure.

19

However, since many patients were on single drug antihypertensive therapy the indications for percutaneous therapy are questionable.

7. Murray SP, Kent C, Salvatierra O et al. Complex branch renovascular disease: management options and late results. J Vasc Surg 1994; 20:338.

   This paper describes a very large series of patients with complex disease of the branch renal arteries managed with a variety of techniques. It also is representative of the excellent follow-up (mean 7 years) noted in many surgical series of renal artery revascularization.

8. Stoney RJ, Messina LM, Goldstone J et al. Renal endarterectomy through the transected aorta: a new technique for combined aortorenal atherosclerosis—a preliminary report. J Vasc Surg 1989; 9:224.

   This report documents the safety and efficacy of transaortic renal endarterectomy done through the orifice of the transected infrarenal aorta. This procedure is particularly applicable for patients with renal artery occlusive disease who also need reconstruction of the infrarenal aorta.

9. Reilly JM, Rubin BG, Thompson RW et al. Long-term effectiveness of extra-anatomic renal artery revascularization. J Vasc Surg 1994; 116:784.

   A long-term follow-up of patients treated with a variety of extra-anatomic bypass procedures for renal artery occlusive disease. This study documents both clinical and angiographic durability of these alternative procedures.

10. Stanley JC, Zelenock GB, Messina LM et al. Pediatric renovascular hypertension: a thirty-year experience of operative treatment. J Vasc Surg 1995; 21:212.

    This report describes the evolution of surgical techniques for pediatric renovascular hypertension and thus documents the technical challenges encountered over time, particularly with aneurysmal changes in pediatric saphenous vein grafts.

CHAPTER 20

Surgical Treatment of Infected Aortic Aneurysms

William J. Quiñones-Baldrich

In 1885 Sir William Osler[1] presented a comprehensive analysis of infected aneurysms and coined the term mycotic aneurysm specifically to refer to patients who presented with infected aneurysms secondary to endocarditis. Since then, however, the term has been used to refer to infected aneurysms regardless of pathogenesis. The fact that other sources of infection could also cause infection in the arterial wall was suggested by Stangel and Wolfed in 1923,[2] describing 30 of 213 patients in whom there was no evidence of bacterial endocarditis and yet they demonstrated infected aneurysms. The potential for bacteremia leading to an infected aneurysm was proposed. In essence arterial wall infection can be caused by bacteremia of any source. It tends to affect more commonly segments of an artery with atherosclerosis or a congenital abnormality. Whether or not an aneurysm forms will depend on the clinical course and the institution of effective antibiotic therapy. When the infection is not treated promptly, continued degeneration of the wall leads to pseudoaneurysm formation and thus the presentation of an infected and/or mycotic aneurysm. Existing aneurysms can also become infected usually in the infrarenal aorta given the higher incidence of aneurysms in that location. Contiguous infection eroding into the aorta can also occur, most often associated with osteomyelitis and/or vertebral or retroperitoneal infection, and present as a mycotic aneurysm. Lastly, posttraumatic infected false aneurysms usually occur secondary to drug abuse or iatrogenic causes, most commonly seen in the femoral, carotid and brachial artery.

In this chapter the term mycotic aneurysm refers to an aneurysm that has formed secondary to infection either from bacterial endocarditis and/or bacteremia of any source. This discussion will specifically exclude bacterial infection with aneurysm formation secondary to primary aortoenteric fistula and/or prosthetic graft infection.

Incidence

Mycotic aneurysms are most common in the femoral artery usually secondary to drug abuse and/or iatrogenic causes. Mycotic aneurysms of the abdominal aorta represent approximately 34% of all reported cases,[3] the second most common site. An incidence of 0.85% has been reported in a review of 2,585 patients with abdominal aortic aneurysms.[4] Interestingly, 50% of these mycotic aneurysms were observed in the perivisceral or thoracoabdominal region.[5] In our experience, six of 12 patients with rupture of the perivisceral aorta proved to have a mycotic aneurysm.[6] Thus, involvement of the perivisceral aorta with a contained rupture should alert the

---

Aortic Surgery, edited by Jeffrey L. Ballard. ©2000 Landes Bioscience.

clinician that a mycotic process may be evolving. Only 31 cases of mycotic periviseceral thoracoabdominal aneurysm had been reported up to 1992.[5] In contrast, it is estimated that there are 5.3 thoracoabdominal aneurysms per 100,000 person years and 21.8 abdominal aortic aneurysms per 100,000 person years.[8]

Bacteriology

The bacteriology of mycotic aortic aneurysms has changed over the years. Although initially the predominant organisms were nonhemolytic *Streptococci, Pneumococci* and *Staphylococci*, recent reviews since 1965 has suggested that *Staphylococcus aureus, Streptococcus* and *Salmonella* are the predominant organisms.[3,5] In 1984 Brown[3] reported that *Staphylococcus aureus* and various streptococcal species were found in 37% of infected aneurysms when all types were considered. Gram negative organisms have been reported with increasing frequency. Of particular importance is Salmonella which appears to have a predilection for the arterial wall, particularly when atherosclerotic, and accounts for most cases of microbacterial arteritis. Patients with positive cultures for Salmonella from an infected aneurysm should also have their gallbladder examined as many of them are carriers and thus cholecystectomy should be considered part of the management. Other gram-negative organisms have been reported in much lower incidence including *Pseudomonas, Escherichia coli, Proteus, Serratia, Enterobacter, Neisseria, Enterococcus* and *Bacteroides*. The latter is more commonly seen in immunosuppressed patients. Fungal infection has also been reported including Candida species. Importantly, up to 25% of patients will have a negative culture in spite of the presence of all other characteristics suggestive of mycotic process.[3] The absence of a positive culture should not deter the clinician from establishing the diagnosis.

Diagnosis

The clinical presentation of patients with mycotic aortic aneurysms is different than those patients presenting with contained rupture of an atherosclerotic aneurysm. In our experience,[5] we noted that all patients with ruptured atherosclerotic aneurysm presented with symptoms of less than 24 hours duration. In contrast, all patients in the mycotic group had symptoms that ranged between two to six weeks with a mean of 3.5 weeks. History of sepsis was absent in all patients presenting with atherosclerotic aortic rupture whereas two-thirds of patients with mycotic aneurysms had history of sepsis. Abdominal, chest and/or back pain was present in all patients regardless of etiology. The age at presentation was similar with a mean age of 73 years in the atherosclerotic group and 74 years in the mycotic group. There were no differences noted in the incidence of cigarette smoking, hypertension or the presence of chronic obstructive pulmonary disease. Coronary artery disease was present in both groups in similar frequency. Previous abdominal aortic aneurysm repair was also present in 50% of the atherosclerotic group and 30% of the mycotic group.

The typical patient with an infected aneurysm presents with no antecedent history of arterial injury, is elderly and usually within the atherosclerotic population. The patient may present with fever of unknown origin. The most common clinical presentation is abdominal pain which occurs in most patients. Fever and leukocytosis can be seen in two-thirds of patients, with positive blood cultures and a palpable abdominal mass occurring in about 50% of patients.[5]

Physical findings may include a tender palpable pulsatile mass. Some patients may present with other signs suggestive of septic emboli such as petechial, occasionally purulent or erythematous lesions in the lower extremities. The presence of a septic foci should be sought such as bacterial endocarditis, pyelonephritis, osteomyelitis, pneumonia or an intraabdominal source of infection.

CT scan remains one of the more important diagnostic studies in the workup of a patient with a suspected mycotic aneurysm. The presence of a contained rupture in the perivisceral and infrarenal aorta with an adjacent normal segment of aorta, particularly in the absence of calcification, is highly suggestive of a mycotic process (Fig. 20.1). On arteriography mycotic aneurysms tend to be saccular whereas atherosclerotic processes tend to be diffuse (Fig. 20.2). Angiography should be included as part of the workup as it will help plan operative repair. The presence of a normal aorta above and below the area of aneurysmal degeneration supports the diagnosis of a mycotic process. This combined with the clinical presentation should give the clinician a high index of suspicion and thus help in planning therapy.

Other imaging modalities include ultrasound which may help establish the presence of an aneurysmal process but will not be helpful in differentiating between a mycotic and an atherosclerotic process. Although radionuclide white blood cell scans can be helpful when positive in the area of the aneurysm, a negative white cell scan does not exclude the diagnosis of a mycotic process.[9]

Imaging studies are aimed at establishing the location of the process with important distinctions between the thoracic, visceral and infrarenal aorta. In addition they may assist in establishing the etiology of the infection, identifying a source of sepsis. Bone erosion of the vertebral bodies in the presence of a diffuse aortic aneurysm perhaps with a contained chronic rupture is suggestive of an infected preexisting atherosclerotic aneurysm (Fig. 20.3). On the other hand bony changes consistent with osteomyelitis in the presence of a contained chronic saccular rupture with normal adjacent aorta is suggestive of a mycotic process secondary to primary bone infection.

Management

Proper management of a mycotic aortic aneurysm includes adequate preoperative preparation with control of overwhelming sepsis if present using broad-spectrum antibiotics, adequate hydration and stabilization of vital signs. On occasion, the process may lead to a cardiac arrest in which case immediate resuscitation and operation will be necessary. In the majority of cases, however, patients present with a contained rupture and, therefore, there is enough time to adequately prepare the patient for major surgical intervention.

Preoperative imaging should establish the proximal and distal extent of the mycotic process with important differences noted in the thoracic, visceral and infrarenal location. General principles at operation include preparatory extra-anatomic bypass particularly for infrarenal mycotic aneurysms. Other important principles include

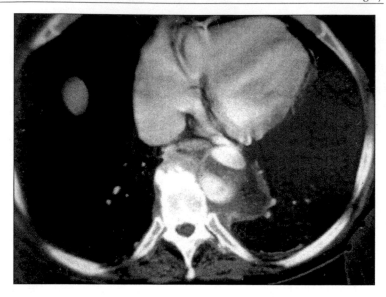

Fig. 20.1. CT scan of the lower descending thoracic aorta region showing a contained rupture of a mycotic aneurysm. Note the absence of calcification in the aortic wall which supports the diagnosis of mycotic aneurysm.

proximal and distal control above and below the contained rupture, resection and debridement of the aneurysm particularly if in-line replacement is anticipated. Gram stain and cultures should be obtained understanding that a negative culture does not exclude the diagnosis of a mycotic aneurysm. Revascularization should be extra-anatomic if feasible or in situ if necessary.

Mycotic aneurysms limited to the descending thoracic aorta can be approached through a left thoracotomy through the fifth intercostal space. The patient should be positioned however in a right semilateral decubitus with the hips flattened so that if extension into the retroperitoneum is necessary, it can be handled by extension of the incision, exposing the infradiaphragmatic aorta in the retroperitoneum.

Extra-anatomic bypass can be used for revascularization in the management of a descending thoracic mycotic aneurysm. A right axillofemoral bypass would be preferable so that a left thoracotomy can be carried out without the encumbrance of a bypass graft. Care must be taken during positioning of the patient so that the axillofemoral reconstruction on the right side is not compressed during the operation. Bypass must be performed prior to resection of the mycotic process, otherwise the ischemia time to the kidneys, gastrointestinal organs and lower extremities would be intolerable. In addition, blood flow through an extra-anatomic bypass may be somewhat limited and the patient may experience renovascular hypertension in the postoperative period. In the author's opinion, in-line replacement is the preferred method for revascularization following resection of a descending thoracic mycotic

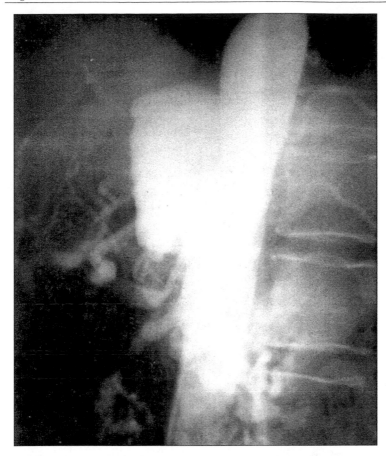

Fig. 20.2. Aortogram of patient with CT scan seen in Figure 20.1. Note normal proximal and distal aorta without calcification or aneurysmal changes. These findings on aortography support the diagnosis of a mycotic process.

aneurysm. It is imperative that the area of the aneurysm be thoroughly debrided and that no purulence be present prior to in-line replacement. In the presence of a mycotic process, reimplantation of intercostals in this region is not advisable, as it would likely include infected aortic tissue increasing the incidence of recurrent infection. Thus the patient should be advised as to the possibility of paraplegia following this intervention. Similarly, utilization of adjunctive procedures to lower the incidence of paraplegia such as spinal fluid drainage should be utilized. On occasion we have routed a descending thoracic graft around the infected aortic bed under a pleural flap to avoid direct apposition of the graft with the infected area (Fig. 20.4).

Mycotic aneurysms involving the visceral segment of the abdominal aorta may be approached through an 11th rib retroperitoneal incision with visceral rotation. If

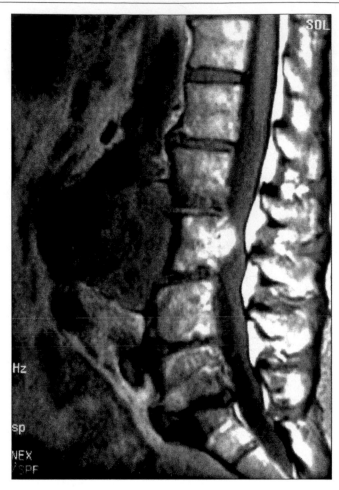

Fig. 20.3. Contained infrarenal abdominal aortic aneurysm with bony erosion. This should raise the suspicion of a secondarily infected abdominal aortic aneurysm.

the proximal process of the aneurysm is much above the celiac takeoff however, a thoracoretroperitoneal incision with division of the diaphragm is preferred so that adequate proximal control can be obtained. In this instance a seventh or eighth interspace incision will provide adequate exposure of the proximal segment of the process. Proximal and distal control should be obtained and the location of the takeoff of at least one of the visceral branches should be noted so that one can anticipate the location of the visceral vessels. In-line replacement is indicated as extra-anatomic revascularization of this process would involve individual bypasses to each one of the visceral branches and thus the utilization of prosthetic material cannot be avoided. We have utilized in-line replacement after wide debridement

20

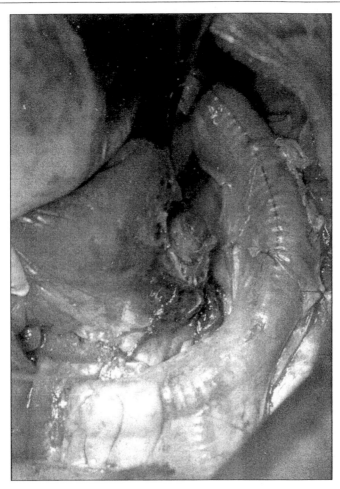

Fig. 20.4. Proximal descending to distal descending aortic reconstruction in a patient with a mid-descending thoracic mycotic aneurysm. Note area of infected aorta which has been debrided and pleural flap coverage of prosthetic graft.

and irrigation of the area with excellent results. The celiac, superior mesenteric and right renal arteries are usually reimplanted in a single patch with the left renal reimplanted as a separate Carrel patch or with a short prosthetic bypass. The use of a patch to close the aortic defect if it is away from the takeoff of the visceral vessels has been reported and we have utilized it successfully one time in a patient who suffered a cardiac arrest upon induction. In that instance an expeditious repair was most important. That patient has now been followed for three years without development of pseudoaneurysm and/or recurrent sepsis. When this method is chosen, wide debridement of the aortic wall should be performed to avoid residual infected aortic tissue.

Management of mycotic aneurysms of the infrarenal aorta follows the same principles as with the visceral and descending thoracic aorta. Extra-anatomic bypass however is an excellent alternative and is preferred by most clinicians if the diagnosis has been established prior to laparotomy. In this instance, an axillobifemoral bypass is performed prior to laparotomy. At laparotomy proximal and distal control with ligation of the infrarenal aorta and the aortic bifurcation is done to complete the procedure. It is extremely important that the aortic stump be thoroughly debrided in the infrarenal location as blowout is a recognized and not infrequent complication of this mode of treatment. In-line replacement can be performed if there is no purulence in the aortic bed and wide debridement can be carried out. If the diagnosis is not established preoperatively, it is the author's preference to proceed with in-line replacement unless findings at operation would dictate otherwise. These would include significant purulence in the aortic bed, inability to debride surrounding tissues properly or the known presence of a gram-negative necrotizing organism, particularly Pseudomonas. If extra-anatomic bypass is to be performed after aortic aneurysm resection, it is important to move expeditiously, as the incidence of lower extremity reperfusion injury is significant given the prolonged ischemia time.

All the alternatives for revascularization during the management of a mycotic aneurysm include the use of cryopreserved aortic homografts or autologous tissue, particularly the superficial femoral vein. The experience with these alternatives is limited and thus long-term results are still uncertain. Particularly with the use of homografts, these have been noted to be relatively resistant to infection and their use has been associated with a decreased incidence of complications and eradication of the infectious process.[10]

Postoperative Care

Postoperative management of patients following mycotic aneurysm resection and revascularization is similar to any other aortic procedure with the exception that antibiotic therapy appropriate for the organisms cultured (if positive) should be continued for at least six weeks. In addition, eradication of the septic foci if present is of paramount importance. If the cultures have been negative, then coverage for gram positive organisms should be carried out for a minimum of six weeks. We have preferred to maintain these patients on suppressive doses of appropriate antibiotics for life. These are usually maintained at a lower than therapeutic dose on a daily basis.

Continued sepsis in the postoperative period should mandate thorough evaluation, particularly with CT scan, to identify the source of sepsis. Most commonly it is either the original source or the aortic bed. When it occurs in the presence of in-line replacement, alternative revascularization should be sought with removal of the prosthetic graft. If this is not feasible, exploration, debridement and proper drainage can actually salvage some of these grafts.

Atherosclerotic aneurysms which are secondarily infected are most difficult to diagnose. Routine cultures of abdominal aortic aneurysms will yield a positive culture in about 15% of instances. Nevertheless, these patients have been managed with routine aneurysm repair and no increased incidence of graft infection has been noted. If at operation for a routine infrarenal atherosclerotic aneurysm purulence is found, and a positive gram stain is obtained, later confirmed with a positive culture, it is the author's preference to place the patient on appropriate long-term antibiotics. If the diagnosis is made at the time of operation, consideration can be given to extra-anatomic bypass to avoid the use of prosthetic graft in an infected bed; however, given the excellent results of both in-situ replacement for mycotic aneurysms and the occasional infrarenal aneurysm repair in the presence of a positive thrombus culture, in-line replacement seems preferable following the same principles of absence of purulence, wide debridement and prolonged antibiotic therapy.

Results

The results of surgical management of infected and/or mycotic aneurysms in essence depend on the location, the microorganism involved and the patient's general condition. Overall results have improved over the years. Prior to 1967, surgical management of infected aneurysms was universally fatal. In a literature review by Wilson et al,[11] it was estimated that 25% of patients with mycotic aneurysms died after treatment. Microbial arteritis with aneurysm had a 75% mortality rate and infected preexisting aneurysms a similar mortality. Our experience suggests, however, that rupture of the perivisceral aorta by a mycotic process has a much lower mortality than a similar atherosclerotic rupture. We feel this is likely the result of the time allowed for preparation of the patient and planning surgical strategy in a mycotic process versus the emergent nature of an atherosclerotic rupture.

Other complications include renal failure in perivisceral and supraceliac mycotic aneurysms, coagulopathy from sepsis and/or abdominal visceral ischemia, paraplegia from spinal cord ischemia during cross-clamping and/or persistent ischemia due to ligation of the anterior spinal artery, wound infection, and/or lower extremity ischemia.

Overall results are also linked to the involved organism. Whereas gram-positive infections tend to be less virulent, gram-negative infections particularly with necrotizing organisms such as Salmonella and Pseudomonas can be particularly morbid.

Diagnosis and treatment of mycotic aortic aneurysms is extremely challenging. Following important principles of diagnosis, surgical approach, debridement and revascularization, this process can be managed effectively. Both early- and long-term results have steadily improved over the last two decades and thus it behooves the clinician to establish the diagnosis promptly and manage these patients following these well-established principles.

Selected Readings

1. Osler W. The Gulstonian lectures on malignant endocarditis. Br Med J 1885; 1:467.
   A classic clinical review of endocarditis causing mycotic aneurysms.
2. Stengal A, Wolferth C. Mycotic (bacterial) aneurysms of intravascular origin. Arch Intern Med 1923; 31:527.
   A clinical review of patients with mycotic aneurysms de novo.

3.   Brown SL, Busuttil RW, Baker JD et al. Bacteriologic and surgical determinants of survival in patients with mycotic aneurysms. J Vasc Surg 1984; 1(4):541-7.
      A review of UCLA's clinical experience of patients with mycotic aneurysms.

4.   Chan FY, Crawford ES, Coselli JS et al. In situ prosthetic graft replacement for mycotic aneurysm of the aorta. Ann Thorac Surg 1989; 47(2):193-203.

5.   Cull DL, Winter RP, Wheeler JR, Gregory RT et al. Mycotic aneurysm of the suprarenal abdominal aorta. J Cardiovasc Surg (Torino) 1992; 33(2):181-4.
      The etiology, bacteriology, diagnosis and principles of management of mycotic aneurysms of the suprarenal aorta are discussed in this report.

6.   Quiñones-Baldrich WJ, Nene SM, Moore WS. Rupture of the perivisceral aorta: Atherosclerotic versus mycotic aneurysm. Ann Vasc Surg 1997; 11(4):331-41.
      Twelve patients with rupture of the perivisceral abdominal aorta were reviewed, with important differences noted in clinical presentation when compared to atherosclerotic TAA.

7.   Bickerstaff LK, Pairolero PC, Hollier LH et al. Thoracic aortic aneurysms: A population-based study. Surgery 1982; 92(6):1103-8.
      Thoracic aortic aneurysms were detected in 72 patients over a 30-year period noting the incidence of aortic dissection, atherosclerosis, aortitis, cystic medial necrosis and syphilis.

8.   Bickerstaff LK, Hollier LH, Van Peenen HJ et al. Abdominal aortic aneurysms: The changing natural history. J Vasc Surg 1984; 1(1):6-12.
      A review of 296 patients with abdominal aortic aneurysms.

9.   Brunner MC, Mitchell RS, Baldwin JC et al. Prosthetic graft infection: Limitations of indium white blood cell scanning. J Vasc Surg 1986; 3(1):42-8.
      This paper discusses a rapid, noninvasive and accurate method to confirm or rule out prosthetic graft infection.

10.   Vogt PR, Brunner-La Rocca HP, Carrel T, et al. Cryopreserved arterial allografts in the treatment of major vascular infection: a comparison with conventional surgical techniques. J Thorac Cardiovasc Surg 1998; 116(6):965-72.
      Seventy-two patients with mycotic aneurysms (n=29) or infected vascular prostheses (n=43) of the thoracic (N=26) or abdominal aorta (n=46) were treated with in situ repair and extra-anatomic reconstruction using prosthetic material (n=38) or implantation of a cryopreserved arterial allograft (n=34).

11.   Wilson SE, Van Wagenen P, Passaro E Jr. Arterial infection. Curr Probl Surg 1978; 15(9):1-89.
      This is an excellent review of the literature on arterial infections.

CHAPTER 21

Thoracoabdominal Aortic Aneurysm Repair

Hazim J. Safi, Charles C. Miller III, Samer Koussayer

Thoracoabdominal aortic aneurysm (TAA) involves the portion of the aorta located in the chest and abdomen from the left subclavian artery to the iliac bifurcation. Because the many aspects of aneurysm graft replacement can affect multiple organs with potentially severe side effects, the operation has always been a formidable endeavor. Surgeons first performed successful TAA graft replacement half a century ago and since then morbidity rates have steadily declined, but patients remain at risk for postoperative complications of the lungs, heart or kidneys. Injury to the spinal cord may be the most dreaded complication, occurring in 13% of nondissecting TAA patients. Ischemia of critical intercostal arteries, which flow to the spinal cord from the upper segment of thoracoabdominal aorta, for as little as 8 minutes can bring about neurologic damage.

Within the thoracoabdominal aorta, aneurysms are classified according to their location in the chest and abdomen. Figure 21.1 shows the original Crawford classification of types I through IV, with the addition of type V, which we believe will help to better interpret causes of neurologic deficit. Crawford reported the relationship of aneurysm types to the neurologic complications of paraparesis and paraplegia in 1986.[1] Researchers have consistently observed the most extensive TAA, or type II, to be at highest risk in the development of neurologic deficit (Fig. 21.2). Clear classification and separate analysis of aneurysm type is of paramount importance to correctly evaluate success or failure of adjuncts used to prevent neurologic deficit. The factors responsible for neurologic deficit, although narrowed to include aortic cross-clamp time, aneurysm extent, etiology (acute dissection), previous aortic surgery, age, preoperative renal function and rupture, are not completely known.

Crawford also popularized the inclusion technique of TAA repair that includes simple clamping and liberal intercostal artery reattachment. His technique, known as "cross-clamp and go", remains in use today although nearly all surgeons have added adjuncts for better spinal cord protection. Adjuncts vary from the widely utilized centrifugal pump bypass to more recently introduced methods such as epidural cooling. Others advocate use of cerebrospinal fluid drainage, somatosensory or motor evoked potentials, or profound hypothermia. In our experience, which we will describe here, we have found the combination of cerebrospinal fluid drainage and distal aortic perfusion, further enhanced by passive moderate hypothermia, to provide the best spinal cord protection.[2] Occlusion of the aorta results in distal

21

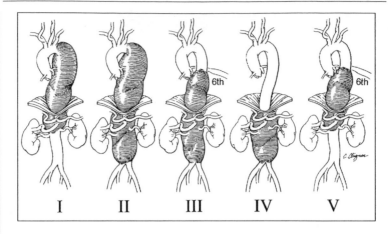

Fig. 21.1. Thoracoabdominal aortic aneurysm classification: Type I: Distal to the left subclavian artery to above the renals. Type II: Left subclavian artery to below the left renal. Type III: Sixth intercostal space to the below the left renal. Type IV: Twelfth intercostal space to the iliac bifurcation (total abdominal aortic aneurysm). Type V: Sixth intercostal space to just above the renal arteries.

hypotension with resultant decrease in spinal cord perfusion pressure. In addition, aortic occlusion also leads to an increase in cerebrospinal fluid pressure that further lowers spinal cord perfusion pressure. Combined, cerebrospinal fluid drainage and distal aortic perfusion counteract the pressure imbalance (Figs. 21.3A-21.3C). Passive moderate hypothermia acts to lower metabolic demands on the spinal cord. On the rare occasion where cerebrospinal fluid drainage and distal aortic perfusion cannot be used, we resort to profound hypothermia which will also be briefly described.

Clinical Presentation and Diagnostic Evaluation

TAA patients are usually asymptomatic. Symptoms, when they occur, may be related to growing aneurysm size or impending rupture, which can cause pain in adjacent organs. Pressure on the recurrent laryngeal or vagus nerves can produce vocal cord paralysis or hoarseness; on the pulmonary artery, a fistula or bleeding leading to pulmonary hypertension and edema; on the esophagus, dysphagia; and on the tracheal bronchial tree, dyspnea. Pressure on the stomach may cause early satiety and weight loss. There may be frank intestinal angina or renovascular hypertension because about 5% of TAA patients also have atherosclerotic occlusive disease of the visceral and renal arteries. An outbreak of pain in a previously asymptomatic patient is highly significant and may indicate rapid expansion, leakage or impending rupture.

Before surgery the patient undergoes at least one diagnostic examination such as computed tomography (CT) scan, magnetic resonance (MRI), transesophageal echocardiography (TEE) or aortography. Chest x-ray may raise the suspicion of TAA (Fig. 21.4). However, we rely on the CT scan to truly confirm TAA and to

21

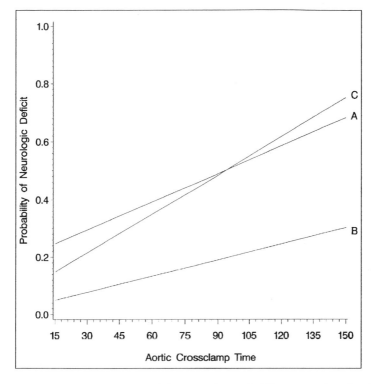

Fig. 21.2. Type II aneurysms. Logistic regression probability curves describe the relationship between probability of neurological deficit on the y-axis, and clamp time and adjunct use on the x-axis. Line A represents the probability associated with simple clamp use, line B that with adjunct.[4] Line C represents Crawford data.[5]

define size, location and extent as well as intraluminal thrombus or calcification (Fig. 21.5). CT scan can also uncover other pathology in the chest and abdomen such as lung or kidney disease. In patient follow-up, the CT scan is indispensable for documenting aneurysm growth rate. Renal insufficiency or allergies to contrast agents may contraindicate CT scan. MRI is as good as CT scan in delineating the presence of TAA, its characteristics and etiology (Fig. 21.6). It is noninvasive and does not require contrast medium. Drawbacks are cost and the time required to run the test. A pacemaker or patient claustrophobia are contraindications. TEE reliably surveys aortic valve disease, aortic dilatation, ascending aortic aneurysm, dissection, thrombi, atherosclerotic disease and mitral valve disease. It provides an assessment of cardiac structure and function and is highly sensitive in aortic pathology diagnosis. TEE nonetheless is a poor identifier of aneurysm below the diaphragm and in the transverse aortic arch. The technique requires a skilled cardiologist to interpret data because of the high rate of false-positive results observed with unfamiliarity of its diagnostic

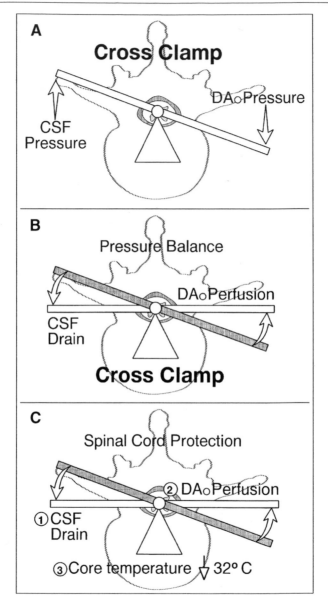

Fig. 21.3A. Dynamics of the aortic cross-clamp. The cross-clamp causes distal aortic hypotension and a decrease in spinal artery pressure followed by an increase in cerebrospinal fluid pressure. B. Dynamics of the aortic cross-clamp. Cerebrospinal fluid drainage and distal aortic perfusion begin to lower cerebrospinal fluid pressure and to increase distal aortic pressure. C. Further cerebrospinal fluid drainage and distal aortic perfusion further counteract the pressure imbalance.

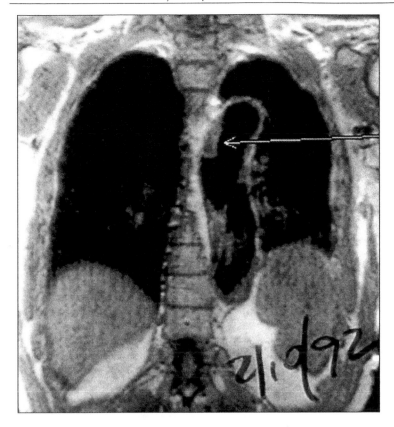

Fig. 21.4. Chest x-ray reveals aneurysm of the descending thoracic aorta.

limitations. Absolute indications for aortography are the presence of renovascular hypertension, intermittent claudication or atherosclerotic occlusive disease of the abdominal aorta. Aortography disadvantages are that it is an invasive procedure that raises the risk of renal failure due to radio-opaque dyes.

Due to risks of myocardial infarction, respiratory failure, renal failure and stroke, preoperative assessment of these organ systems is essential. Cardiac catheterization evaluates concomitant atherosclerotic occlusive disease of the coronary arteries that can be corrected before or at the same time as the aortic aneurysm. Pulmonary function tests, spirometric tests and arterial-blood gas analysis may be required in patients with chronic pulmonary disease. Adequate preoperative hydration is particularly important in patients with preoperative renal dysfunction to reduce the risk of hypotension, low cardiac output and hypovolemia. Patients at risk for cerebrovascular disease undergo carotid artery duplex imaging to detect carotid disease and surgical reconstruction in order to minimize stroke.

21

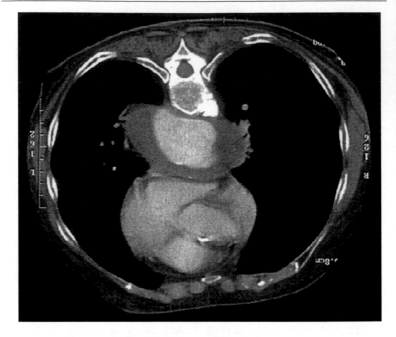

Fig. 21.5. CT scan of TAA showing clot.

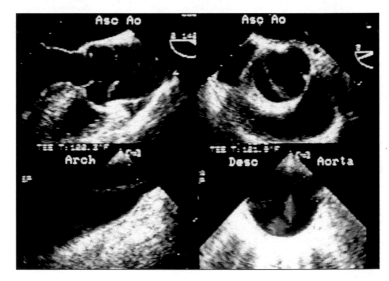

Fig. 21.6. MRI shows ascending aorta, arch and descending aorta dissection.

Conventional Surgical Technique

A team approach delivered by anesthesiologists, surgeons, blood bank directors and hematologists has become increasingly important for successful results in TAA repair. Anesthesiologists are responsible for placement of all catheters for blood management, hemodynamic monitoring and drug administration. Catheters are placed in both radial arteries to continuously monitor blood pressure and to retrieve blood gas specimens. A left subclavian vein to right atrial catheter is inserted for the administration of drugs and measurement of central venous pressure. A Swan-Ganz catheter placed into the right pulmonary artery records pulmonary artery pressure and pulmonary capillary wedge pressure, cardiac output and peripheral resistance. Intravenous catheters are inserted into four peripheral veins for volume replacement therapy with an additional large bore catheter in the jugular vein for rapid intravenous resuscitation. Arterial blood gases, serum electrolytes, acid-base balance, and plasma osmolarity are measured before operation and every 30 minutes during operation. Urine output is measured through a bladder catheter. Tracheal intubation with a double lumen tube facilitates left lung collapse, which provides good exposure, and protects the left lung from manual manipulation. Intraoperatively, the anesthesiologist attends to the patient's massive blood volume requirements. We use a cell saver, which processes blood units in less then 3 minutes and is vital to intraoperative volume resuscitation. A rapid infuser is essential for large quantities of blood and blood component therapy, such as fresh frozen plasma, platelets, packed red blood cells and cryoprecipitate. Cardiac function is measured by TEE, which can also detect atherosclerosis in the thoracic aorta and establishes the competency of the aortic valve before beginning surgical therapy. The patient's temperature is permitted to drift downward to produce moderate hypothermia (nasopharyngeal temperature, 32-33°C).

Aortic cross clamping decreases distal aortic pressure, while creating an increase in cerebrospinal fluid pressure. Therefore, we use distal aortic perfusion to increase the pressure of the clamped aorta and cerebrospinal fluid drainage to decrease cerebrospinal fluid pressure. These maneuvers augment perfusion of the spinal cord. Cerebrospinal fluid drainage is used both intraoperatively and postoperatively at 10 mm Hg. With the patient in a lateral position, a catheter for cerebrospinal fluid drainage is inserted in the space between lumbar vertebrae 3 and 4 and advanced 3-5 cm (Fig. 21.7). If there is a bloody tap the site is changed or drainage is abandoned. Other contraindications for lumbar drainage are a previous spinal operation and mycotic aneurysm. The spinal fluid is drained by gravity. The patient is positioned in a right lateral oblique decubitus fashion and held in place with the support of a beanbag. After preparing and draping the patient, an incision is made in the left groin to expose the left common femoral artery for cannulation. The thoracoabdominal incision is tailored to the extent of the aneurysm. In type I or type V aneurysms (Figs. 21.8A-21.8B), which taper to the level of, or just below, the celiac axis, we use a modified thoracoabdominal incision. After removing the 6th rib and excising the costal cartilage, an incision is made in the anterior rectus muscle about 3 cm beyond the rib cage. We no longer cut the diaphragm. Previously, the outer muscular portion and trefoil-shaped central tendon were completely incised.

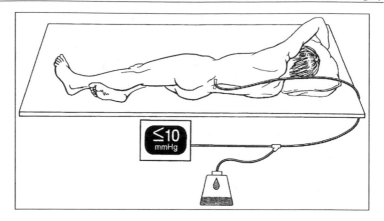

Fig. 21.7. Cerebrospinal fluid drainage catheter insertion.

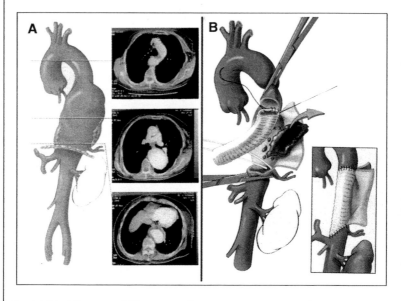

Fig. 21.8A. CT scan and illustration of type V TAA. B. Repair of type V TAA.

Now we divide only the muscular portion of the diaphragm and the intact central tendinous portion retains its mechanical integrity. We found that diaphragm preservation promotes earlier weaning from the ventilator. To gain access to the celiac access the muscular portion around the aorta is dissected. In type I or type V TAAs, which involve the superior mesenteric artery, abdominal exposure is essential, and the incision is extended from the umbilicus to the chest. For types II, III, or IV

TAAs, (Figs. 21.9A-21.11B) the incision is from the symphysis pubis, midline to the umbilicus, and straight toward the costal cartilage into a posterolateral thoracotomy incision along the 6th rib. Usually the sixth rib is removed. The spleen, left colon and kidney are reflected medially and extraperitoneally. The retroperitoneum is entered to expose the aorta from the aortic hiatus to the iliac bifurcation. A self-retaining retractor holds the chest and abdomen open.

We dissect the aortic hiatus, cutting the muscular structures around the aortic hiatus both in the chest and abdomen. If the aneurysm is a type I or type II, then the proximal dissection is carried up to the left subclavian artery. Dissection should start at the level of the pulmonary hiatus to expose the left vagus nerve and proceed proximally until the recurrent laryngeal nerve is in sight. Subsequently, the dissection is carried proximal or distal to the left subclavian artery and posterior to the aorta to completely encircle it at this level. The pericardium posterior to the left phrenic nerve is opened. Using a pursestring suture and Rummel tourniquet to hold the cannula in place we cannulate either the left pulmonary vein or the left atrium for distal aortic perfusion outflow. The arterial end of the Biomedicus pump is inserted into the left common femoral artery and secured. Then the pump is started. Proximal arterial pressure is kept above 100 mm Hg and if the pressure goes below 90 mm Hg, distal aortic perfusion is decreased or stopped altogether.

In sequential clamping, pairs of clamps are applied in succession from the upper to the lower portions of the aorta (Figs. 21.12A-D). This method of clamping with the assistance of the pump permits continuous blood flow to all but the clamped portions of the aorta. The distal arch should first be mapped intraoperatively by using a hand held probe or TEE to detect any atheromatous debris. We then begin with two clamps applied in the proximal and mid-descending thoracic aorta at about the 6th or the 8th intercostal space. Before clamping the proximal and mid-descending aorta, I put my fingers all the way around the aorta to insure safe application of the clamps. The aneurysm between the proximal and distal clamp is opened. As we proceed, aneurysmal walls are retracted using #2 silk retraction sutures. We inspect intercostal arteries T3 through T6, and if patent, we ligate them. The proximal descending thoracic aorta is completely cut circumferentially and lifted off the esophagus. An appropriate sized graft is sutured to the descending thoracic aorta using a running 3-0 polypropylene suture. All anastomoses are methodically checked for bleeding and reinforced with 3-0 pledgeted polypropylene sutures if necessary. The distal clamp is moved down to the infrarenal abdominal aorta and the remainder of the aneurysm is opened longitudinally. The walls of the aneurysm are retracted laterally using #2 silk retraction sutures. Patent intercostal arteries T9 through T12 are occluded using a #3 ballooned tip catheter, and the rest of the intercostal arteries are oversewn using 2-0 silk sutures. The patent intercostal arteries are attached with 3-0 polypropylene suture to a hole cut in the graft. While the aortic segment that includes celiac axis, superior mesenteric and both renal arteries is open, the viscera are perfused with cold oxygenated blood using the octopus (Fig. 21.12C). Renal temperature is monitored and kept below 15°C if possible.

The graft is passed underneath the diaphragm and retrieved in the operative field in the abdomen. We cut an elliptical side hole opposite the visceral orifices and

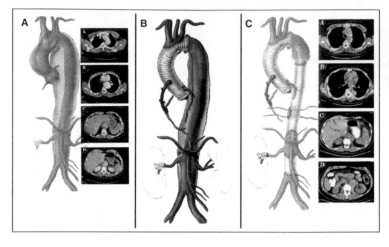

Fig. 21.9A. CT scan and illustration of type II TAA and type A aortic dissection. B. First stage repair of type A dissection (elephant trunk technique). C. Second stage repair of type II TAA.

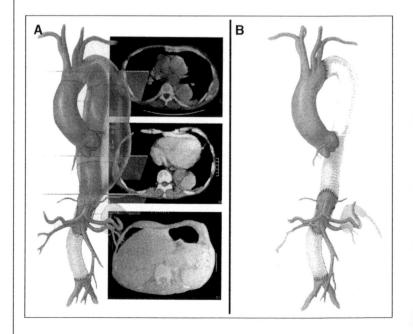

Fig. 21.10A. CT scan and illustration of type III TAA. B. Repair of type III TAA.

21

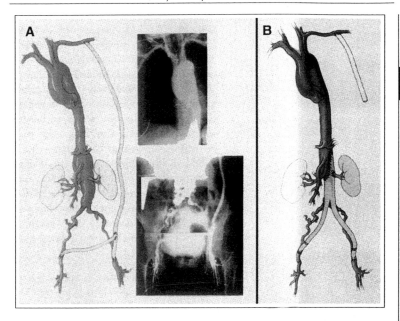

Fig. 21.11A. CT scan and illustration of type IV TAA previously treated with axillo-bifemoral bypass for Leriche syndrome. B. Repair of type IV TAA with excision and ligation of previous graft

either attach the celiac axis, superior mesenteric and both renal arteries in a single patch or, more often, we reattach the left renal artery separately in a patch or bypass. The patient is placed in a head-down position, the graft is flushed to remove all air and debris and the clamp is slowly released to restart the flow to the intercostal and visceral arteries. The patient's head is raised and attention is turned to the infrarenal abdominal aorta. If we are able to clamp above the iliac arteries we do so, otherwise, at this time the pump is stopped while the infrarenal abdominal aorta is opened. Any lumbar arteries are ligated using 2-0 suture ligature. The graft is stretched and cut to length and then sutured to the infrarenal abdominal aorta above the aortic bifurcation using 3-0 or 2-0 polypropylene suture. The pump is restarted with the flow moving distally to remove any air or debris. The proximal infrarenal aortic clamp is released to remove all air and debris proximally. Subsequently, we complete the distal anastomosis. We slowly release the clamps and pulsatile flow returns to the legs. The patient is rewarmed to a rectal temperature of 36°-37°C. Once this is completed, the left atrial and femoral arteriotomy cannulas are removed and the femoral artery incision closed using 5-0 polypropylene suture. All bleeding points are checked and stopped. We check renal function by injecting indigo carmine. Indigo carmine appearing in less than 30 minutes predicts an incidence of renal failure of less than 6%. The abdominal incision is closed in two layers; the pericostal space with interrupted #2 Vicryl, the muscular fascia with #1 polypropylene and

21

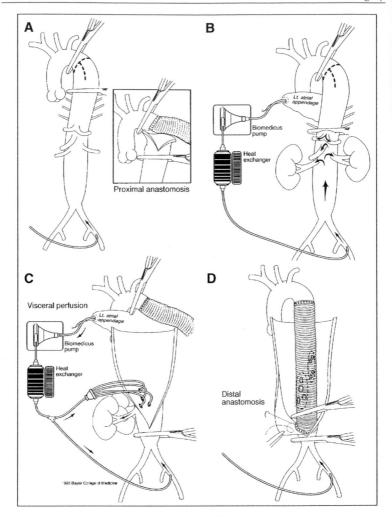

Fig. 21.12A. Sequential clamping. Proximal and mid-descending thoracic aortic clamp. Inset: Proximal anastomosis. B. Sequential clamping. The clamp is moved down on the aorta; aneurysm is opened; visceral vessels are perfused, intercostal arteries are occluded. C. Sequential clamping. Distal clamp is again moved downward and the remainder of the aneurysm is opened. Prior to reattachment, intercostal arteries are occluded, with active visceral cooling. Flow continues to femoral artery. The heat exchanger is used at the end of the procedure to rewarm the patient. D. Sequential clamping. The intercostal and visceral arteries have been reattached to graft; proximal clamp moved down on the graft; distal anastomosis is completed before withdrawal of clamps.

abdominal fascia using #1 polypropylene. The skin is closed using stainless steel staples. We place two #36 Argyle tubes in the chest for drainage.

Postoperative Care

After closing the patient, he or she is placed in a supine position. The double lumen endotracheal tube is changed to a single lumen tube unless there is severe edema of the vocal cord or if the patient is unstable in which case double lumen tube is kept in place and removed 24-48 hours later. Blood pressure is maintained and the transfer to the intensive care unit is not done until the patient is stable. Once the patient is in the intensive care unit all effort is made to keep blood pressure in the range of 100 mm Hg. We avoid Nipride unless blood pressure gets very high, because of experimental and clinical evidence that Nipride may be a causative factor in the development of paraplegia. Cerebrospinal fluid drainage pressure is checked every hour and if it rises above 10 mm Hg, we drain 10-20 ml at a time until the pressure falls below 10 mm Hg. The catheter is removed on the third postoperative day. We closely observe and document the patient's movements as soon as the patient awakes. When extubated, the patient can sit upright in a chair. Physical therapy is started in the intensive care unit. Once the CSF catheter is removed and the patient is up and about, he is transferred to regular care where physical and rehabilitation therapies are started at once.

Results

Much progress has been made in the field of TAA repair in the last 10-15 years. The incidence of the major complications—neurologic, renal, respiratory and hepatic—has been reduced. The decline in morbidity and mortality rates is mainly due to improvements in surgical technique, especially the adoption of perfusion adjuncts to maintain distal aortic blood flow and cerebrospinal fluid drainage to decrease spinal cord ischemia. Reimplantation of intercostal arteries, which has become practical since the introduction of perfusion adjuncts, has also improved results dramatically[3] (Fig. 21.13). While complications following TAA surgery do remain a threat, the current short-term mortality is 5 to 10 percent, compared to 20-25% ten years ago. The neurological deficit rate for the most troublesome type II aneurysms has fallen to 10-12% from 30-40.[4,5] The main risk factors for poor neurologic outcome are aneurysm extent (particularly type II aneurysms), preoperative renal function and aortic cross-clamp time. Table 21.1 shows neurologic deficit risk from two of the largest clamp-and-go series and our recent adjunct series.[1,4,5]

Renal Failure

Renal complications in TAA patients are generally related to preoperative renal failure or insufficiency. The incidence of acute renal failure after TAA repair varies between 4-29% and has been associated with age, male sex, renal occlusive disease, preoperative renal failure, stroke, elevated preoperative creatinine and visceral ischemia (Table 21.2). The simple cross-clamp technique is associated with a worse renal outcome. The adjunct of distal aortic perfusion has demonstrated a protective effect against acute renal failure.[6]

21

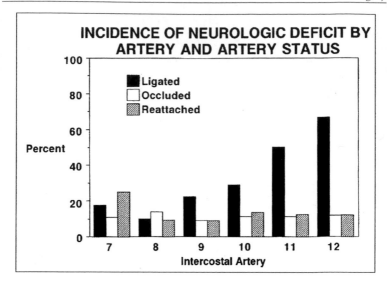

Fig. 21.13. Percent of patients with neurologic deficit by intercostal artery and artery status.[3] The lower the position of the artery on the spine, the higher the risk of deficit if the artery is ligated.

Table 21.1. Statistically significant risk factors for neurologic deficit

Clamp-and-Go Era

Acute aortic dissection	30%
Type II aneurysm	25-30%
Ruptured aorta	25-30%
Proximal aortic aneurysm	27%
Preoperative renal insufficiency	15-20%
Clamp time ≥ 90 Min:	
Type II aneurysms	>50%
Other aneurysms	15-30%
Intercostal artery reattachment	23%

Adjunct Era

Type II aneurysm	7%
Clamp time ≥ 90 Min:	
Type II aneurysms	10%
Other aneurysms	2%
Intercostal artery reattachment	5-8%

Table 21.2. Statistically significant risk factors for postoperative renal failure*

Age > 65	15-20%
Male gender	21%
Type II aneurysm	15-25%
Ruptured aorta	36%
Acute dissection	31%
Creatinine level > 2 mg/dL	20-50%
Previous distal aortic operation	23%
History of gout	32%
History of coronary disease	24%
History of hypertension	20%
Renal artery disease	20-30%
Previous stroke	28%
Clamp and go	17%
Adjuncts	7%

*Based on Svensson and Safi articles.[5,6]

Respiratory Failure

We evaluated the effect of preoperative and intraoperative risk factors on prolonged postoperative respiratory insufficiency, which we defined as the need for mechanical ventilation beyond 72 hours.[7] Statistically significant predictive risk factors following multivariate analysis included advanced age, aortic cross-clamp time, number of packed red blood cells transfused and tobacco use (Table 21.3). The diaphragm is most often completely incised during TAA repair. If, however, instead of this complete division, only the muscular portion of the diaphragm is divided, the intact central tendinous portion will retain its mechanical integrity. This results in a closer and more rapid approximation of preoperative respiratory dynamics. We found that diaphragm preservation during TAA repair results in a significant improvement in early ventilator weaning. In addition, this benefit remains present even when the effects of advanced age, tobacco use, extended clamp time and greater transfusion requirements are accounted for.

Liver Dysfunction

Complex TAA repair exposes patients to ischemic insult and puts them at risk for end-organ damage.[8] TAA type II carries the longest total ischemic time and we have found postoperative liver dysfunction to be highest in these patients. Analysis of liver function-related laboratory tests indicate that prior history of hepatitis, as a marker for pre-existing liver disease, acute rupture, and emergency presentation, as markers of ischemia, are risk factors for hepatic injury following TAA repair (Table 21.4). Visceral perfusion during type II aneurysm repair effectively negates the rise in postoperative laboratory values associated with repair done with the simple cross-clamp technique.

Delayed Paraplegia

The infrequent, but ever-dreaded neurologic complication of paraplegia most commonly becomes evident when the patient awakes, immediately following surgery.

21

Table 21.3. Statistically significant risk factors for postoperative ventilator dependence beyond 3 days*

Current smoking	52%
Type II aneurysm	51%
Cross-clamp time $\geq$ 45 minutes	50%
> 10 units packed red blood cells	55%
> 20 units fresh frozen plasma	51%
> 20 units platelets	56%
Split diaphragm technique	48%
Preserved diaphragm technique	33%

*Based on Safi.[7]

Table 21.4. Statistically significant risk factors for at least one abnormal postoperative liver function test*

History of hepatitis	38%
Type II aneurysm	21%
Ruptured aorta	35%
Emergency operation	35%

*Based on Safi.[8]

Less often, this sort of complication will appear several hours or sometimes days following surgery. Why the onset is delayed is uncertain. Steroids, physical therapy, and methods of blood pressure stabilization have been ineffective in reversing this discouraging outcome. We know of no cases of spontaneous improvement. Since September of 1992, we have combined the traditional supportive therapies for delayed neurologic deficit with the free drainage of cerebrospinal fluid.[9]

Delayed neurologic deficit is a complex phenomenon, related to arterial blood pressure control and postoperative bleeding. The rationale for the use of cerebrospinal fluid drainage postoperatively is to decrease spinal cord edema, which may be an important factor, in delayed neurologic deficit. As we know from experimental and clinical studies, the effect on the spinal cord of clamping the aorta is two-fold.[10] First, spinal artery pressure falls, resulting in decreased spinal cord perfusion and second, cerebrospinal fluid pressure goes up, leading to further deterioration of blood flow to the spinal cord. Because the spinal cord is housed in a rigid structure, we propose that the condition is similar to postoperative brain edema and compartmental syndrome, which require urgent decompression. Immediate cerebrospinal fluid drainage should be introduced when signs of neurologic deficit appear.

Profound Hypothermia

In our clinical experience over the last four years, we have found the adjuncts of cerebrospinal fluid drainage and distal aortic perfusion to reduce neurologic deficit (paraplegia or paraparesis) in TAA repair.[2,4] Because of the good results using these adjuncts, we use them in all but rare instances when cross-clamping of the distal arch or proximal descending aorta is hazardous due to rupture, excessive aortic size, or atheromatous plaque and debris. We then resort to profound hypothermic circulatory arrest (PHCA). First used by Borst and colleagues in 1964 in the repair of a traumatic distal aortic arch-innominate vein fistula,[11] today the technique is most often used in surgery of the ascending aorta and arch.

We make the same incision as described above. After making a left groin incision we expose the left common femoral artery and vein for cannulation and cardiopulmonary bypass. The patient is anticoagulated with sodium heparin and cooling begun. The left atrium is cannulated to augment venous return and also to decompress the left ventricle. The patient's temperature is lowered to approximately 15°C, but we wait until the patient's pupils are fixed and dilated and the electroencephalogram (EEG) is isoelectric, to place the patient in a head-down position and arrest the circulation. We monitor both nasopharyngeal and rectal temperatures. A single clamp placed on the descending thoracic aorta above the diaphragm establishes cerebral ischemia while the distal aorta is perfused. The aneurysm is opened and a graft sutured proximally to the distal arch or proximal descending aorta or, on rare occasion, to the ascending aorta. Following completion of the proximal anastomosis, a side-arm graft is sutured to the proximal aortic graft or an arterial line is inserted directly into the graft and flow is established to the cerebral and coronary circulation. We reattach any patent intercostal artery between T9 and T12 to the graft as described previously. On completion of the distal anastomosis, all clamps are removed and blood flow is restored to the intercostal arteries. Rewarming through the side-arm graft continues until the rectal temperature reaches 37ºC. Once the heart is defibrillated to sinus rhythm, establishing a good heart rate and blood pressure, the patient's head is elevated. We wean the patient from cardiopulmonary bypass and remove all venous and arterial cannulas. The anticoagulated state is reversed using protamine sulfate.

Results

In our recent series of 21 patients, the 30-day mortality was 29%. Of those cases in which PHCA was used on an emergent basis, the mortality was 50%. The high rate of pulmonary complications played a predominant role in an extensive average recovery of 30 days. We believe that high mortality and pulmonary complications warn against the regular use of this technique. Although we consider profound hypothermic circulatory arrest to be a required adjunct in the treatment of some patients with complex aortic pathology, we believe that the technique should be reserved for situations where there is no other alternative, and when aortic cross-clamping would present the greater risk. While the protective properties of hypothermia are well documented in surgery of the ascending aorta and transverse aortic arch, the drawbacks of lowering systemic temperature are also well known.

Conclusion

TAA repair remains a formidable procedure. Multiple complications of the spinal cord, kidneys, viscera, lungs, heart and brain continue, the most catastrophic of which is neurologic deficit. With assistance of excellent cardiovascular anesthesia,

21

left heart bypass with distal aortic perfusion and intraoperative echocardiography to monitor cardiac function, we are better able to act promptly to correct impending problems. Clamping the proximal descending thoracic aorta must be done with care, with particular attention to the possibility of atheromatous debris traveling to the brain to cause stroke. In our practice we have found cerebrospinal fluid drainage and distal aortic perfusion to offer great protection to the spinal cord. With regard to protection of the kidneys, we believe that cooling is important and that visceral perfusion also protects the liver and intestines from the side effects of prolonged ischemia. In short, continued efforts toward multisystem organ preservation will make the TAA repair a safer operation.

Selected Readings

1. Crawford ES, Crawford JL, Safi HJ et al. Thoracoabdominal aortic aneurysms: Preoperative and intraoperative factors determining immediate and long-term results of operations in 605 patients. J Vasc Surg 1986; 3(3):389-404.
    This seminal report reviews immediate and long-term results of TAA repair in 605 patients with median age of 65 years. The patients were divided into four groups based on the extent of aneurysm. There were 54 (8.9%) perioperative deaths and 151 late deaths. Impressively, 400 (66%) patients were still alive 3 months to 20 years after TAA repair, including 60% at 5 years! Age, aortic clamp time and COPD were found to be significant predictors of early death by multivariate analysis. Variables predictive of lower extremity neurologic events were rupture, reattachment of intercostal/lumbar arteries (surprising result that is more than likely related to prolonged clamp time), dissection and aneurysm extent.

2. Safi HJ, Hess KR, Randel M et al. Cerebrospinal fluid drainage and distal aortic perfusion: reducing neurologic complications in repair of thoracoabdominal aortic aneurysm types I and II. J Vasc Surg 1996; 23(2):223-228; discussion 229.
    This study evaluated the role of CSF drainage and distal aortic perfusion in the prevention of postoperative neurologic complications in 94 patients with types I and II TAA. Early and late neurologic complications occurred in only 5% and 3% of patients, respectively. These excellent results compare favorably to a control group of 42 patients (also treated by Dr. Safi) who had simple clamp-and-go technique without CSF drainage or distal aortic perfusion. Neurologic complications in this group was 19% (p=0.09).

3. Safi HJ, Miller CC 3rd, Carr C et al. The importance of intercostal artery reattachment during thoracoabdominal aortic aneurysm repair. J Vasc Surg 1998; 27:58-68.
    This review of 343 TAA patients demonstrates that reimplantation of patent thoracic intercostal arteries from T_9 through T_{12} lowers the overall risk of lower extremity neurologic complications.

4. Safi HJ, Campbell MP, Miller CC, 3rd et al. Cerebral spinal fluid drainage and distal aortic perfusion decrease the incidence of neurological deficit: the results of 343 descending and thoracoabdominal aortic aneurysm repairs. Eur J Vasc Endovasc Surg 1997; 14(2):118-124.
    CSF drainage and distal aortic perfusion decreased the incidence of postoperative neurologic deficit. These adjuncts were particularly effective for patients with type II TAA who have the highest risk.

5. Svensson LG, Crawford ES, Hess KR et al. Experience with 1509 patients undergoing thoracoabdominal aortic operations. J Vasc Surg 1993; 17(2):357-368; discussion 368-370.

Retrospective review of an enormous patient series to identify variables associated with perioperative morbidity and mortality following TAA repair. The 30-day survival rate of 92% and mean aortic cross clamp time of 45 minutes are a reflection of a true master surgeon (Dr. Crawford). Variables significantly associated with early death included increasing age, elevated preoperative creatinine, concurrent aortic arch aneurysm, coronary artery disease, COPD and total aortic cross clamp time. With these improved survival rates, two major complications of TAA repair (paraplegia and renal failure) become increasing apparent.

21

6. Safi HJ, Harlin SA, Miller CC et al. Predictive factors for acute renal failure in thoracic and thoracoabdominal aortic aneurysm surgery [published erratum appears in J Vasc Surg 1997 Jan;25(1):93]. J Vasc Surg 1996; 24(3):338-344; discussion 344-345.
   This study analyzed risk factors that were associated with acute renal failure following thoracic and TAA repair. The following variables were found to be significant predictors of acute postoperative renal failure: elevated preoperative creatinine, visceral perfusion, need for left renal artery reattachment and clamp-and-go technique.

7. Engle J, Safi HJ, Miller CC, 3rd et al. The impact of diaphragm management on prolonged ventilator support after thoracoabdominal aortic repair. J Vasc Surg 1999; 29(1):150-156.
   The purpose of this study was (1) to determine whether preservation of the diaphragm had a significant effect on postoperative ventilator duration and (2) to determine if any other pulmonary risk factors influenced the outcome of TAA repair. A total of 256 patients had TAA repair; in 150 the diaphragm was divided and in 106 it was left intact. An intact diaphragm resulted in a higher probability of early extubation (p=0.02) independent of other well known pulmonary risk factors.

8. Safi HJ, Miller CC, 3rd, Yawn DH et al. Impact of distal aortic and visceral perfusion on liver function during thoracoabdominal and descending thoracic aortic repair. J Vasc Surg 1998; 27(1):145-152; discussion 152-153.
   This study demonstrates that visceral perfusion negates the rise in postoperative liver function-related clinical lab values in patients undergoing repair of type II TAA.

9. Safi HJ, Miller CC, 3rd, Azizzadeh A et al. Observations on delayed neurologic deficit after thoracoabdominal aortic aneurysm repair [see comments]. J Vasc Surg 1997; 26(4):616-622.
   This report describes the clinical course of eight patients who had delayed neurologic complications between 1 and 14 days after TAA repair. Immediate CSF drainage was instituted in these patients as soon as symptoms were recognized. Interestingly, all 8 patients improved by at least 2 points (modified Tarlov score) when examined by an independent neurologist.

10. Svensson LG GD, Bednarski M, Cosgrove DM et al. Appraisal of cerebrospinal fluid alterations during aortic surgery with intrathecal papaverine administration and cerebrospinal fluid drainage. J Vasc Surg 1990; 11:423-429.
    This report is an extension of previous work demonstrating the technique of intrathecal administration of papaverine and CSF drainage to prevent paraplegia after complex aortic reconstruction. No complications were noted with the technique and there were instances of postoperative paraparesis or paraplegia in 11 treated patients.

11. Borst HG SA, Rudolph W. Arteriovenous fistula of the aortic arch: Repair during deep hypothermia and circulatory arrest. J Thorac and Cardiovasc Surg 1964; 48:443-447.

CHAPTER 22

Alternate Approach for Type III and Type IV Thoracoabdominal Aortic Aneurysm Repair

Jeffrey L. Ballard

End-organ damage from ischemia and reperfusion of abdominal viscera, spinal cord and lower extremities contributes greatly to the morbidity and mortality associated with thoracoabdominal aortic aneurysm (TAA) repair. Adjunctive techniques such as left heart bypass with distal aortic and visceral perfusion, cerebrospinal fluid (CSF) drainage, monitoring of spinal somatosensory evoked potentials, reattachment of intercostal arteries, epidural cooling, passive hypothermia, cardiopulmonary bypass with hypothermia and profound hypothermic circulatory arrest are all selectively utilized in order to diminish this end-organ ischemia. These adjuncts appear to be successful in decreasing morbidity and mortality particularly associated with repair of type I and II TAAs which extend from the subclavian artery to above the celiac axis or opposite the superior mesenteric artery (SMA) but above the renal arteries (type I), or through the visceral vessels to the aortic bifurcation (type II). However, even those who have championed these methods do not necessarily use them for repair of type III or IV TAAs where the risk of spinal cord ischemia is less but the risk of gastrointestinal, hepatic, renal and lower extremity ischemia remains the same. These TAAs involve all four visceral vessels and extend through the aortic bifurcation with a type III beginning in the mid-descending thoracic aorta and a type IV beginning at the diaphragm.

Pioneers in the treatment of TAA recognized the danger of producing ischemic damage to these vital organs. Temporary shunts made of compressed polyvinyl sponge (Ivalon) were originally used to reduce the period of circulatory arrest to the visceral beds, kidneys and lower extremities. In 1955, Etheredge et al successfully repaired a large aneurysm that extended from the diaphragm to just above the right renal artery using a temporary 5 mm polyethylene aorto-aorta shunt and reattaching the celiac and superior mesenteric arteries onto the body of an aortic homograft. TAA excision with aortic homograft replacement and reanastomosis of the visceral and renal vessels evolved, as knitted Dacron became available as a satisfactory synthetic arterial replacement. Later, DeBakey et al demonstrated that a Dacron graft could function as a temporary bypass during TAA repair and then remain as a permanent vascular replacement. Step-wise grafting using 8 mm Dacron side limbs to the celiac, superior mesenteric and renal arteries decreased the average period of end-organ ischemia

---

to a tolerable limit. However, as noted by Crawford in 1974, the DeBakey procedure was arduous and notable for prolonged operating time and significant blood loss.

These intraoperative observations were the impetus for Dr. Crawford to develop his classic "inclusion technique" for TAA repairs. In the previous chapter, Dr. Safi thoroughly and elegantly discussed his vast experience in the management of extensive thoracoabdominal aortic disease. This brief chapter will describe a variation of what Crawford referred to as a type I operation for repair of type III and IV TAAs that minimizes ischemia to the abdominal viscera, spinal cord and lower extremities and decreases operating time and blood loss.

22

Patients and Methods

Over a recent 25 month period, five type IV TAAs (one recurrent with a large pseudoaneurysm and one with contained rupture) and three type III TAAs (one with contained rupture) were repaired at Loma Linda University Medical Center using a trifurcated graft to bypass 3 of 4 visceral vessels and another graft to reconstruct the thoracoabdominal aorta. The men were 71, 66, 62 and 54 years of age and the women 72, 71, 70 and 66 years old. Hypertension was present in all (100%) patients. Cardiac symptoms such as prior myocardial infarction, history of angina or congestive heart failure were noted in 5 (63%) patients. Incidence of preoperative renal insufficiency (creatinine > 1.3) and chronic obstructive pulmonary disease was 38% and 50%, respectively. All patients were previous or active smokers (100%).

In the operating room, the patient was placed in a modified right lateral decubitus position to facilitate a thoracoabdominal incision and access to both femoral arteries. The incision began paramedian below the level of the umbilicus and was carried across the costal margin into the 6th, 7th or 8th interspace. The left retroperitoneal space was developed in a retronephric extraperitoneal plane and in the thorax, the inferior pulmonary ligament was divided to expose the descending thoracic aorta. Distally, division of the median arcuate ligament and lumbar tributary to the left renal vein improved aortic exposure. This facilitated further medial rotation of the abdominal viscera and left kidney. The proximal portions of the celiac, superior mesenteric and left renal arteries were then dissected free of surrounding tissue and looped for vascular control. Control of distal target vessel(s) completed the dissection. The reader is referred to Chapter 8 for a more thorough discussion of this surgical exposure.

Before administering heparin (80 units/kg), a trifurcated graft was constructed by attaching a third 6 mm PTFE (Gore-Tex, Flagstaff, AZ) graft limb onto the body of a 12 x 6 mm bifurcated PTFE stretch graft (Fig. 22.1). This graft was then sewn end-to-side to an unaffected area of descending thoracic aorta. Use of a side-biting aortic clamp preserved distal perfusion. Direct end-to-end bypasses to the left renal, superior mesenteric and celiac arteries were then sequentially accomplished with limited ischemia time to each vessel as shown in Table 22.1. The remaining TAA was then replaced with an in-line Dacron tube (2 cases) or bifurcated graft (6 cases) by clamping distal to the trifurcated graft so as to maintain visceral and left renal artery perfusion. Open intercostal arteries at the proximal level of the open descending thoracic aorta were incorporated into the proximal anastomosis. Otherwise more

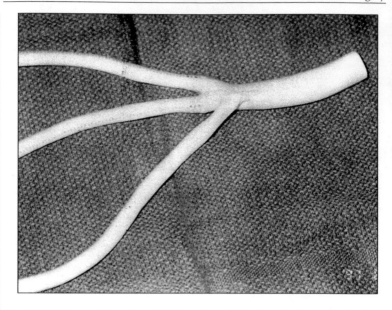

Fig. 22.1. Trifurcated 12 x 6 mm PTFE stretch graft. Reprinted with permission from Ballard JL. Thoracoabdominal aortic aneurysm repair with sequential visceral perfusion: a technical note. Ann Vasc Surg 1999; 13:217.

Table 22.1. Visceral vessel ischemia times

Patient	Left Renal	SMA	Celiac	Right Renal
1	10.5 mins.	12 mins.	13 mins.	44 mins.
2	9 mins.	12 mins.	11 mins.	29 mins.
3	11 mins.	11 mins.	15 mins.	30 mins.
4	10 mins.	9.5 mins.	12 mins.	35 mins.
5	11 mins.	11 mins.	15 mins.	42 mins.
6	11 mins.	10 mins.	20 mins.	25 mins.
7	9 mins.	11 mins.	10 mins.	35 mins.
8	7 mins.	11 mins.	10 mins.	30 mins.
Mean	**10 mins.**	**11 mins.**	**13 mins.**	**34 mins.**

*From Ballard JL. Repair of thoracoabdominal aortic aneurysms with sequential visceral perfusion: A technical note. Ann Vasc Surg 1999;13:216-221.

distal ones were suture ligated. Implantation of the right renal artery into the Dacron graft using the inclusion technique completed visceral artery reconstruction. Fig. 22.2 shows how the trifurcated graft limbs lie in relation to the Dacron graft.

Closure was uncomplicated, as the diaphragm reapproximates around the PTFE graft limbs without creating a potential space for herniation of abdominal contents

Fig. 22.2. Trifurcated PTFE graft secured to uninvolved descending thoracic aorta. Note how graft limbs sweep over top of graft used for in-line repair of TAA. Graft limbs are anastomosed to celiac (top), superior mesenteric (middle) and left renal (bottom) arteries. Reprinted with permission from Ballard JL. Thoracoabdominal aortic aneurysm repair with sequential visceral perfusion: A technical note. Ann Vasc Surg 1999; 13:218.

into the chest. Figures 22.3 and 22.4 demonstrate postreconstruction arteriographic patency of the trifurcated graft, visceral artery bypasses and reimplanted right renal artery.

Results

Mean ischemia time was 11 minutes for each sequential visceral bypass and 34 minutes for the right renal artery. Average blood loss during the operation was 4,100 cc (range 1,500-8,550 cc) and with experience operating time decreased to a mean of 4.7 hours. Mean ICU and hospital stays were 4 and 11 days, respectively. No patient developed signs of visceral/extremity hypoperfusion, distal embolization, coagulopathy, renal failure or spinal cord dysfunction. In addition, there were no postoperative pulmonary complications in this group. However, two patients with preoperative renal insufficiency (creatinine level 1.4 and 1.8, respectively) demonstrated a transient postoperative rise in creatinine and one patient died unexpectedly on POD #5 after a myocardial infarction. This patient required urgent repair of a painful type III TAA with contained rupture.

Seven patients are well at latest follow-up ranging from 1-29 months (mean, 8 months). Duplex ultrasound surveillance of the visceral artery bypasses has demonstrated continued patency with normal flow velocities in all cases. No patient has developed late symptoms of paraparesis, paraplegia, renal insufficiency/failure or mesenteric ischemia.

Discussion

This approach for repair of Type III and IV TAAs arose from experience with two challenging redo ruptured TAA repairs. In each case, with careful dissection, the left renal, superior mesenteric and celiac arteries could be isolated before entering the pseudoaneurysm/old graft. However, the remaining visceral patch segment of aorta was extremely friable and unyielding. Despite prompt proximal aortic control and technical success using the inclusion technique, both cases were complicated by prolonged visceral and renal ischemia, massive bleeding from coagulopathy, multiorgan failure and patient death. When a third patient presented electively with a large pseudoaneurysm of the visceral patch segment of a previously repaired Type IV TAA, the DeBakey/Crawford techniques were re-engineered to avoid a potentially degenerated aortic visceral patch segment and to diminish renal, abdominal viscera and spinal cord ischemia.

This new technique is similar in concept to the type I operation for TAA repair referred to by Crawford in his seminal presentation to The Southern Surgical Association in 1973. However, there are a number of key differences. The first modification concerns anatomic exposure. As originally described by DeBakey et al and Crawford, these procedures were approached with separate thoracic and midline abdominal incisions. Therefore, the aneurysm was not exposed in its entirety and transperitoneal exposure of all four visceral vessels was arduous. Crawford modified this approach by using a continuous thoracoabdominal incision with medial visceral rotation which afforded better exposure of the visceral vessels. However, the retronephric extraperitoneal exposure as described in this new approach greatly

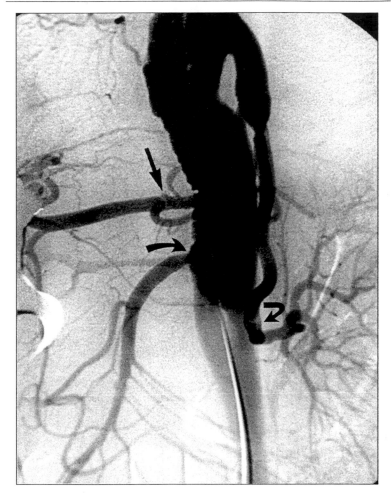

Fig. 22.3. Arteriographic demonstration of patent bypasses to celiac (straight arrow), superior mesenteric (slightly curved arrow) and left renal (curved arrow) arteries. Reprinted with permission from Ballard JL. Thoracoabdominal aortic aneurysm repair with sequential visceral perfusion: a technical note. Ann Vasc Surg 1999; 13:218)

facilitates dissection of the visceral vessels as well as complete TAA exposure. Risk of splenectomy is reduced because there is no need for transperitoneal medial visceral rotation. In addition, the peritoneum remains unopened. Therefore, the patient has a better chance of remaining warm during the procedure and of having prompt return of bowel function.

The second conceptual modification concerns potential ischemic damage to the visceral beds, kidneys, spinal cord and lower extremities. As originally described,

22

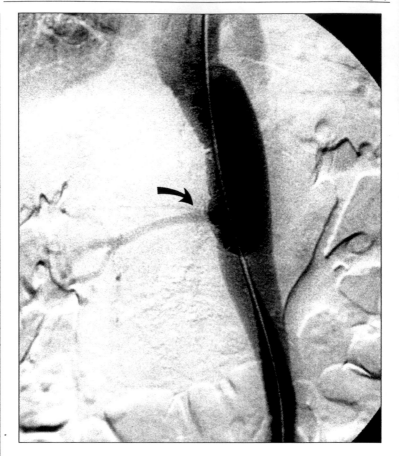

Fig. 22.4. Arteriographic demonstration of implanted right renal artery (arrow). (Reprinted with permission from Ballard JL. Thoracoabdominal aortic aneurysm repair with sequential visceral perfusion: a technical note. Ann Vasc Surg 1999; 13:219.

DeBakey et al[3] first used a Dacron graft as a temporary bypass by attaching it end-to-side above and below the TAA. Step-wise bypass to the celiac, superior mesenteric and renal arteries was then followed by aneurysm resection. Suture closure of the proximal cut end of the descending thoracic aorta distal to the dacron graft and of the distal aorta or iliac arteries above the distal graft attachment site completed the procedure. This left a blind proximal thoracic aortic stump and ischemia to the visceral beds and kidneys ranged from 10-30 minutes. This procedure was further modified by Crawford, who began using his well-known inclusion technique to decrease operating time at the expense of increased visceral and spinal cord ischemia. During these cases, visceral organ ischemia time ranged from 20-49 minutes for the celiac, SMA and right renal artery and up to 60 minutes for the left renal artery.

However, average operating time was decreased from 5.5 hours to approximately 3 hours!

Operating time with this newly described approach for TAA repair is not excessive and distal perfusion is maintained during attachment of the proximal trifurcated graft by the utilization of a side-biting thoracic aortic clamp. Thereafter, sequential bypass of the celiac, superior mesenteric and left renal arteries minimizes circulatory arrest to the visceral beds and left kidney. The right kidney, spinal cord and lower extremities receive their normal blood flow during this portion of the operation as each limb of the trifurcated graft is successively clamped rather than occluding the descending thoracic aorta. This is followed by direct in-line TAA replacement with another graft by clamping between the aneurysm and the trifurcated PTFE graft. During this portion of the operation the visceral beds and left kidney are well perfused via the trifurcated graft and only the right kidney and lower extremities remain to be revascularized.

Like the inclusion technique described by Crawford, this new approach eliminates a potentially disastrous thoracic aortic stump because it is the trifurcated graft and not the TAA replacement graft that is attached to the side of the descending thoracic aorta. However, ischemia to the visceral beds and kidneys is reduced and since circulatory arrest to these vital organs is kept well within the limits of ischemia tolerance, adjuncts such as left heart bypass, hypothermia and CSF drainage are not required. Without the need for cardiac exposure, the thoracic portion of the incision can be made in a lower interspace and cannulation of a potentially atherosclerotic femoral artery is also avoided. Blood loss that averaged 6,250 cc for a type I operation is reduced closer to that reported by Crawford for type II and III operations (average 3,000 cc) because of minimal heparinization, the ability to sequentially clamp back-bleeding vessels and total extraperitoneal exposure. Finally, distal embolization during application of the side-biting thoracic aortic clamp has not been observed, although this is a theoretical concern.

Late complications such as progression of aneurysmal disease in the proximal thoracic aorta or dehiscence of the suture line at the end-to-side anastomosis have not occurred, although follow-up at this time is limited. These potential complications are not unique to this new method of TAA repair. Clearly, aneurysmal degeneration is possible above or at the proximal aortic anastomosis with standard TAA repair. Reoperation has been described for false aneurysm of the proximal suture line, the site of intercostal artery reattachment and site of visceral artery reattachment. Aneurysmal degeneration or suture line dehiscence/pseudoaneurysm of the visceral patch is greatly diminished with this technique as 3 of 4 visceral vessels are directly bypassed using end-to-end configurations. In addition, the right renal artery is implanted into the Dacron graft with the suture line placed as close as possible to the artery orifice without creating stenosis. Additionally, there have been no problems to date associated with diaphragm closure around the three graft limbs and no evidence of thoracic herniation of abdominal contents.

This newly described approach eliminates many of the ischemia related problems encountered by simply trying to reinsert another graft for redo TAA repair or using a clamp-and-sew inclusion technique for primary type III and type IV TAA repair. However, we continue to favor a multi-adjunct approach for repair of Type I and II TAAs. This typically involves cerebrospinal fluid drainage, distal aortic and visceral perfusion from the left heart or pulmonary vein using a Bio-Medicus pump and selective intercostal artery reimplantation. However, this patient series demonstrates the applicability of this new modification of an operative technique that evolved from first description in the 1950's, to elective or redo TAAs that begin in the distal thoracic aorta.

Selected Readings

1. DeBakey ME, Creech O Jr et al. Aneurysm of thoracoabdominal aorta involving the celiac, superior mesenteric and renal arteries. Report of four cases treated by resection and homograft replacement. Ann Surg 1956; 144:549.

    This classic manuscript is difficult to find. It describes the original "DeBakey" procedure for thoracoabdominal aortic aneurysm repair using an arterial homograft. These pioneering surgeons laid the groundwork for modern day complex aortic reconstruction by demonstrating the feasibility of surgical treatment for these daunting problems.

2. Etheredge SN, Yee J, Smith JV et al. Successful resection of a large aneurysm of the upper abdominal aorta and replacement with homograft. Surgery 1955; 38:1071-1081.

    The first successful resection of a suprarenal aortic aneurysm on September 20, 1954, at the Oakland Veterans Administration Hospital is described in detail by Dr. Etheredge et al. The comment section is as appropriate today as it was at the time of publication in 1955.

3. DeBakey ME, Crawford ES, Garrett HE et al. Surgical considerations in the treatment of aneurysms of the thoracoabdominal aorta. Ann Surg 1965; 162:650-662.

    This work describes the various surgical approaches used for thoracoabdominal aortic aneurysm repair in 42 patients including the four mentioned in reference #1. Detailed drawings of the surgical procedures and technical considerations are worth a thousand words. The importance of having minimal periods of ischemia to the abdominal viscera during resection and graft replacement is emphasized. It is truly remarkable that the nine-year survival in this complex patient group was 63%!

4. Crawford ES. Thoracoabdominal and abdominal aortic aneurysms involving renal, superior mesenteric, and celiac arteries. Ann Surg 1974; 179:763-772.

    This seminal work was presented at the Annual Meeting of the Southern Surgical Association in December 1973. In it Dr. Crawford details three different techniques (Type I, II and III) for thoracoabdominal aortic aneurysm repair. Type I repair represented a variation of the original DeBakey procedure with stepwise visceral bypass grafts but with in-line graft repair of the aneurysm. Type II and III repairs represented variations of his now well-known inclusion technique.

5. Crawford ES, Crawford JL. Redo aortic operations. In: Crawford ES, Crawford JL, eds. Diseases of the Aorta. Baltimore: Williams & Wilkins, 1984:317-339.

    This classic text is full of excellent large-scale drawings as well as pathologic and radiographic images of pre and postoperative surgical cases managed by Dr. Crawford during his distinguished career at Baylor College of Medicine.

6. Ballard JL. Thoracoabdominal aortic aneurysm repair with sequential visceral perfusion: A technical note. Ann Vasc Surg 1999; 13:216-221.

    A re-engineered approach for Type III and Type IV thoracoabdominal aortic aneurysm repair is described in detail. Discussion section compares and contrasts this new technique with those that have been previously described.

22

CHAPTER 23

Endovascular Management of Aortic Aneurysmal Disease

Frank J. Criado and Robert J. Falconer

Endoluminal grafting for treatment of aortic aneurysms is the most exciting topic in vascular surgery today. Two stent-graft devices—Ancure (Guidant) and AneuRx (Medtronic AVE)—have just been approved by the FDA this year. It is anticipated that as many as 50% (or more) of aneurysms in the infrarenal abdominal and descending thoracic aorta will be repaired endovascularly in the near future.

Historical Evolution

Carrel wrote of the "intubation" of blood vessels as early as 1912.[1] However, this idea lay dormant and was essentially ignored for more than 50 years. It was Charles Dotter in his classic paper of 1964 that first envisioned the need for an "intraluminal splint" to prop the vessel open and promote "reintimalization" following percutaneous angioplasty.[2] Dotter again, in 1969,[3] reported on the first series of experiments with endoluminal "coil spring endarterial tube grafts" in a canine animal model. And finally, in 1983, he culminated his work with a report on clinical application of these devices, using for the first time the term stent within the context of a noncardiac peripheral intervention.[4] Over the ensuing several years, further refinements and innovations contributed to the establishment of stents as important tools for endovascular intervention. These early developments can appropriately be considered to be the precursors of stent-grafts that were to evolve shortly thereafter.

While a stent (or any other intravascular implant) may be considered an "endoluminal graft", a more narrow definition of stent-grafts will be used for this chapter: transluminally-placed devices, containing a cloth (or another impervious) cover capable of effecting segmental vessel exclusion or "intraluminal bypass".

Early Designs and Initial Experience

Most, if not all, endoluminal grafts are stent-based devices (Table 23.1). The metallic stent portion is used as a fixator or anchor, or as a skeleton to be covered or enveloped by the cloth or plastic material. Additionally, it provides full-length support to the tubular structure. Maas and Balko were amongst the first investigators to design endoluminal grafts (using polyurethane over a nitinol or steel frame) for transfemoral aortic aneurysm exclusion. Dacron (Lawrence, 1987) and nylon (Mirich, 1989) prostheses were reported shortly thereafter. These followed earlier designs by Choudhury, Kornberg, and Lazarus. The majority of these developments involved

Table 23.1. Aortic stent grafts—key initial investigators

- Choudhury (1979)
- Volodos (1986)
- Balko
- Maas
- Cragg
- Kornberg
- Lazarus (1988)
- Parodi-Barone-Palmaz (1988)
- Mirich (1989)

23

theoretical conceptions, patents, animal experimentation and occasional clinical application of "home-made" devices.[5,6] Volodos was probably first in the world to treat an aortic (thoracic) aneurysm with a stent-graft of his own conception and construction in 1986.[7] But it was left to Parodi of Buenos Aires, Argentina to "push the envelope" and introduce endoluminal repair of AAA as a revolutionary new approach that was destined to usher in a whole new era of minimally-invasive vascular therapy.

Modern Developments: The 1990s

Endoluminal exclusion by endograft placement was an established research concept by the late 1980s, albeit unknown to most vascular specialists. Dr. Juan C. Parodi had envisioned several technical possibilities beginning during his vascular training at the Cleveland Clinic in the late 1970s. Several conceptions and designs were proposed, but none proved workable. In 1988, Parodi met Julio Palmaz (another Argentinian) at the first TCT meeting in Washington, D.C.: "discovery" of the Palmaz stent enabled Parodi to overcome difficulties with conception and practical implementation of early endograft designs. The Palmaz balloon-expandable stent appeared to him as the "ideal" anchor or fixator of an aortic endoluminal graft at the proximal aneurysm neck.[8] Without delay, a balloon-expandable system was created in collaboration with Hector Barone (a bioengineer and device industry leader in Buenos Aires), and now with the active participation and contribution of Julio C. Palmaz. A thin-walled Dacron graft could thus be delivered transluminally, and securely attached to the vessel wall at the proximal neck to effect intraluminal bypass (exclusion) of the AAA (Fig. 23.1). The concept was tested in a canine model, and proved valid. The first AAA clinical implant took place at the Instituto Cardiovascular de Buenos Aires on September 1, 1990. Several more cases followed in rapid sequence. The initial publication of Parodi's early clinical experience with five cases had profound and long-lasting impact.[9]

Parodi's initial approaches (and that of others soon to follow) evolved in this manner:

Design #1 (Fig. 23.2)

Straight aorto-aortic—proximal stent only.

This first design assumed that a "good fit" of the endograft and aorta at the distal neck would result in good apposition, with little or no risk of reflux into the sac.

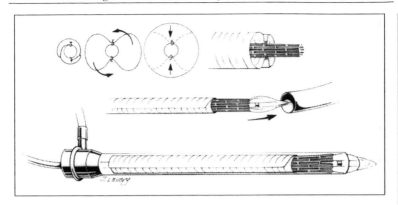

Fig. 23.1. The original Parodi-Barone-Palmaz design combined a large balloon-expandable stent and thin-wall Dacron graft mounted on a balloon angioplasty catheter.

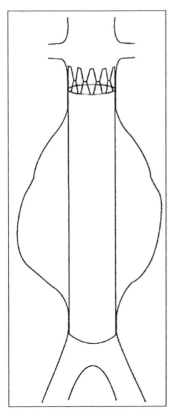

Fig. 23.2. Tubular stent-graft concept; proximal stent only.

23

Design #2 (Fig. 23.3)

Straight aorto-aortic—proximal and distal stents

The second design became necessary to obtain a blood-tight seal at the distal neck. It had become obvious by then that a nondistally stented endograft would result in primary or secondary reflux in nearly every case.

Both designs #1 and #2 were based on the "erroneous surgical view" that tube endografts could be used to exclude half or more of AAA's, as is the case with operative therapy.[10] In reality, less than 10% of patients are amenable to such tubular stent-graft configuration.

Design #3 (Fig. 23.4)

Aorto-Uni-Iliac + exclusion of contralateral iliac + femorofemoral bypass

This was also introduced by Parodi (in late 1991) in an effort to expand applicability of endoluminal repair.[11] It rapidly became the most common approach in his hands, and those of several others in the 1992-95 time period. It continues to be used frequently by a number of well-known investigators.[12-14]

Design #4 (Fig. 23.5)

One-piece bifurcated nonsupported stent-graft

Originally championed by Chuter,[15] this design represented a natural evolution and the result of lessons learned with earlier approaches. However, it proved technically complex and impractical.

Design #5 (Fig. 23.6)

Modular, fully-supported, bifurcated aortoiliac stent-graft

This was the most significant technological achievement.[5,6] It incorporated several features that are currently viewed as critical components of endovascular AAA technology, namely: a) modular design permitting construction of the stent-graft by joining two or more sections within the aortoiliac lumen, and the opportunity for adding extensions both cephalad and caudad in order to optimize deployment and exclusion in a given case; b) full-length support to achieve the columnar strength that is necessary for stability and integrity with preservation of a normal flow channel, even when placed across tortuous anatomy. Another design aspect that has recently become the focus of attention relates to the desirability of suprarenal fixation (of the uncovered stent at the proximal end) allowing secure attachment to a more healthy segment of aorta that is less prone to progressive dilatation.[17] Currently, the Talent (Medtronic AVE), Vanguard (Boston Scientific Vascular), and Zenith (Cook) devices incorporate such a feature.

Current Status (Mid-1999)

There are two stent-graft devices that were recently approved by the FDA for treatment of AAA: a) the Ancure EVT device (Guidant), which is an early design balloon-expandable, one-piece bifurcated stent-graft (Fig. 23.7), and b) the AneuRx device (Medtronic AVE), a self-expanding, modular-design, fully supported bifurcated stent-graft (Fig. 23.8).

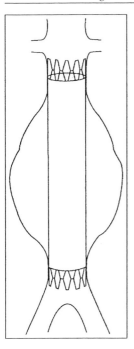

Fig. 23.3. Tubular stent-graft concept; proximal and distal stents.

23

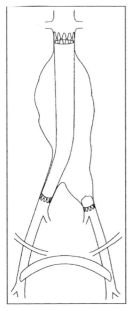

Fig. 23.4. Aorto-uni-iliac stent-graft concept. It implies need for contralateral iliac artery exclusion, and crossover femorofemoral bypass.

Fig. 23.5. One-piece bifurcated stent-graft.

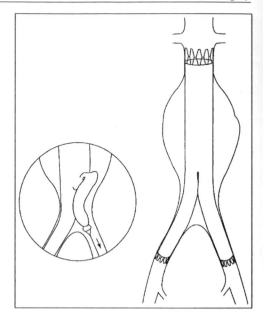

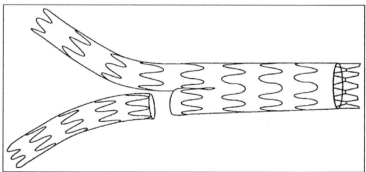

Fig. 23.6. Modular, bifurcated, fully-supported stent-graft.

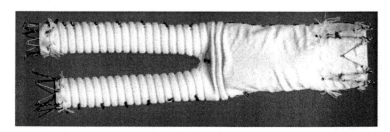

Fig. 23.7. Ancure EVT device (Guidant).

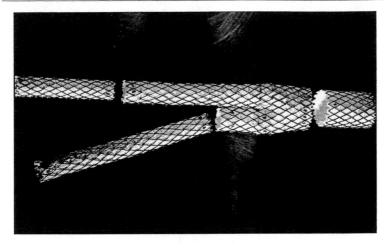

Fig. 23.8. AneuRx device (Medtronic AVE).

Additionally, several other stent-grafts are currently under clinical investigation, including the Vanguard (Boston Scientific Vascular) (Fig. 23.9), Talent (Medtronic AVE) (Fig. 23.10), Excluder (W. L. Gore) (Fig. 23.11), and Zenith (Cook) (Fig. 23.12). They are all self-expanding, modular-design endografts, made of a combination of nitinol or stainless steel stents with a Dacron or PTFE fabric.

Principles of Stent-Graft Implantation Techniques

Endovascular grafting procedures require a combination of surgical maneuvers and approaches with refined interventional skills. They are often difficult, and involve catheter techniques and imaging requirements that are not readily available in most vascular surgery practices today. The collaboration between surgeons and interventionalists is often necessary and occasionally mandated in an investigational protocol!

The following critical steps must be successfully completed in a typical AAA stent-graft procedure utilizing a modular bifurcated device:

Bilateral femoral cutdown approach to the common femoral arteries. In some cases, contralateral limb deployment can be performed percutaneously. It is anticipated that truly percutaneous stent-graft devices may well become available in the future, with one new design (by Cordis Endovascular) set to begin clinical trials in late 1999.

Percutaneous brachial artery catheterization is practiced selectively by some investigators. It can be very useful to facilitate several important steps of the procedure.[18]

High-resolution imaging, including digital subtraction and road-mapping capabilities are mandatory.

Deployment requires retrograde introduction of the device-carrying delivery sheath through the femoral/iliac arteries. Access-related difficulties are often the

Fig. 23.9. Vanguard device (Boston Scientific Vascular)

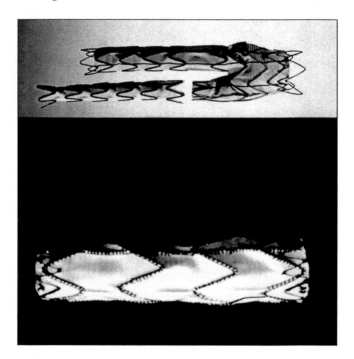

Fig. 23.10. Talent device (Medtronic AVE).

result of challenging anatomy and/or small vessel size and the presence of calcific atherosclerotic occlusive disease. This constitutes one of the two most frequent reasons for anatomical unsuitability for endoluminal repair (the other being the adequacy of the length of proximal aneurysm neck).

Precise deployment in the juxtarenal aorta is most important. Some devices (Talent, Zenith) incorporate a design that allows transrenal fixation of the uncovered proximal stent.

Contralateral limb deployment first necessitates guidewire access across the short leg.

Modular designs allow cephalad (aortic cuff) and caudad (iliac) extensions that may be necessary to optimize placement and correct endoleaks.

Fig. 23.11. Excluder device (W. L. Gore).

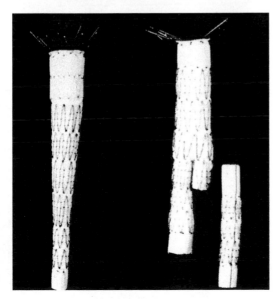

Fig. 23.12. Zenith device (Cook).

Fig. 23.13. Two-piece Talent stent-graft for the thoracic aorta.

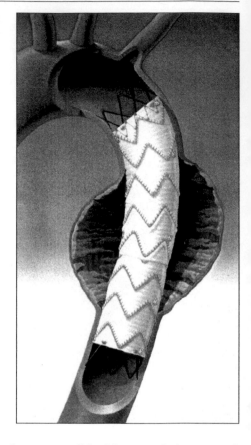

23

The term endoleak denotes the presence of blood flow outside the stent-graft but within the confines of the lumen of the native aorta or iliac arteries. They are usually the result of poor sealing at an attachment site (proximal, distal) or junctions, or expression of branch backflow from patent inferior mesenteric or lumbar arteries.[19]

Endoluminal repair of aneurysms in the descending thoracic aorta is another area under active investigation at this time.[20] Talent (Fig. 23.13), AneuRx and Excluder technologies have developed endografts configured for placement in the thoracic aorta distal to aortic arch branches. Some forms of aortic dissection[21] and traumatic rupture are also being managed with endovascular approaches. However, available data are only preliminary at this time. A much larger clinical experience with longer follow-up will be necessary before a definitive view can be attained concerning the performance of these endografts for treatment of aneurysmal and nonaneurysmal thoracic aortic diseases. It is our preliminary impression that stent-graft repair of descending thoracic aortic aneurysms will rapidly become a popular

Table 23.2. Aortic stent grafts device requirements for technical success

1. Deliverable to target area
2. Secure fixation to vessel wall
3. Bloodtight seal at all junctions

Table 23.3. Aortic stent grafts optimal clinical performance (proposed goals)

• Applicability	> 50%
• Technical success	> 90%
• Procedure time	< 3 hours
• Blood loss	< 500 ml
• Endoleak rate	< 10%
• 30-day mortality	< 3%
• Length of stay	< 3 days
• Overall costs	< surgical Rx

23

approach given the extensive nature and severe morbidity of conventional surgical treatment.

Summary and Overview

Endovascular grafting of aortic aneurysms is clearly feasible and capable of achieving a high degree of technical success. The question of whether it can justifiably replace surgical treatment will not be answerable for several more years until the results of ongoing trials and long-term follow-up data become available. The essential requirements of a successful stent-graft device have been defined (Table 23.2). Optimal clinical performance (Table 23.3) will have to be achieved before endovascular grafting becomes standard treatment for the majority of patients with aneurysms.

Selected Readings

1. Carrel A. Results of the permanent intubation of the thoracic aorta. Surg Gyn Obst 1912; 15:245-248.
2. Dotter CT, Judkins MP. Transluminal treatment of arteriosclerotic obstruction: description of a new technique and a preliminary report of its application. Circulation 1964; 30:654.
3. Dotter CT. Transluminally-placed coil spring endarterial tube grafts. Invest Radiol 1969; 4:329-332.
   Classic article describing percutaneous placement of an expandable nitinol coil stent for peripheral intervention.
4. Dotter CT, Buschman R, McKinney M et al. Transluminal expandable nitinol coil stent grafting: Preliminary report. Radiology 1983; 147:259-160.
5. Donayre CE. Intraluminal grafts: Current status and future perspectives. In: White RA, Fogarty TJ eds. Peripheral Endovascular Interventions. St. Louis: Mosby-Yearbook, 1996; 364-405.
6. Criado FJ, ed. Endovascular Intervention: Basic Concepts and Techniques. Armonk, NY: Futura 1999.

7. Volodos NI, Karpovich IP, Troyan VI et al. Clinical experience with the use of self-fixing synthetic prostheses. Vasa (Suppl) 1991; 33:93-95.

8. Parodi JC. Personal communication (1989).

9. Parodi JC, Palmaz JC, Barone HD. Transfemoral intraluminal graft implantation for abdominal aortic aneurysms. Ann Vasc Surg 1991; 5:491-499.
    This seminal report details Parodi's initial animal and clinical experience with transfemoral intraluminal graft implantation for AAA repair. Feasibility of this technique was demonstrated in animals using a proximal balloon-expandable stent-anchored knitted Dacron graft introduced via retrograde femoral artery cannulation.
    The results of five hi-risk patients who received an individually tailored endograft are also reported. In 3 cases, the endograft had only a proximal stent and in the other two, the graft had stents at both ends. One patient required conversion to open repair because of stent misplacement and in 3 other cases the aneurysm was noted to have decreased in size. This article has obviously had quite an impact on the practice of vascular surgery worldwide.

10. Lazarus HM. Endovascular grafting for the treatment of abdominal aortic aneurysms. Surg Clin North Am 1992; 72:959-968.
    Overview of endovascular AAA repair by the surgeon who was intimately involved with the development of the EVT device.

11. Parodi JC, Criado FJ, Barone HD et al. Endoluminal aortic aneurysm repair using a balloon-expandable stent-graft device: A progress report. Ann Vasc Surg 1994; 8:523-529.
    Twenty-four patients with AAA had 25 endoluminal repair procedures using a stent-graft device. Eighty-three percent of the patients were deemed to be hi-risk for conventional AAA repair. Various device configurations were used including aorto-aortic in 16 patients and aorto-uni-iliac combined with femoral-femoral bypass in 7 patients. Some key technical points are emphasized such as iliac pull-down maneuver for tortuous vessels and temporary prosthetic graft attachment to the common iliac artery to facilitate delivery of the device. Results of this series encouraged the authors to continue to develop this new technique for AAA repair.

12. Yusuf SW, Baker DM, Hind RE et al. Endoluminal transfemoral abdominal aortic aneurysm repair with aorto-uni-iliac graft and femorofemoral bypass. Br J Surg 1995; 82:916.

13. Thompson MM, Sayers RD, Nasim A et al. Aortomonoiliac endovascular grafting: Difficult solutions to difficult problems. J Endovasc Surg 1997; 4:174-181.
    This report details the technique of aortomonoiliac endograft exclusion of AAAs. Contralateral common iliac artery occlusion and extra-anatomic bypass with either femoral-femoral or ilio-femoral graft configurations complete this procedure. Short-term results are reported as acceptable, but the authors' caution that long-term efficacy must be addressed before they can recommend widespread use of this procedure.

14. Lipsitz EC, Ohki T, Veith FJ. What are the indications for endovascular stent-graft repair of abdominal aortic aneurysms: Present status. In: Greenhalgh RM ed. Indications for Vascular and Endovascular Surgery London: WB Saunders, 1998; 211-220.

15. Chuter TA, Green RM, Ouriel K et al. Transfemoral aortic graft placement. J Vasc Surg 1993; 18:185-197.
    This report describes the authors' initial laboratory experience with an endovascular delivery system for straight and bifurcated grafts (patent is held by Dr. Chuter). The technique of endovascular graft insertion was studied in dogs and graft attachment was

23

assessed in human cadaveric aortas. Both types of graft configurations consisted of barbed, self-expanding stents attached to woven polyester fabric.

Immediate postprocedure angiograms demonstrated that the endografts could be deployed within 4.6 ± 1.6 mm of the intended site. No migration or leakage of the device was seen on follow-up angiograms and at 3 months all endografts were patent. These preliminary results demonstrated that these devices could be positioned accurately and securely with the abdominal aorta.

16. Lawrence-Brown M, Sieunarine K, Hartley D et al. Should an anchor stent cross the renal artery orifices when placing an endoluminal graft for abdominal aortic aneurysm? In: Greenhalgh RM ed. Indications for Vascular and Endovascular Surgery London: WB Saunders, 1998; 261-269.

17. Criado FJ, Abul-Khoudoud O, Wellons E et al. Treatment of AAA with the Talent Stent-Graft System: Techniques and Problem Solving. In: Katzen BT and Semba CP eds. Techniques in Vascular and Interventional Radiology. Philadelphia: WB Saunders (In Press).

18. Criado FJ, Abul-Khoudoud O, Barker C et al. Brachial artery catheterization to facilitate endovascular grafting of AAA: safety and rationale. J Vasc Surg (in press).

19. White GH, May J. Failure of endovascular repair of abdominal aortic aneurysms: endoleak, adverse events and grading of technical difficulty. In: Greenhalgh RM, ed. The Durability of Vascular and Endovascular Surgery London: WB Saunders 1999; 357-373.

20. Mitchell RS, Dake MD, Semba CP et al. Endovascular stent-graft repair of thoracic aortic aneurysms. J Thorac Cardiovasc Surg 1996; 111:1054-1062.

    This report demonstrates the feasibility of endovascular repair of aneurysms of the descending thoracic aorta. Thoracic aortic stent-grafts were deployed in 44 patients. Each graft was individually constructed from a self-expanding Z stent covered with Dacron polyester fabric. In 12 cases open surgery was performed in conjunction with graft deployment. Patients were followed for a mean of 12.6 months with computed tomography and angiography.

    One of the three early deaths was from graft failure and two of the late deaths were likely from aneurysm rupture. Paraparesis or paraplegia occurred in 2 patients and in one, this complication was associated with early death. Immediate aneurysm thrombosis was achieved in 36 patients, and late thrombosis occurred in 3 others. Five patients did not experience complete thrombosis of their aneurysm. Admirably, conversion to an open procedure was required in only 1 patient. Distal embolization and stent migration were not observed during the short follow-up period.

21. Nienaber CA, Fattori R, Lund G et al. Nonsurgical reconstruction of thoracic aortic dissection by stent-graft placement. N Engl J Med 1999; 340:1559-1545.

    The safety and efficacy of elective transluminal stent-graft insertion in 12 consecutive patients with type B aortic dissection was compared to surgical repair in 12 matched controls. Stent-graft repair was successful in all patients and there was no morbidity or mortality! However, there were 4 deaths (33%, p=0.09) in the surgery group and five serious adverse events (42%, p=0.04) within 12 months of the procedure. Interestingly, in the endograft group there was no instances of paraplegia, stroke, embolization, side-branch occlusion or infection. Nine patients in this group did experience "postimplantation syndrome" with transient elevation of body temperature, C-reactive protein plus mild leukocytosis.

23

CHAPTER 24

Endovascular Management of Aortoiliac Occlusive Disease

Reese A. Wain and Frank J. Veith

Over the past two decades, treatment of atherosclerotic aortoiliac occlusive disease has changed dramatically. In the past, patients were treated with either operative endarterectomy, anatomic or extra-anatomic bypasses. Now patients can be treated with less invasive techniques such as balloon angioplasty and intra-arterial stenting. However, despite many apparent advantages of angioplasty and stenting, their overall utility and long-term efficacy remain a matter of ongoing debate. Endovascular grafts (endoluminally inserted prosthetic grafts attached to metallic stents) have been used extensively for the treatment of aortic aneurysmal disease but, can also be used to treat stenotic and occlusive aortoiliac lesions. By combining the durability and proven efficacy of prosthetic bypass grafts with the less invasive characteristics of angioplasty and stenting, these devices are poised to assume an increasing role in the future management of aortoiliac occlusive disease. The purpose of this chapter is to provide an overview of endovascular grafts and endovascular grafting techniques as they apply to the treatment of atherosclerotic lesions in the aorta and iliac arteries.

An endovascular graft consists of a prosthetic graft that is mated to an attachment device, typically consisting of one of several varieties of metallic stents. This device, in an unexpanded state, is loaded into a specially designed delivery sheath. After percutaneous access is achieved or a surgical cut-down is performed, the delivery sheath is inserted over a guidewire into an access vessel and advanced to the site of disease. The delivery sheath is then removed leaving the endovascular graft in place. Finally, the endovascular graft is expanded so that the stent attaches the prosthetic graft to the arterial wall. In this fashion, prograde blood flow is directed into the graft and the arterial lesion is effectively bypassed.

Currently, two varieties of endovascular devices are being used clinically to treat symptomatic aortoiliac lesions. The first type is inserted percutaneously, usually in an interventional suite, and consists of a short self-expanding stent that is covered along its entire length by prosthetic material. These types of devices, also known as covered stents, are similar to conventional stents and have been used to treat short segmental lesions that have undergone balloon angioplasty. At Montefiore Medical Center in New York, our focus has been on using a device which is conceptually more similar to a surgically inserted bypass graft than a conventional stent. We perform our procedure in the operating suite and obtain open exposure of a relevant

Aortic Surgery, edited by Jeffrey L. Ballard. ©2000 Landes Bioscience.

access vessel- usually the common femoral artery. Fluoroscopic guidance is used to insert a device consisting of a long prosthetic graft attached to a Palmaz balloon-expandable stent (Johnson & Johnson Interventional Systems, Warren, NJ, USA). The stent portion of the device fixes the graft to the luminal surface of the artery proximal to the site of disease. The distal aspect of the graft is retrieved from within the arteriotomy and the distal anastomosis is hand sewn according to the patient's pattern of outflow disease. In contrast to covered stents, these endovascular grafts reline the entire length of the diseased vasculature. Therefore, they can be used to treat patients with long segment aortoiliac disease. In addition, because the distal anastomosis can be tailored to the patients' pattern of infrainguinal occlusive disease as well, a wider range of potential patients can be treated.

Covered Stents

24

Early reports on the use of covered stents for the treatment of aortoiliac occlusive disease have come from centers using the "Cragg CndoPro System 1" (Mintec, Inc., Grand Bahama Island, The Bahamas) and the Hemobahn endograft (W.L. Gore & Associates, Flagstaff, Arizona).

The Cragg CndoPro System 1 is a self-expanding Nitinol stent with a woven polyester covering. In Europe, Henry et al used this device to treat nonocclusive iliac artery lesions varying in length between 3 and 20 cm. The 19 treated patients had typical risk factors for peripheral vascular disease and were predominantly treated for claudication. These patients underwent covered stent insertion to manage stenoses, dissections or recurrences following balloon angioplasty. Local anesthetics were administered and percutaneous access to the femoral artery ipsilateral to the lesion was achieved to facilitate treatment. Guidewire and catheter based techniques were used to cross the lesion and an angioplasty balloon was used for dilatation purposes. The appropriate size covered stent was then chosen and inserted through a 50 cm long 9Fr introducer sheath. A "pusher" catheter held the graft in place as the delivery sheath was removed and the graft was allowed to expand. An angioplasty balloon was then used to dilate the covered stent to improve its fixation to the luminal surface of the artery.

In their experience, technical success was achieved in all patients as assessed by an improvement in the percent stenosis of the lesion treated and by a decrease in the pressure gradient across the lesion. In addition, improved postprocedure noninvasive vascular lab studies were noted in all treated patients. Long-term patency was not available. However, all of the grafts were open at 8 months. One of the covered stents protruded from the common iliac artery into the aorta and obstructed flow in the contralateral limb necessitating placement of a stent in the previously unaffected limb. Based on this early clinical experience, the authors concluded that covered stents do appear to be useful in the treatment of some iliac lesions.

Pernes et al also used the Cragg Endopro system to treat 10 patients with iliac lesions 6 cm or greater in length with fifteen covered stents. These patients were also primarily claudicants. In this series, technical success was achieved in 90% of the patients treated. Technical failure occurred in one patient whose external iliac artery ruptured when the lesion being treated was dilated by an angioplasty balloon. An attempt was made to treat this complication with a covered stent, however, the stent thrombosed the following day and the patient required an operative bypass. Two of the patients in this series developed recurrences; one patient was successfully managed with additional balloon dilatation and the fate of the second patient was not reported. Finally, one of the treated patients developed an asymptomatic stenosis within a covered stent. This patient required an additional intervention to balloon dilate the lesion.

Clinical use of the Hemobahn endograft (an ePTFE tube which is supported by a Nitinol exoskeleton) was reported in 1998 by Allen et al. They treated 7 patients with long-standing iliac artery occlusive disease. Contrary to the patients treated in the previously mentioned studies, many of these patients had limb-threatening ischemia. The length of lesion averaged 4.6 cm. A 100% technical success rate was achieved and the postprocedure ankle-brachial indices improved as well in all patients. Three patients experienced iliac artery dissection during the procedure, which in no case necessitated further intervention. One patient did require further intervention when embolic matter rendered the contralateral extremity acutely ischemic.

Endovascular Grafts

The Montefiore Experience

The endovascular grafts we use are constructed from 30 mm Palmaz balloon expandable stents and 6 mm polytetrafluoroethylene (PTFE) grafts (W.L. Gore and Associates, Flagstaff, Arizona, USA). Each graft is attached to a stent at one end with CV-6 PTFE sutures (W.L. Gore and Associates) so that approximately one-half of the stents predeployment length is covered. This endovascular graft is loaded onto an 8 mm x 3 or 4 cm angioplasty balloon (Blue Max or PMT, Medi-tech, Inc., Watertown, MA, USA) which, when inflated, expands the stent. The graft-balloon complex is then inserted into a hemostatic sheath which delivers the device to its deployment site. A second angioplasty balloon (tip balloon) is inserted into the delivery sheath adjacent to the endovascular graft and is positioned so that it protrudes from the open end of the sheath. Inflation of this balloon provides a tapered end to the delivery sheath to facilitate its insertion. In addition, it provides a seal so that the sheath can be pressurized to increase its pushability (Fig. 24.1).

These procedures are performed in the operating room under local, regional or general anesthesia and in contradistinction to those who insert covered stents, we obtain open arterial control of the remote access vessel. After a cut-down is performed and the femoral artery is controlled in standard fashion, a 16-gauge single wall needle is used for a direct arterial puncture. A 7Fr hemostatic sheath is then inserted in an over-the-wire fashion and catheter-guidewire techniques are utilized to cross stenotic lesions under fluoroscopic guidance. If an arterial occlusion is being treated, the vessel must be recanalized before the endovascular graft can be deployed. Recanalization is preferentially performed via an over-the-top approach using a guidewire inserted through a percutaneous puncture of the contralateral femoral artery. This approach is not undertaken if the contralateral femoral or iliac artery is occluded. The over-the-top approach more reliably establishes a recanalization plane

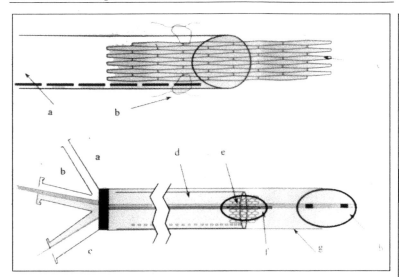

Fig. 24.1. Components of an endovascular graft. (Top) An ePTFE graft (a) has been sutured with PTFE sutures (b) to a Palmaz balloon expandable stent (c). (Bottom) The endovascular graft, which consists of the PTFE material (d) and the Palmaz stent (e) are mounted on an angioplasty balloon (f) and placed within a delivery sheath (g). The "tip balloon" (h) is alongside the endovascular graft within the delivery sheath. The sheath has hemostatic ports for saline infusion (a) and for the tip (b) and endovascular graft (c) balloon catheters.

within the true lumen of the vessel than does a retrograde approach which often results in a subintimal recanalization plane.

Once a guidewire has crossed the diseased arterial segment, the patient is systemically anticoagulated and the entire length of the iliac artery being treated is dilated with an 8 mm angioplasty balloon. This dilatation maximizes the luminal diameter of the vessel so that the delivery sheath containing the endovascular graft can be delivered without excessive friction. In addition, it ensures that the endovascular graft, once deployed, can expand to its full diameter.

Next, an appropriately sized longitudinal arteriotomy is fashioned in the common femoral artery and the delivery sheath is inserted. The delivery sheath is advanced under fluoroscopic guidance until the stent containing portion of the graft abuts the proximal most portion of the diseased vessel. The tip balloon is then deflated and partially withdrawn along with the delivery sheath. These maneuvers leave the endovascular graft and its associated deployment balloon in place. The deployment balloon is then inflated to secure the stent and proximal portion of the endovascular graft to the arterial wall. When the delivery sheath is totally withdrawn, the distal unstented portion of the endovascular graft can be retrieved from within the arteriotomy (Figs. 24.2-24.10). Finally, the entire length of the endovascular graft is dilated with an angioplasty balloon to fully expand the graft and reduce the possibility of kinking.

Fig. 24.2. After a cut-down was performed, a sheath has been placed into the common femoral artery.

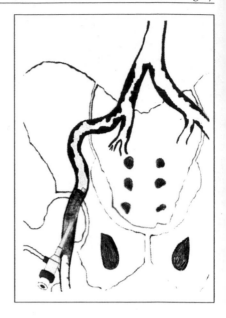

Fig. 24.3. Guidewire and catheter based techniques have been used to traverse a diffusely diseased iliac artery.

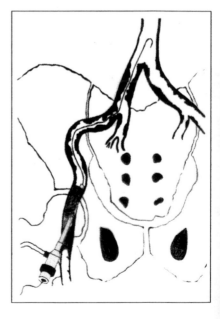

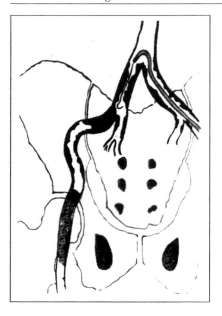

Fig. 24.4. In the presence of an iliac artery occlusion, an over-the-top approach is utilized to establish a recanalization plane.

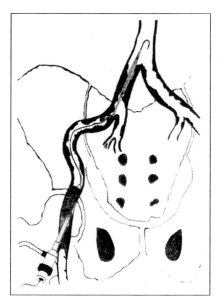

Fig. 24.5. An angioplasty balloon has been inserted at the proximal most portion of the diseased vessel and is ready to be inflated.

Fig. 24.6. Balloon angioplasty of the proximal common iliac artery is undertaken.

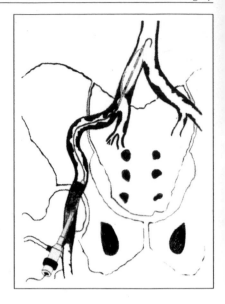

Fig. 24.7. The balloon angioplasty catheter has been deflated and pulled back to a more proximal location before being reinflated.

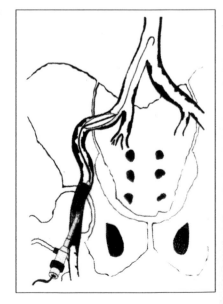

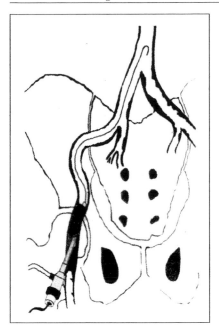

Fig. 24.8. The entire length of the iliac artery being treated has undergone sequential balloon angioplasty. The balloon catheter has been removed to facilitate insertion of the delivery sheath housing the endovascular graft.

24

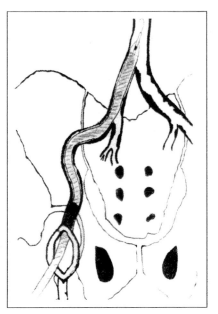

Fig. 24.9. An arteriotomy has been performed and the hemostatic delivery system is advanced into position.

Fig. 24.10. The delivery sheath has been removed and the endovascular graft was deployed. Note that the distal aspect of the endovascular graft has been retrieved from within the arteriotomy.

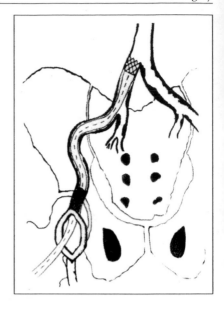

Once the graft has been successfully deployed, the distal anastomosis is constructed. Typically, we perform an endoluminal anastomosis within the common femoral artery and close the overlying arteriotomy with a prosthetic patch (Fig. 24.11A-B). Early in our experience we did not routinely patch the arteriotomies and several instances of anastomotic narrowing occurred. In the presence of coexisting bilateral occlusive disease, the arteriotomy can be covered with the hood of a femorofemoral crossover graft. Alternatively, if the ipsilateral femoral artery bifurcation vessels are occluded, the endovascular graft can be brought out from the femoral arteriotomy and anastomosed in a conventional fashion to a more distal vessel or bypass graft (Fig. 24.12A-B).

Completion arteriography is routinely performed in the operating room following the insertion of our devices. One of the most common postinsertion arteriographic finding mid-graft stenosis. These stenoses can result from inadequate expansion of the endovascular graft or from the graft being compressed by residual disease within the native vasculature. To treat these lesions, repeat balloon dilatations are undertaken and stents are placed as needed. All patients also undergo postoperative duplex ultrasonography of their grafts and lower extremity pulse-volume recordings. These tests are repeated at three months and six months after surgery and then every six months thereafter. Additional arteriograms are obtained if there is a significant change in the patient's pulse examination, if there is a decrease of greater than 0.15 in the ankle-brachial index or if a duplex study documents a hemodynamically significant flow disturbance.

Over a four-year interval, we have treated 52 patients with aortoiliac occlusive disease using endovascular grafts. Twenty-five of the patients were men and 27 were

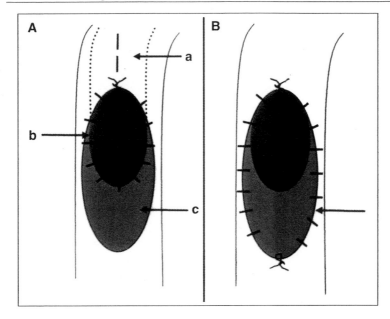

24

Fig. 24.11. Endoluminal Anastomosis. A. The distal portion of the PTFE graft (a) is hand sutured to the luminal surface of the common femoral artery using a running PTFE suture (b). The anastomosis is performed entirely through the arteriotomy(c). B. After the anastomosis has been completed; the arteriotomy is closed with a suitably sized prosthetic patch (arrow).

women. The mean age of these patients was 65 years and the percentage of patients with diabetes, hypertension, coronary artery disease and cigarette smoking was 63, 60, 50 and 50 respectively. Seventy-three percent of the patients had two or more of these risk factors and two-thirds of the patients had previously undergone aortoiliac or infrainguinal bypass. In contradistinction to many patients treated with covered stents, none of the patients treated were considered candidates for management with conventional balloon angioplasty and stenting largely because of long segment occlusions, eccentrically calcified stenoses and disadvantaged outflow. Similarly, most of these patients were judged to be medically unfit for aortic reconstruction.

Eighty-one percent of patients had severe lower extremity ischemia with tissue loss (gangrene or ulceration) and the remaining patients had rest pain. Fifty-eight endovascular grafts were inserted to treat 68 at-risk limbs. At the beginning of the series, six patients with bilateral lower extremity ischemia received separate iliofemoral grafts on each side. Of late, 10 patients with bilateral symptomatic limbs were treated with unilateral aortofemoral endovascular bypass combined with a femorofemoral bypass. Slightly more than half of the patients we treated required concurrent lower extremity bypasses and most of these terminated at the popliteal artery level.

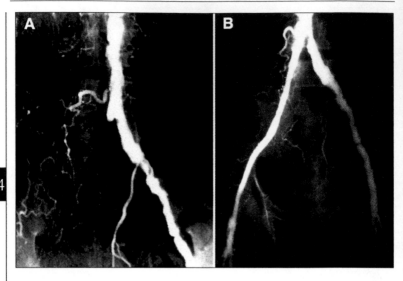

Fig. 24.12. A. Preoperative arteriogram of a patient with limb threatening right leg ischemia secondary to iliac artery and superficial femoral artery occlusions. B. The patient was treated with an endovascular graft originating within a recanalized right common iliac artery. The graft terminated within the right common femoral artery and the arteriotomy was covered with the hood of a femoropopliteal bypass graft.

Eighty-eight percent of patients treated with endovascular grafts had complete follow-up for between three and 57 months. Median length of follow-up was 22 months following surgery and only six patients were lost to follow-up. Four-year primary endovascular graft patency was 66%. Fifteen endovascular grafts in 14 patients lost their primary patency a mean of seven months postoperatively. Of these, seven grafts in six patients were reopened by operative thrombectomy and graft revision. Four additional grafts were salvaged following infusion of thrombolytic agents and the remaining four grafts stayed closed. Total secondary patency was 72% over four years. Eleven grafts in nine patients failed a mean of 11 months postoperatively and could not be reopened. Three of these patients went on to require major extremity amputation.

In total, six patients required an amputation (four above knee, two below knee) during the study interval for a four-year limb salvage rate of 89%. Twenty-three patients (44%) died within four years of surgery for a cumulative survival rate of only 37%. Of the deaths, only three occurred in the perioperative (30-day) period. One of these patients suffered from visceral and lower extremity microembolization and two succumbed to myocardial infarctions. Mean length of time to death in patients surviving their perioperative course was 21 months.

Other Experiences

Nevelstein et al recently reported their initial experience using endovascular grafts to treat patients with aortoiliac occlusive disease. Using a similar approach 29 endovascular grafts were inserted to treat 17 patients with limb-threatening ischemia and seven patients with claudication. Technical success was achieved in 15 patients and in the remaining two patients, they were unable to recanalize occlusive lesions. The reported follow-up varied between two and 22 months with an average of 13 months. Primary and secondary endovascular graft patency was 85% and 95% respectively at one year.

Discussion

Although results achieved in our series are inferior to those generally reported for aortofemoral bypass, the patients treated were unsuitable candidates for aortic bypass procedures. In fact, these results compare favorably with those for high-risk patients treated with axillofemoral and femorofemoral bypass. By inserting an endovascular graft in patients with multiple and severe coexisting medical problems, local or regional anesthesia can be used and the cardiac and pulmonary stress of general anesthesia and aortic cross clamping can be avoided. In addition, transperitoneal access to the abdominal aorta can be averted in patients with colostomies, hernias, prosthetic mesh, adhesions from multiple previous operations and intraabdominal infections.

Favorable midterm patency rates for endovascular aorto- or iliofemoral grafts are probably explained by their origin in high-flow central vessels and by their comparatively short lengths. These factors may allow endovascular grafts to perform better than axillofemoral grafts which are longer and originate in smaller, more peripheral vessels which themselves may be diseased. In addition, an in-line endovascular graft, unlike an extra-anatomic bypass, does not put an uninvolved extremity at risk for complications such as infection, seroma, anastomotic disruption or distal embolization.

A potential advantage of endovascular grafts over balloon angioplasty and stenting is that the entire length of a diseased vessel can be treated rather than just a short isolated segment of the vessel. When isolated lesions are treated with angioplasty and stenting, the subsequent development of proximal or outflow lesions can jeopardize the extremity. Endovascular grafts may have an advantage in this regard in that the entire iliac artery is lined with a prosthetic graft which is less likely to be thrombogenic than a diffusely diseased vessel that is unlined and has been subjected to mechanical intervention. Throughout our experience we have been concerned that by dilating the entire length of an iliac artery, graft constriction could occur secondary to disease progression or recoil of the native arterial wall. However, there were no intragraft lesions in the follow-up period. Instead, late graft failure resulted from intimal hyperplasia at the anastomotic sites or progression of infrainguinal outflow disease.

Another advantage of endovascular grafts over standard angioplasty and stenting procedures is that the grafts can be inserted through an open arteriotomy. This approach permits concomitant treatment of existing disease within the common and deep femoral arteries. In addition, conventional stenting may be contraindicated when there is circumferential calcification of the aorta or iliac vessels and arterial rupture can occur. Endovascular grafts may be placed in the presence of severe calcification and have in fact been used to treat patients in whom arterial rupture has occurred secondary to vigorous balloon dilatation.

Limitations of endovascular grafts include the need to sacrifice collateral vessels along the course of the grafts and the relatively large diameter delivery sheaths that current devices require. Sacrificing collateral vessels such as the hypogastric artery or those originating from the external iliac or femoral arteries, can render patients more ischemic than they had been previously if the endovascular graft should fail. In addition, if the graft fails and the patient requires an amputation, the level of the amputation may be higher for the reasons cited above than if a standard graft had failed. This was the case in two of our patients who required high above knee amputation. Finally, the presence of the intraluminal graft may limit further options for revascularization. Currently, patients with small iliac vessels cannot be treated with our delivery sheaths (19F outer diameter). However, technologic innovations may render future generations of these devices smaller, easier to insert and more applicable to a wider range of patients.

Conclusions

At the present time, patients with symptomatic localized or short focal aortoiliac lesions are likely best served by angioplasty with or without stenting. However, covered stents should probably continue to be evaluated as an alternative treatment in these patients. Patients with long segmental stenoses or occlusions without severe coexisting medical problems or prohibitive anatomy should undergo standard aortofemoral bypass. However, based on our four-year results, we believe that endovascular grafts are a viable alternative to aortofemoral and extra-anatomic bypass in high-risk patients with diffuse aortoiliac involvement and anatomic contraindications to standard procedures. In the future, innovations in endovascular graft design and insertion techniques should lead to expanded indications for this evolving less-invasive procedure.

Selected Readings

1. Henry M, Amor M, Ethevenot G et al. Initial Clinical Experience with the Cragg Endopro System 1 for Intraluminal Treatment of Peripheral Vascular Disease. J Endovasc Surg 1994; 1:31-43.
    This manuscript represents one of the earliest reported series documenting the feasibility of using covered endovascular prostheses to treat stenotic iliac artery lesions. The authors were able to show that these devices could be safely inserted via a percutaneous route and maintain high initial vessel patency rates with a small number of complications.
2. Allen BT, Hovsepian DM, Reilly JM et al. Endovascular Stent Grafts for Aneurysmal and Occlusive Vascular Disease. Am J Surg 1998; 176(6):574-80.
    This paper included a more contemporary series of patients treated with a low profile industry made device. The number of patients reported in this manuscript is small. However, the authors successfully treated patients with long lesions and limb-threatening ischemia rather than an easier to treat cohort of claudicants. Despite a moderate complication rate, the authors achieved a 100% technical success rate and were able to

24

    demonstrate how covered stents could successfully treat complications of balloon angioplasty such as intimal dissection.

3.   Ohki T, Marin ML, Veith FJ et al. Endovascular aortounifemoral grafts and femorofemoral bypass for bilateral limb-threatening ischemia. J Vasc Surg 1996; 24:984-997.

    This is an excellent primer on the use of endovascular grafts combined with conventional femorofemoral bypass to treat patients with bilateral limb-threatening ischemia. The manuscript includes a detailed description of the construction of endovascular grafts and an equally complete tutorial on how they should be inserted.

4.   Wain RA, Veith FJ, Marin ML et al. Analysis of endovascular graft treatment for aortoiliac occlusive disease. What is its role based on midterm results? Annals of Surgery 1999; 230(2):145-151.

    This manuscript chronicles one institution's experience using homemade endovascular grafts to treat a series of patients with aortoiliac occlusive disease and limb-threatening ischemia. The paper not only provides a detailed description of how endovascular grafts are constructed but has enough information on insertion techniques to allow a surgeon with the necessary endovascular skills to begin deploying his/her own devices. In addition, the longest and most complete published follow-up of patients with endovascular grafts placed for occlusive disease is reported.

24

CHAPTER 25

Management of Intra-abdominal Disease in Conjunction with Aortic Surgery

John J. Ricotta and Paul S. van Bemmelen

Much of the available literature on concomitant intra-abdominal surgery predates minimally invasive procedures such as ERCP and laparoscopic cholecystectomy. Furthermore, rapid changes occur in diagnostic imaging technology, which lead to new and different coincidental findings during the work-up of various intra-abdominal conditions. Management of intra-abdominal pathology encountered during aortic surgery is based on anecdote and personal experience more than it is on hard data. The coexistence of aortic and other intra-abdominal pathology is uncommon enough that no large or randomized series exist to provide level one data for the clinician. Rather, therapeutic decisions must be made based on clinical assessment of several factors. These include relative severity of the aortic and nonaortic conditions, risk of aortic graft infection (which should be considered a highly lethal complication), risk of aortic rupture if aneurysmorrhaphy is delayed, indication for concomitant procedure (prophylactic versus therapeutic) and complexity of the proposed procedure. In each case, the goal should be to minimize patient risk while avoiding an unnecessary second operation. The ensuing chapter will discuss rationale for a selective approach to these problems.

As a general rule, resection of an aortic aneurysm will take precedence over any other intra-abdominal operation. This is based on the risk of death from rupture of the aorta. While the risk of rupture increases with aneurysm diameter, most patients will come to operation because their aneurysm meets size criterion, which cause significant concern of rupture. There are anecdotal reports of aneurysm rupture after nonvascular surgery.[1] While this issue remains speculative, there is no doubt that any series of events which postpones the resection of an aneurysm which is large enough for resection will expose the patient to some increased risk of rupture during the interval. Since complications may attend any surgery, it is always best judgement to perform the most critical operation first under the assumption that unforeseen events may postpone a second procedure. Exception to this rule occurs when intra-abdominal emergencies are present such as hemorrhage, perforation or obstruction. In these cases aneurysmorrhaphy is usually deferred because of the fear of infecting the aortic graft. However, as will be discussed below, there are even exceptions to this generalization.

Aortic Surgery, edited by Jeffrey L. Ballard. ©2000 Landes Bioscience.

Unanticipated Concurrent Disease

Due to sophisticated diagnostic and imaging modalities usually employed prior to elective aortic surgery, concomitant disease is often anticipated prior to celiotomy. However, there are occasions when a patient is operated on for an acute gastrointestinal problem and an incidental aneurysm is discovered, or conversely, additional intra-abdominal pathology is discovered during routine exploration at the time of aneurysmorrhaphy. These situations will be discussed separately.

Patients may undergo urgent laparotomy for an acute abdomen (including the preoperative diagnosis of ruptured AAA) and be found to have an intact aneurysm with concomitant intra-abdominal pathology. In general aneurysmorrhaphy is deferred under these circumstances and the acute event is addressed. Valentine et al,[2] recently reported an exceedingly high mortality for patients operated on emergently for presumed rupture of an aortic aneurysm when the aneurysm was intact. This was often due to the occurrence of other acute pathology, most often myocardial ischemia. Thus, when these patients are encountered, we believe that aneurysmorrhaphy should be deferred and the acute problem identified and addressed. In many cases, the problem is infectious (appendicitis, cholecystitis, diverticulitis), obstructive or an intestinal perforation. In each circumstance the risk of infection of the aneurysm and the instability of the patient makes delay of aneurysm surgery judicious. Operation should be directed at removing the source of potential contamination as completely as possible and minimizing the chance of postoperative complications. Copious irrigation of the peritoneal cavity, including antibiotic solutions, should be employed to reduce the rate of late contamination. This is particularly true when the aneurysm is >6 cm., since postoperative complications can delay future aneurysm resection. In general, small intestinal anastomoses are acceptable but any large bowel anastomosis should be avoided because of the possibility of an anastomotic leak or intra-abdominal abscess. In the case where resection of the large bowel is indicated, diverting colostomy should be performed. If operation on the stomach or duodenum is required, procedures with the low risk of anastomotic leak and least chance of contamination should be selected. When operation on the gall bladder is required, manipulation of the common bile duct should be minimized and whenever possible common duct exploration deferred in favor of delayed endoscopic approaches. In these cases, aneurysm resection should be considered after 2-4 months, when the inflammatory process has subsided. There is some data suggestion that bacteria may be harbored in intestinal or retroperitoneal lymphatics for months after an acute abdominal process, thus increasing the risk of contamination at subsequent aortic surgery. However delay must be balanced against the risk of rupture. In general, it is our recommendation to perform a CT scan to exclude active intra-abdominal processes or residual inflammation before planning secondary elective aneurysmorrhaphy. In these cases we suggest bowel prep and prophylactic antibiotics which cover intestinal flora as well as skin flora.

On occasion, intestinal perforation occurs during operative exposure for elective aneurysm resection. This is usually the result of lysing adhesions. If the perforation is in the small intestine or the stomach and spillage is limited, we are comfortable with proceeding with aneurysm resection after copious irrigation of the abdomen and secure closure of the gastrointestinal tract. However if the colon is injured, even in the presence of bowel prep and prophylactic antibiotics, we believe that aneurysm resection should be deferred for at least 4-6 weeks. In such cases, since they are usually occasioned by dense adhesions, reoperation is performed through the retroperitoneal approach.

During elective surgery for either aneurysm or nonvascular abdominal conditions, unexpected pathology may be encountered during preliminary exploration of the abdomen. Several reports suggest that biliary pathology occurs in about 10% of patients. Nonbiliary gastrointestinal pathology may be present in as many as 5% of cases.[3,4] Exploration should always include palpation of the infrarenal aorta, particularly in men > 65 years of age. In this cohort the incidence of aortic aneurysm is 2-4%. When an aneurysm is found, decision on how to proceed will depend on the indication for celiotomy and aneurysm size. Small aneurysms (< 5 cm) can be observed and evaluated electively for resection. The unexpected finding of a large aneurysm may prompt aortic resection, as will be discussed below. Conversely, the vascular surgeon may encounter unexpected gastrointestinal, gynecologic or genitourinary pathology during a planned aortic resection. In the majority of cases the patient has not been adequately prepared for bowel resection and this must be deferred and aneurysmorrhaphy performed. If the lesion is inflammatory this should be dealt with as discussed above and the aortic procedure postponed. When it appears that there may be an unanticipated malignancy, treatment should be individualized. In all cases, a thorough evaluation for potential metastasis should be undertaken, including evaluation of lymph nodes and the liver as appropriate. Nodes may be sent for permanent or frozen section without compromising the potential for aneurysm resection. Ovarian lesions may be removed without excessive fear of contamination, however we are hesitant to treat uterine lesions. If it appears that the patient has disseminated malignancy, attempts should be made to establish this diagnosis by frozen section. If this proves to be the case, the surgeon must consider whether aneurysm resection is still indicated. In general, most vascular surgeons would not perform aneurysmorrhaphy in the face of widely disseminated malignant disease. On rare occasions, a surgeon will encounter an asymptomatic nearly obstructing lesion of the intestinal tract. Management of these lesions will be discussed later in the chapter.

Planning the Management of Combined Lesions

Most often, surgeons are aware of combined vascular and nonvascular pathology prior to operation. This allows for planning the management of these lesions. As stated above, the basic principles of care are to minimize the risk to the patient, the most important of which are death from aortic rupture and graft infection. In most situations this results in sequential operations, however in some circumstances concomitant procedures are acceptable. These situations will be discussed individually below.

Aorta Surgery and Gallstones

Controversy exists in the literature regarding the appropriateness of removal of the gallbladder during an operation on the aorta. At least three different scenarios should be considered separately:

1. Asymptomatic gallstones
2. A patient with symptoms that could be attributable to gallstones, which may have led to the incidental discovery of an aortic aneurysm
3. Acute cholecystitis, with an asymptomatic aortic aneurysm.

Asymptomatic Gallstones: The Case for a Combined Approach

This is one of the more common scenarios of combined disease, due to the relative frequency of gallstones in the aneurysm population. The near universal use of ultrasound and/or CT scanning in the diagnosis of aneurysm disease often provides this information to the surgeon preoperatively. When gallstones are diagnosed before aortic operation, the surgeon should attempt to elicit any symptoms of biliary tract disease from the patient. This may not always be initially apparent, since the symptoms of biliary disease are often nonspecific, however the questions must always be asked. Laboratory investigation to evaluate the possibility of choledocholithiasis (alkaline phosphates, bilirubin and liver enzymes) should be performed prior to surgery. If there is suggestion of choledocholithiasis, this should be evaluated and if possible, treated endoscopically prior to laparotomy. If the biliary tract lesion can be treated by simple cholecystectomy this is performed at the time of aneurysm resection, after the aortic graft is in place and the posterior peritoneum closed. This approach is based on experience over several decades which suggests that cholecystectomy in such cases is associated with minimal additional morbidity.[5] While the risk of post-operative cholecystitis is small, the diagnosis may be difficult to make in a patient recovering from a laparotomy, since symptoms of abdominal pain, ileus, fever and even jaundice may be ascribed to other conditions. The late incidence of symptomatic cholelithiasis is low in patients following aneurysmorrhaphy, however the occurrence of this problem will likely require laparotomy or at least a laparoscopic procedure. It follows from this discussion that prophylactic cholecystectomy for asymptomatic or mildly symptomatic cholelithiasis is acceptable practice, yet this is not a universally held opinion. Several authors believe that prophylactic removal of the gall bladder is unnecessarily meddlesome and exposes the patient to increased risk of perioperative complication, a position outlined below. Patients do need to be carefully selected and discretion in case selection is likely the reason for low complication rates in reported series of combined procedures. Prophylactic removal of a contracted or scarred gallbladder or one that is partially intra-hepatic, is not recommended, nor is common bile duct exploration. These are the cases associated with increased complications and prophylactic operation in these cases should be avoided. If the biliary tract disease is symptomatic, if a complex operation is anticipated, or if there is evidence of biliary sepsis combined procedures are contraindicated. In general symptomatic or infected cases are done before aortic surgery while complex asymptomatic cases are not operated upon. The basic principle is to provide the patient the benefit of removing a pathologic organ without undue increased risk. In cases where a patient is explored for an acute aneurysm and cholecystitis is found, cholecystectomy alone should be performed. It is important to emphasize that when biliary tract disease is known or suspected, prophylactic antibiotic coverage should include gram negative organisms known to be associated with the biliary tract.

As stated, when cholecystectomy is combined with aneurysm resection, the biliary operation is deferred until aneurysmorrhaphy is completed, the posterior peritoneum closed and heparin reversed. Cholangiography or any manipulation of the common bile duct should be minimized and the sub-hepatic space is not drained unless absolutely necessary. With proper patient selection drainage rarely becomes an issue. If the patient is unstable or the aneurysm resection complex, cholecystectomy is deferred. However we do feel there is benefit to removing the abnormal gallbladders of patients with ruptured aneurysms if they have tolerated resection well and the additional operation is expeditious. We justify this seemingly paradoxical approach based on the increased risk of biliary problems, and the difficulty of diagnosis, in the patient with a ruptured AAA. When cholelithiasis is noted at surgery and the gallbladder is not removed, the surgeon must have a heightened sensitivity to the possibility of postoperative complications from biliary sources.

Asymptomatic Gallstones: The Case for a Conservative Approach

The most common situation, due to the high incidence of gallstones in the age group with aortic disease is the combination of asymptomatic gallstones in a patient scheduled to undergo elective aorta surgery. Evans et al[6] performed screening of 394 aortic-reconstruction patients using preoperative oral cholecystography and found gallbladder disease in 73 patients (18%). The risk of postoperative cholecystitis was low and the long-term sequelae of those with retained diseased gallbladders were not judged to be significant. Concomitant cholecystectomy in the asymptomatic patient is not justified by these data. Asymptomatic cholelithiasis is generally a benign disease, with development of symptoms at the rate of approximately 1%/year.[6,7] Postoperative cholecystitis after AAA resection is mainly seen after a ruptured AAA and may be acalculous.[7]

Gallstones with Symptoms: The Case for a Conservative Approach

No prospective randomized study is available to answer whether simultaneous cholecystectomy is advisable or not. On one hand, several relatively small retrospective patient-series are showing that it is possible to safely remove gallbladders, without a statistically significant increase in graft infections.[5,8] On the other hand, theoretical arguments are made, that an unnecessary increased risk of graft infection is likely.[8] Over age 70, the percentage of positive bile cultures taken at cholecystectomy is as high as 72%. The lymphatic drainage of the biliary tree can go to peri-aortic nodes.

Dissection at the level of the left renal vein will lacerate some of these lymphatics and can expose the proximal anastomosis to potential contamination even if the posterior peritoneum is closed over the graft prior to the cholecystectomy.[8]

An increase in serious complications with concomitant cholecystectomy was reported by Bickerstaff et al[4] of 45 patients with concomitant cholecystectomy, 36% developed complications and 4.4% died. The interpretation of this is difficult, however, as these complications did not seem directly related to the cholecystectomy itself, suggesting that patient selection rather than the operation was the deciding factor.

For symptomatic gallstones, a series by Fry[8] mentioned no instances of aneurysm rupture, when the gallbladder was removed first. Anecdotal reports of postoperative rupture of AAA after laparotomy started speculation about generalized increase in collagenase activity. However, many of these were large aneurysms, which were probably about to rupture whether the patient underwent a laparotomy or not. Subsequent animal studies showed no increase in aortic collagenase after laparotomy and a prospective study[1] cast further doubt on whether unrelated surgical interventions hasten the time of rupture of an AAA.

Acute Cholecystitis

In cases of acute cholecystitis, which have the highest likelihood of positive cultures, cholecystectomy needs to be performed first and the asymptomatic AAA can be left for a later time.

Aorta Surgery and Colorectal Operations

In the past, unexpected malignancies of the colon were often first encountered during laparotomy for aortic-reconstruction. The largest experience[9] with this predates the widespread use of CT-scanning for the work-up of AAA. Since these patients usually have not received complete bowel prep, the unanticipated colon lesion should be left alone.

Nowadays, the coexistence of a colon lesion and AAA are usually known preoperatively. The question then arises which problem should be dealt with first. As one would expect, long term survival is only possible when both the AAA and colon lesion are ultimately removed.[10] Since colon surgery is often followed by small anastomotic leaks and localized abscess formation, this can delay AAA resection for a prolonged period of time. On the other hand, if the AAA is resected first, a second intra-abdominal procedure can usually be carried out after about two weeks. For this reason, rather than the rupture risk, it usually is preferable to repair the AAA first. Komori et al,[3] recommend resection of the malignancy first if both the AAA and the tumor are asymptomatic. However, he is in the minority in this opinion.

If a colon tumor is causing obstruction, appears to perforate, or has resulted in significant bleeding, one will have to individualize the approach and address the colon lesion first in some cases. Reports have appeared of simultaneous operations.[3] These commonly involve the retroperitoneal approach for the aneurysm and transperitoneal approach for the malignancy. Transperitoneal abdominoperineal resection for rectal cancer has been combined with transperitoneal repair of AAA, but this is probably best reserved for exceptional situations in which an obstructing tumor has led to direct infection of the aorta with bowel microorganisms.[11] Under such circumstances one might postulate that either aortic resection with revascularization via extra-anatomic bypass would obviate placement of prosthetic material in a potentially infected field. Alternately, in the absence of intestinal perforation, resection with Hartman's procedure might minimize the risk of abdominal infection and should be considered if in-situ aortic replacement is performed. These situations are too rare for definitive recommendations to be made. A consensus to the dilemma does not exist: one third of professors in general and vascular surgery would excise the aneurysm first, one third the carcinoma first and the remaining third would decide during laparotomy.[11]

Aortic Surgery and Miscellaneous Procedures

Appendectomy

This is mainly of historical interest: incidental appendectomy used to be a common procedure with AAA resection. In a series of 640 AAA repairs combined with other procedures, Ochsner[12] reported no increase in complications when 480 incidental appendectomies were performed, as compared to AAA without appendectomy. Because of the low incidence of appendicitis in the age group with AAA, incidental appendectomy is no longer performed in this setting.

Gynecologic Lesions

Gynecologic lesions are rarely encountered during resection for aortic aneurysm, owing to the male predominance of aneurysmal disease. An ovarian mass encountered in a woman with aortic aneurysm must be considered malignant until proven otherwise. If this is encountered, gynecologic consultation should be obtained early in the procedure to insure proper staging of the lesion. This involves washing of the peritoneum and subphrenic spaces. In general such lesions can be treated synchronously with aortic pathology. Evidence of disseminated ovarian malignancy must be considered in the decision to continue with aneurysm resection and a joint decision should be made with gynecologic consultation. Uterine lesions are usually deferred, since many of these are benign and nonoperative treatment may be appropriate. Furthermore, hysterectomy involves transection of the vaginal cuff, thereby introducing a possible source of contamination.

Adhesiolysis

After prior abdominal surgery or peritonitis, adhesions between bowel loops and the abdominal wall can make access to the abdominal aorta difficult. Careful lysis of adhesions can usually be performed, without injury to the bowel. After multiple abdominal procedures, or after therapeutic radiation, adhesions may become so dense that the abdomen becomes "hostile" to surgeons. Alternate approaches such as retroperitoneal or endovascular repair may be more appropriate. Since extensive adhesions can present a major problem when one needs to obtain rapid control of a ruptured AAA, this should be taken into consideration when considering the need for elective repair of a relatively small AAA.

Hernia Repair

When a midline abdominal incision is used, one often encounters small epigastric, umbilical, or cicatricial herniations, which are repaired during the closing phase.

Inguinal hernia repair is not truly an intra-abdominal procedure and, therefore, is outside the scope of this chapter. Thomas[13] found a significantly increased complication rate with combined procedures, in the subgroup of aortic reconstructions done for limb salvage; therefore, we generally discourage patients from undergoing combined procedures for benign elective conditions that can be addressed at a later date.

Selected Readings

1. Durham SJ, Steed DL, Moosa HH et al. Probability of rupture of an abdominal aortic aneurysm after an unrelated operative procedure: A prospective study. J Vasc Surg 1991; 13:248-52.

    This retrospective review examines the fate of thirty-three patients with known AAA (average size was 5.6 cm) who underwent 45 unrelated surgical procedures. General anesthesia was used in 29 procedures, spinal/epidural in 6 and regional/local in 10 and these included abdominal, cardiothoracic, head/neck, other vascular, urologic and breast procedures. One patient died of ruptured AAA 20 days after coronary artery bypass (1/33 patients – 3%, 1/45 procedures – 2%). Otherwise, 14 patients had elective AAA repair at a later date, 4 patients were deferred because the AAA was deemed too small and 4 patients were considered too high risk for AAA repair. Five thoracoabdominal AAA's were not repaired and 4 patients were awaiting surgery when the manuscript was sent to press. Interestingly, during the same 40-month period, two other patients with unknown AAA died of rupture 21 and 77 days after another unrelated surgical procedure. All three ruptured AAAs were > 5 cm in diameter.

2. Valentine RJ, Barth MJ, Myers SI et al. Nonvascular emergencies presenting as ruptured abdominal aortic aneurysms. Surgery 1993; 113:286-289.

    This interesting study examines outcome of patients presenting with symptoms and signs of ruptured AAA but who actually have other mimicking diseases. Over a 10-year period, 16 patients presumed to have ruptured AAA were found at operation to other diseases that accounted for the symptoms. Fifteen (94%) had abdominal pain, 9 (56%) had a pulsatile abdominal mass and 7 (44%) were hypotensive at presentation. Ten of the 16 patients had intact AAAs at surgery. Eight (50%) patients died in the perioperative period from widespread metastases (4), overwhelming sepsis (3) and myocardial infarction (1). None of the 10 patients with AAA ruptured after emergency laparotomy and 2 of these patients went on to have uneventful staged AAA repair.

3. Komori K, Okadome K, Itoh H et al. Management of concomitant abdominal aortic aneurysm and gastrointestinal malignancy. Am J Surg 1993; 166:108-11.

    This study evaluates nineteen patients with concomitant AAA and gastrointestinal malignancy. Group I (11 patients) had a 1- or 2-stage operation for both problems and groups II patients either had an operation for only one lesion (6) or had no operation (2). Four patients in group I had had the malignancy resected first, two had AAA repair first and the rest had both lesions repaired/resected during the same anesthetic. Survival was better in group I (73%) than in group II (13%) at follow-up.

25

The following guidelines were recommended by the authors: (1) The urgent problem should be repaired/resected first. (2) Resect the malignancy first if both lesions are asymptomatic. (3) Simultaneous resection may be considered in some patients. (4) Both lesions should eventually be resected/repaired for better long-term survival.

4. Bickerstaff LK, Hollier L, Van Peenen HJ et al. Abdominal aortic aneurysm repair combined with a second surgical procedure B Morbidity and mortality. Surgery 1984; 95:487-91.

    This study compares morbidity and mortality rates of patients having combined procedures to patients who have AAA repair alone. 356 patients had AAA repair alone (group I), 115 had at least one additional vascular procedure (group II) and 113 had one or more concomitant nonvascular procedures combined with AAA repair (group III). Morbidity and mortality rates in the three groups were 12.8%, 26.1%, 18.5% and 2.6%, 3.5%, 6.0%, respectively. Deaths in group I were largely due to myocardial infarction and those in groups II and III were largely due to postoperative or underlying disease complications. Patients who had concomitant cholecystectomy had an increase in serious complications.

5. Ouriel K, Ricotta JJ, Adams JT et al. Management of cholelithiasis in patients with abdominal aortic aneurysm. Ann Surg 1983; 198:717-9.

    Gallstones were detected in 42 of 865 patients with AAA (4.9%). Eighteen patients had concomitant AAA repair and cholecystectomy. Eleven had AAA repair alone and 13 had cholecystectomy alone. There were no significant differences in operative mortality, duration of operation or hospital stay when cholecystectomy was added to AAA repair. However, there was one (5.6%) case of graft infection in a patient who did not have closure of the posterior peritoneum prior to the gallbladder procedure. Nine of the 11 "AAA alone" patients experienced an episode of acute cholecystitis during a mean follow-up of 2.9 years. Two of these were perioperative and one patient died of biliary sepsis. Therefore, concomitant AAA repair and cholecystectomy is reasonable in patients with cholelithiasis as long as there are no other precluding circumstances.

6. Evans WE, Hayes JP, Waltke EA et al. Screening for cholelithiasis prior to aortic reconstruction. Am J Surg 1989; 157:208-9.

    This study was performed to determine incidence and complications of cholelithiasis in patients having aortic reconstruction. Incidence of postoperative cholecystitis was 0.8% (3 of 381 patients). Cholelithiasis was noted before AAA repair in only one of these patients and the other two had normal gallbladders noted on preoperative oral cholecystography. On the basis of these data, the authors conclude that cholecystectomy during aortic reconstruction is not contraindicated and that the risk of postoperative cholecystitis in asymptomatic patients is negligible.

7. Ouriel K, Green RM, Ricotta JJ et al. Acute acalculous cholecystitis complicating abdominal aortic aneurysm resection. J Vasc Surg 1984; 1:646-8.

    This review of 6 patients demonstrates significant morbidity and mortality when acute cholecystitis complicates AAA repair. Three patients had ruptured AAA repair and symptoms (right upper quadrant pain, fever, elevated white count and slight elevation of liver function tests) appeared at a mean of 3 weeks postoperatively. Treatment consisted of cholecystostomy (3 patients) or cholecystectomy (3 patients), with an overall mortality of 50%. These results underscore the need for early diagnosis and treatment in patients with suspected acute cholecystitis after AAA repair.

8. Fry RE, Fry WJ. Cholelithiasis and aortic reconstruction: The problem of simultaneous surgical therapy. Conclusions from a personal series. J Vasc Surg 1986; 4:345-50.

Thirty-five (5.1%) of 682 patients having aortic reconstruction also had a biliary tract operation performed before (21 patients), during (2 patients) or after (12 patients) the aortic procedure. These authors comment that concomitant cholecystectomy and AAA repair rarely need to be performed and that combined procedures should be reserved for patients in whom risk of not treating both problems is greater than total operative risks.

9.　Szilagi DE, Elliott JP, Berguer R. Coincidental malignancy and abdominal aortic aneurysm. Arch Surg 1967; 95:402-11.

10.　Nora JD, Pairolero PC, Nivatvongs S et al. Concomitant abdominal aortic aneurysm and colorectal carcinoma: Priority of resection. J Vasc Surg 1989; 9:630-6.
Seventeen patients underwent operation for concomitant AAA and colon carcinoma over a contemporary 12-year period. Thirteen patients had colon resection first, two had AAA repair first and two had concomitant procedures. Only five patients (29%) were long-term survivors without evidence of recurrent carcinoma and all had previously had both lesions treated by repair/resection. Three late deaths occurred as a result of complications from untreated AAA in eight patients who had had colon resection only. These authors conclude that AAA repair should precede colon resection unless the carcinoma is symptomatic. Further, both lesions should be treated to enhance long-term survival.

6.　Lobbato VJ, Rothenberg RE, LaRaja RD et al. Coexistence of abdominal aortic aneurysm and carcinoma of the colon: A dilemma. J Vasc Surg 1985; 2:724-6.
Incidence of concomitant colon carcinoma and AAA is approximately 2%. In this study, 46 professors of general and vascular surgery gave their response as to which condition (AAA or carcinoma) should receive treatment priority. One-third favored excision of carcinoma first, one-third favored AAA repair first and the remaining third would decide at laparotomy. Two professors indicated that they would simultaneously repair the AAA and resect the colon!

12.　Ochsner JL, Cooley DA, DeBakey ME. Associated intra-abdominal lesions encountered during resection of aortic aneurysms. Dis Colon Rectum 1960; 3:485-90.

13.　Thomas JH, McCroskey BL, Iliopoulos JI et al. Aortoiliac reconstruction combined with nonvascular operations. Am J Surg 1983; 146:784-7.
Aortoiliac reconstruction associated with intraabdominal procedures in 76 patients was compared to 445 patients having aortoiliac reconstruction alone. The authors were interested to know if there was an increase in morbidity and mortality by adding the nonvascular procedure to aortoiliac reconstruction. There was a significant increase in perioperative complications if an abdominal procedure was combined with aortoiliac reconstruction (p < 0.01). However, none of the perioperative deaths could be directly attributed to the abdominal procedure. The surgeon must ultimately weigh any potential benefits of a combined operation against definite risks.

25

CHAPTER 26

Management of Aortic Disease and Associated Urologic Problems

Aileen M. Takahashi and Fred A. Weaver

On occasion, surgeons may encounter aorta-iliac aneurysms, which coexist with genitourinary neoplasms of the prostate, bladder or kidney. Both processes predominantly occur in the same age group, have a male predominance and may have one or more risk factors in common such as tobacco use. In addition, both organ systems occupy the retroperitoneum and are anatomically in close proximity.

When concomitant disease exists, this presents a surgical dilemma as to the appropriate timing and staging of surgical therapy. Present day complex oncologic urologic procedures such as radical cystectomy require opening the gastrointestinal tract for construction of a neobladder. Performing both urologic and vascular procedures simultaneously may potentially increase the risk of graft infection.[1] Also, combined procedures of this magnitude may result in unacceptable morbidity and increased mortality. Conversely, staging of the two procedures risks interval progression of the neoplastic process or rupture of the aneurysm.[2] This patient population, most of whom are elderly, are then subjected to two major intraabdominal procedures usually within a three-month period during which the morbidity and mortality is cumulative. In addition, the retroperitoneal dissection required for either the oncologic or aortic procedure renders the second procedure technically more difficult. One may also elect not to treat a small aortic aneurysm (< 5 cm in diameter). However, an increased risk of aneurysm rupture has been reported after laparotomy, thoracotomy and sternotomy. Nora has observed that in patients with concomitant colon cancer and aortic aneurysms, when the aneurysm was not resected, there were no long-term survivors.[3] Finally, a stent-graft approach to the aortic aneurysm, which could be performed before or after the urologic procedure, is now feasible. However, any technical failure, graft migration or endoleak which would require an open operation would be particularly problematic and potentially compromise the subsequent urologic procedure or injure a previously constructed urinary diversion.[4]

Our early experience with a staged approach to coexistent urologic and aneurysm disease demonstrated the formidable challenge of undertaking a major urologic resection or aneurysm resection in an abdomen obliterated by the first-stage procedure. What follows is an overview of our experience and present recommendations for this clinical problem, including technical modifications and sequence of procedures, which has provided satisfactory results.

Aortic Surgery, edited by Jeffrey L. Ballard. ©2000 Landes Bioscience.

Preoperative Management

In general, the aneurysm is first recognized during diagnostic evaluation for the urologic neoplasm, usually as an incidental finding on the abdominal or pelvic CT scan. However, on occasion the vascular surgeon may be called to the operating room to evaluate an aortic-iliac aneurysm in a patient undergoing resection of bladder, prostate or renal neoplasm.

When known preoperatively, any infrarenal abdominal aortic aneurysm or iliac aneurysm greater than 4 cm in diameter should be considered for resection. A thorough, mechanical bowel prep should be administered 24 hours prior to the procedure. Perioperative antibiotic coverage should cover intestinal and colonic bacteria. On those occasions, when the vascular surgeon is called to the operating room to evaluate an unexpected aortic aneurysm a decision to resect the aneurysm should consider size, aneurysm location, age of the patient, extent of the neoplastic process, associated medical comorbidities, amount of gastrointestinal tract contamination and course of the urologic procedure. In general, patients with infrarenal abdominal aortic aneurysms greater than 4 cm with localized, potentially curable, neoplastic disease and minimal gastrointestinal tract spillage, are good candidates for concomitant resection.

26

Operative Technique

Required simultaneous procedures are performed with the urologic team first completing the oncologic resection and urinary diversion. Radical cystectomy and prostatectomy for neoplastic disease requires limited or extensive iliac lymph node dissection, and for renal cell neoplasms, complete removal of juxtarenal periaortic nodal tissue. Radical cystectomy requires creation of a neobladder or ileal conduit, both of which are made from small intestine and located just below the aortic bifurcation. The neobladder stoma is either placed as a continent cutaneous reservoir or is sewn to the urethral remnant.

Aortic disease is addressed after completion of the urologic procedure. This sequence of events provides exposure of iliac vessels, since the lymph node dissection associated with the bladder or prostate, procedures includes an iliac lymphadenectomy. This greatly facilitates the vascular reconstruction and conversely may complicate any open approach at a later date if replacement is not performed. Only infrarenal aortic and/or iliac aneurysms should be addressed simultaneously. Juxtarenal or thoracoabdominal aneurysms are much too complex to perform concomitantly.

Vascular reconstruction begins with mobilization of the aorta and iliac vessels above and below the level of the aneurysm (Fig. 26.1).[5,6] For aortic aneurysms with concomitant iliac artery involvement, a modification of the standard approach has been used so as to maintain the aneurysm wall and to optimize graft coverage. Once appropriate vascular control is secured, the patient is heparinized. The aneurysm is opened and the proximal anastomosis is performed. Leaving the iliac aneurysm intact, the distal limbs of the graft may then be passed through their lumen (Fig. 26.2).[5,6] The iliac bifurcation is then transversely opened, and the graft tailored to the appropriate length and sutured to the common cuff of the external and internal iliac arteries (Fig. 26.3).[5,6]

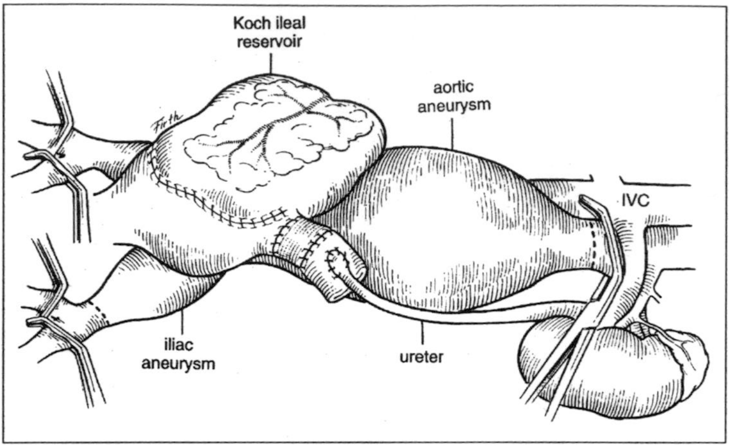

Fig. 26.1. The completed neobladder is located immediately anterior to the bifurcation of the aorta.

Fig. 26.2. The proximal anastomosis of the aneurysm repair is completed. The distal limb of the graft is passed within the iliac aneurysm to the site of the distal anastomosis at the common cuff of the internal and external iliac arteries.

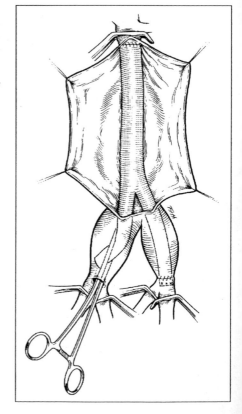

26

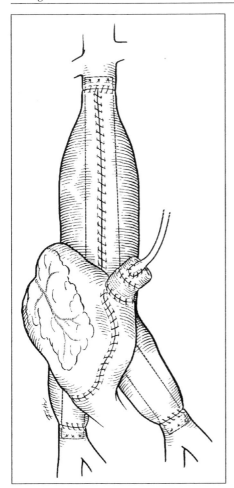

Fig. 26.3. The urologic resection and reconstruction and AAA resection are completed with the aneurysm sac closed over the aortic graft.

Soft tissue coverage to protect the graft from the urinary diversion is critical and may be provided by the aneurysm wall, any available retroperitoneal soft tissue (since lymphadenectomy may remove much of the pelvic soft tissue), small bowel mesentery or omentum. The soft tissue barrier between the prosthetic graft and the continent urinary reservoir protects the graft from urine leaks. A combination of closed suction and penrose drains are then placed near the neobladder to drain urine leaks.

In those cases where the vascular surgeon is asked to see a patient with a known abdominal aortic aneurysm and an oncologic urologic procedure has been performed in the past, the aorta may be approached either retroperitoneal or transabdominal. Both approaches may present difficulties. The transabdominal approach may be complicated by small bowel adhesions, but the iliac vessels are most easily exposed by this approach. A retroperitoneal approach, either left or right, in patients with iliac involvement and existing urinary diversion is problematic. The location of the ileal conduit or neobladder just below the aortic bifurcation makes the dissection and control of the iliac vessels contralateral to the retroperitoneal approach extremely difficult, if not impossible. Any injury to the neobladder during dissection of the iliacs exposes the graft to high bacterial counts since bacterial colonization of a neobladder uniformly occurs. The ureters may also be adhesed to the aneurysm wall and in close proximity to the aortic bifurcation. Careful dissection is required to avoid injury. If there is a concern during the course of the operation that a ureter has been injured, intravenous administration of methylene blue can help to localize the injury. In general, we prefer the transabdominal approach when iliac aneurysms exist. For localized infrarenal aneurysms without iliac involvement both approaches have been satisfactory.

Postoperative Management

Postoperative management is similar for any open aneurysm procedure. For combined procedures, since bladder and prostate procedures have a significant incidence of venous thromboembolism, combination prophylactic therapy with pneumatic compression and low dose heparin is important. Parenteral antibiotics continue until drains are removed. This may require a combination of parenteral and oral antibiotics for 5-7 days, and for 3-5 days after removal in those patients with indwelling bladder catheters.[5]

Results

At the University of Southern California we have both staged and combined urologic and vascular procedures. When the two procedures were staged with the aneurysm addressed first, the subsequent urologic procedure was complicated by profound retroperitoneal cicatricial changes, resulting in a technically difficult identification and mobilization of the ureters. This resulted in a major urine leak in one patient and necrosis of the ureter in another. In seven patients, when urologic neoplasms alone were resected and the aneurysm left in situ, four patients required subsequent aortic reconstruction since the aneurysm increased in size. All operations were technically very challenging with increased operating time and blood loss. One other patient in this group, with a 4.2 cm aneurysm, developed bacteremia from an obstructed neobladder. This seeded the aortic aneurysm, resulting in patient demise.

The complications of staged procedures have resulted in simultaneous correction of vascular and urologic disease now being the standard approach used in most patients. Compared to staged procedures, the overall operative time, blood loss and perioperative morbidity has been less. Despite their relatively advanced age, patients have tolerated this approach well. There have been no perioperative deaths and morbidity has been confined to one instance of pancreatitis. Vascular complications have not occurred. More importantly, the occurrence of a late graft infection has not materialized at a mean follow up of 31 months. Longer follow up will certainly be needed to confirm this finding.

Conclusion

Combining repair of coexistent abdominal aortic aneurysm and excision of urologic neoplasms, although technically difficult, appears to be a safe and satisfactory
approach. Anatomically, both of these organ systems occupy the retroperitoneum
and the areas of operative dissection are the same allowing simultaneous exposure of
both systems. Mechanical bowel preparation, perioperative antibiotics, meticulous
surgical technique and coverage of the aortic graft with soft tissue, are important in
order to minimize the risk of vascular graft contamination. When these principles
are followed, the risk of graft contamination and subsequent infection appears to be
rare.

Selected Readings

1. Krupski WC. Infected vascular graft. In: Current Surgical Therapy. Cameron JC,
    ed. St. Louis: Mosby 1995; 690-701.
    *Current and comprehensive overview of incidence, etiology and treatment of infected
    vascular prostheses. Controversies concerning graft infections are discussed with a thor-
    ough review of the literature.*

2. Swanson RJ, Littooy FN, Hunt TK et al. Laparotomy as a precipitating factor in
    the rupture of intra-abdominal aneurysms. Archives of Surgery 1980; 115: 299-304.
    *Classic paper describing rupture of existing abdominal aortic aneurysm shortly after
    laparotomy for unrelated disease. Authors postulated systemic lysis of collagen due to
    laparotomy as possible causative factor. The same observation has also been made for
    patients undergoing median sternotomy.*

3. Nora JD, Pairolero PC, Nivatvongs S et al. Concomitant abdominal aortic aneu-
    rysm and colorectal carcinoma: Priority of resection. J Vasc Surg 1989; 9:630-6.
    *This paper describes the surgical dilemma of coexisting neoplastic (colon) and aortic
    aneurysm disease. Importance of aneurysm resection is emphasized since three of eight
    patients in whom the aneurysm was not resected died of aneurysm related complications.*

4. Zarins CK, White RA, Schwarten D et al. AneuRx stent graft versus open surgical
    repair of abdominal aortic aneurysms: Multicenter prospective clinical trial. J Vasc
    Surg 1999; 29(2): 292-308.
    *Recent report of proprietary (AneuRx) stent-graft versus open repair for aortic aneu-
    rysms. These early results are favorable for a stent-graft approach, but graft migration
    and endoleaks remain a concern.*

5. Ginsberg DA, Esrig D, Grossfeld GD et al. Technique of radical cystectomy and
    simultaneous repair of an abdominal aortic aneurysm. Urology 1996;
    47(1):120-122.
    *Case report that emphasizes urologic technique and approach for patients udnergoing
    concomitant oncologic urologic and aortic aneurysm procedures.*

6. Ginsberg DA, Modrall JG, Esrig D et al. Concurrent abdominal aortic aneurysm
    and urologic neoplasm: An argument for simultaneous intervention. Ann Vasc
    Surg 1995; 9(5):428-433.
    *Advantages and disadvantages of staged versus combined procedures for coexistent uro-
    logic neoplasms and aortic aneurysms are discussed. Benefits of combining the two pro-
    cedures include less blood loss, shorter operating times and no graft-related complica-
    tions at a mean follow up of 34 months.*

26

CHAPTER 27

Management of Aortic Graft Infection

Nancy Schindler, Keith D. Calligaro, Matthew J. Dougherty

Aortic graft infection is one of the most dreaded problems faced by vascular surgeons. Although not common, these infections have tremendous implications in terms of morbidity and mortality. Aortic graft infection has been found to occur in approximately one to two percent of all aortic graft procedures. When infection occurs it is associated with a mortality rate of 15 to 75 percent and an amputation rate of 8 to 37%. These cases are challenging not only from a treatment perspective but also from a diagnostic standpoint. Graft infection may present a few days after insertion of an aortic graft or many years later. The patient may appear well or floridly septic. There may be massive gastrointestinal bleeding, only a small draining sinus or no symptoms at all. This chapter reviews the etiology, presenting symptoms, diagnosis and treatment of these difficult clinical problems.

Risk Factors/Epidemiology

A number of different mechanisms of aortic graft infection have been proposed. Most investigators believe that infection commonly occurs at the time of graft insertion even though infection may present clinically many years later. Possible sources of contaminating bacteria include skin flora, bacteria in an aneurysm wall or thrombus, break in aseptic technique, lymphatic drainage associated with an infected limb lesion, transudate of bowel bacteria or contamination from a nonvascular procedure.

Multiple investigators have noted a higher incidence of graft infection when aortic grafts extend to the level of the femoral artery than when surgery is confined to the abdomen. This is not surprising given the general poor hygiene in the groin region and the proximity to fecal and urinary contents. We try to avoid groin incisions, and will preferentially bypass to the distal external iliac artery in the abdomen for aortoiliac occlusive disease if the distal external iliac, common femoral and deep femoral arteries are widely patent. When groin incisions are necessary, technique must be meticulous to avoid lymphatic disruption.

Other factors have been shown to increase risk of aortic graft infection including reoperative or emergent surgery, prolonged hospital stay or operating time, and colonic ischemia after surgery. The graft material itself has been suggested to play a role as well. Knitted Dacron may be less susceptible to infection than woven grafts in experimental animal models, and both may be more susceptible than PTFE. Data in humans, however, has not clearly demonstrated this to be true.

Prophylactic antibiotics have been shown in several randomized double-blinded studies to reduce the risk of prosthetic infection when given preoperatively. Antibiotics

---

Aortic Surgery, edited by Jeffrey L. Ballard. ©2000 Landes Bioscience.

should be given intravenously approximately thirty minutes prior to skin incision and throughout the course of prolonged operations. Dosing frequency needs to be increased during the operative period to maintain adequate tissue levels while large fluid shifts are occurring. The current recommended antibiotic is a first generation cephalosporin, which should be administered every four hours intraoperatively.

In general, simultaneous gastrointestinal procedures should be avoided during aortic surgery, though cholecystectomy may be an exception. Ouriel reported an incidence of postoperative cholecystitis of 18% in patients with gallstones undergoing aortic repair without cholecystectomy.[1] Several series have documented the safety of performing simultaneous cholecystectomy after closure of the posterior peritoneum over the aortic graft.

Diagnosis

The diagnosis of an infected aortic graft may at times be simple and on other occasions may be extraordinarily difficult. One must suspect an infected aortic graft in any patient with a history of aortic graft placement who presents with fever, wound drainage, sepsis or pseudoaneurysm. Patients with a history of an aortic graft who present with a GI bleed should be considered to have an aorto-enteric fistula until proven otherwise.

Patients presenting with infection of superficially placed grafts usually present little diagnostic dilemma. Findings may include tenderness, erythema, a pulsatile mass, exposed graft, drainage or bleeding. These are all obvious signs of infection but should prompt a complete evaluation of the graft to determine the extent of the infection. The mere presence of a pseudoaneurysm without other abnormality may be the presenting sign of graft infection in as many as 13.5% of cases.

Many diagnostic modalities have been used to aid in the evaluation of aortic graft infection. As always, the diagnosis begins with a thorough history and physical exam, though these may be unrevealing. Leukocyte count, blood cultures and sedimentation rate are nonspecific, but frequently helpful in supporting the diagnosis. Imaging modalities are usually required to identify the nature and extent of the problem.

Ultrasound is inexpensive, simple and readily available. It may be useful in identifying pseudoaneurysms and/or perigraft fluid, but it is not as sensitive as other modalities such as CT scan and MRI. It can be used to guide aspiration of perigraft fluid for microbiologic evaluation.

Contrast sinography is a simple test that may help to delineate the extent of graft involvement in patients presenting with draining sinus tracts. Contrast is injected into the sinus and may be seen tracking along the unincorporated portion of a graft. Appropriate antibiotic coverage is recommended as this procedure may cause bacteremia.

Perhaps the most frequently obtained and most useful test is a CT scan. This may show fluid or air in or around the graft, or the presence of a pseudoaneurysm. The sensitivity and specificity of CT scan has been reported to be 94% and 85%,

27

respectively. Perigraft fluid or air may be a normal finding for six to seven weeks postoperatively.

MRI was first reported to diagnose a prosthetic infection in 1985. This imaging modality is best able to distinguish between fluid and surrounding tissue. Perigraft fluid is seen as low to medium intensity on T1 weighted images and as high intensity on T2 weighted images, while perigraft tissue such as native aortic wall wrapped around the graft will appear as low intensity on both T1 and T2 images. Olofsson and colleagues compared CT and MRI in the diagnosis of graft infection and found that MRI was more accurate.[2] Sensitivity and specificity of 100% and 85%, respectively have been reported. Unfortunately, this test may be difficult to obtain in patients who are unstable, and at many institutions, is not as readily available as CT scan.

Angiography is not especially helpful in making the diagnosis of graft infection, but is frequently necessary in order to plan treatment. It may provide useful information including the length of aortic neck above the proximal anastomosis and the status of outflow vessels to be used for subsequent new bypass. It may on rare occasion demonstrate a pseudoaneurysm or graft-enteric fistula. Contrast arteriography, or possibly CT angiography, should routinely be performed in the evaluation of infected aortic grafts once operative intervention is deemed necessary, unless hemodynamic instability precludes further testing.

In cases where aorto-enteric fistula is suspected, upper endoscopy (EGD) should be performed. This test should include the entire duodenum up to and including the fourth portion. A fistula may appear as ragged mucosa, a red spot or rarely as a portion of graft visible through bowel wall. EGD may also identify alternate sources of bleeding such as an ulcer or gastritis, though the presence of such a finding does not rule out a fistula. Commonly, EGD will not demonstrate any abnormality. In one series of aorto-enteric fistulas, endoscopy was negative in half of cases. In the setting of hemorrhage in patients with an aortic graft in whom an exhaustive search yields no source, it is appropriate to proceed with exploratory laparotomy to rule out graft-enteric fistula. Unfortunately, some negative laparotomies may occur. However, this is better than missing the diagnosis. Nuclear medicine examination may also demonstrate evidence of graft infection. This test is very sensitive, but not always specific. In the early postoperative period, the study may be falsely positive. Gallium-67, Indium-111, polyclonal human IgG and technetium-99m Hexametazime scanning have all been used for this purpose. The latter has recently been shown to have an accuracy of 96.2% in the identification of an aortic graft infection. We rarely perform radionuclide studies, although they may be useful to rule out infection if the study is normal.

Bacteriology

The most common bacteria involved in aortic graft infections was formerly *Staphylococcus aureus*, but more recently, less virulent *Staphylococcus epidermidis* has become more widespread. *Staph epidermidis* is notoriously difficult to identify and frequently assumed to be the responsible pathogen when fluid cultures are negative. Routine evaluation should include aspirates of pus or perigraft exudate and biopsy of inflammatory tissue. Swab specimens may not be sufficient. Blood cultures should be performed as well, and some have advocated both arterial and venous specimens. Aggressive attempts to isolate *Staphylococcus epidermidis* including sonication of the graft material itself or broth cultures will frequently provide the highest yield.

Coagulase negative *staphylococcus* has several characteristics which play an important role in its pathogenesis including an ability to adhere to prosthetics and resist host defenses. It may produce a significant mucin capsule that enhances adhesiveness. This makes the bacterium relatively resistant to antibiotics. The capsule is a viscous polysaccharide coating over the outer surface of the cell membrane.

Staph aureus is a more virulent pathogen than staph epidermidis and is able to flourish in a variety of environments and thwart many host defenses. Its cell wall is composed of peptidoglycan interspersed with ribitol-teichoic acid. The teichoic acid binds to fibronectin and allows adherence to host cells and thrombus. In fact the expression of teichoic acid correlates with the invasiveness of the organism. In most strains of *Staph aureus*, the cell wall has surface proteins such as protein A, which has a high affinity for the Fc portion of IgG. The Fab portion is then directed externally which inhibits opsonization. *Staph aureus* also secretes substances that include coagulase and exotoxins. These cell products control the perigraft environment and enhance the infectious process.

Gram negative infections are a less common cause of aortic graft infection but are clinically very aggressive. *Escherichia coli, klebsiella, proteus* and *pseudomonas* as well as other gram-negative bacteria have all been reported to cause graft infection. *Pseudomonas* is of particular concern as it can cause a very aggressive and destructive process. It is a gram-negative rod equipped with a polar flagellum that provides motility. *Pseudomonas* has adherence mechanisms and produces exotoxins as well. It can produce an extracellular polysaccharide similar to *Staph epidermidis*. *Pseudomonas aeruginosa* is capable of rapid tissue invasion, produces large amounts of elastase and collagenase, and therefore is known to digest the vascular wall in the region of anastomoses. This infection is frequently associated with anastomotic disruption and hemorrhage.

27

Treatment

The traditional treatment of aortic graft infection is removal of all infected graft material, debridement of surrounding tissue and extra-anatomic bypass. This has been reported in some series to yield unacceptable morbidity and mortality rates, and has led investigators to question the necessity of complete graft removal in all cases. Graft conservation, both complete and partial, have been suggested as alternative methods of treatment when the infection is confined to the distal limb of aortobifemoral grafts. In situ replacement has also been championed as a possible option. Graft replacement with prosthetic grafts in very selected cases has been reported as well as with allografts and autogenous conduits.

Patient suspected to have an infected aortic graft should have appropriate cultures obtained and should be started immediately on appropriate intravenous antibiotic coverage. Unlike antibiotic prophylaxis at the time of initial surgery, antibiotics used for the treatment of graft infection should initially be broad spectrum and then may be tapered after culture and sensitivity data become available. Data from Calligaro et al suggest that only 25% of graft infections are actually sensitive to a first generation cephalosporin and that initial gram stain results reflect final culture results in only 32% of cases.[3] They recommend empiric treatment with vancomycin and either ceftazidime or ticarcillin/clavulanic acid until final cultures and sensitivities are available. This antibiotic regimen resulted in adequate coverage in 95-96% of cases.

Intra-Abdominal Graft Infection

If the infection involves the intracavitary portion of an aortic graft, the most commonly accepted treatment is removal of the infected intra-abdominal prosthesis, wide debridement and drainage, appropriate antibiotics and revascularization via extra-anatomic bypass through separate, clean operative fields. Though this is the recommended treatment, results of early reports varied and demonstrated a 25-50% amputation rate and a 36-79% mortality rate when total graft excision precedes extra-anatomic revascularization. Current reports in which extra-anatomic bypass precedes graft removal suggest an overall mortality of approximately 19% and an amputation rate of about 14%. Difficulties encountered with aortic graft excision include obtaining control of the proximal scarred aorta and preventing proximal stump blowout. This devastating complication can occur in as many as 25% of cases. Massive bleeding may also occur as the inflamed tissue is debrided. Preoperative angiography is helpful in delineating the length of aorta present below the renal arteries to determine if there is enough for oversewing of the infrarenal aortic stump. If the neck is short it is necessary to gain supraceliac control. If there is inadequate length to oversew below the renal arteries, then the aorta must be oversewn below the superior mesenteric artery and kidney perfusion restored with splenorenal and/or hepatorenal bypass, assuming that graft replacement is not performed. An attempt should be made to remove all of the infected graft and then to cover the aortic and iliac stumps with adjacent soft tissue or omentum. Wide drainage should be established. It is recommended that excision of infected aortic tissue be carried out to an area free of infection that is documented with negative intraoperative gram stain. Positive cultures warrant prolonged intravenous antibiotics.

Revascularization should be performed through uninfected planes. If groin infection is not present, bilateral axillo-femoral bypass, or axillobifemoral bypass can be performed. Alternate inflow sources include the thoracic or supraceliac aorta. If the patient is known preoperatively to have a graft infection and is hemodynamically stable, it is recommended to perform the extra-anatomic bypass prior to removing the infected graft. This will minimize ischemic time and decrease the hemodynamic effects of aortic clamping. Although theoretical concerns might suggest secondary infection of the remote bypass done first, this complication has been reported in less than 5% of patients undergoing extra-anatomic bypass as the first procedure. Trout and others have shown that mortality rates are lower when revascularization is performed prior to graft removal.[4,5]

An alternative option which has been reported in settings when there is no evidence of bleeding or anastomotic breakdown is graft excision and in situ replacement. This may be the only reasonable option for infected grafts involving the celiac and mesenteric vessels. In situ replacement has been done with a variety of conduits including antibiotic impregnated prosthetic grafts, allografts or a variety of autogenous tissue. The latter has been reported with superficial femoral vein or with endarterectomized segments of iliac, common femoral or superficial femoral artery. Reports have demonstrated mortality rates of 20-35% and amputation rates of 7-25% using this approach. Clagett has recently reported his experience with aortoiliac and femoral reconstruction using lower extremity deep veins.[6] He has reported 41 such operations and found that there were no immediate operative deaths, but three patients died of multi-system organ failure after one month for an overall mortality of 7.3%. Of the 27 patients in the series who underwent reconstruction for infected aortic prostheses, the mortality was 10.5%. The amputation rate in Clagett's series was 5%, and the five-year primary and secondary patency rates were 83 and 100%, respectively. Mean follow-up was 32 months. Significant complications occurred in 49% of patients and included amputation (5%), deep vein thrombosis (12.2%), pulmonary embolism (2.4%), compartment syndrome (12.3%), paralysis (7.3%), pneumonia (12.3%) and acute graft thrombosis (7.3%). This alternate approach is very labor intensive, and carries with it significant added stress to the patient, but initial results are promising. Results of this procedure in patients with aortoenteric fistula have not been favorable and Clagett suggests that it is not indicated in those patients.

In situ replacement of infected aortic grafts with prosthetic grafts is associated with unacceptable rates of reinfection, and therefore is not recommended unless *Staph epidermidis* is the only causative organism. In the setting of these low virulent infections, success with this treatment has been reported. Promising research is being performed on antibiotic impregnated grafts. Rifampin has been used because it is hydrophobic and leaches out of grafts at a slow rate. Assays of biologic activity of collagen-bonded rifampin grafts displayed antibacterial activity for periods of 29 days. Little data is available in humans regarding the ability of these grafts to resist recurrent infection. Allografts are another potential conduit to use in situ in the setting of infection. Kieffer has had the largest experience with allografts and has suggested that they may be the treatment of choice for infected grafts.[7] From 1988 to 1993 he treated 58 patients with infected grafts by replacement with cadaver allografts. There was a 13.8% 30-day mortality. Eight percent of surviving patients had early allograft complications, including thrombosis and rupture, but each was treated with redo allograft and resulted in patent allografts in all cases. Twenty-four percent of patients had late allograft related complications including stenosis, limb occlusion and pseudoaneurysm. Mean follow-up was 19.6 months. Previous reports have suggested late deterioration of allografts and long-term results of this treatment are not well known.

Infections of Bifurcated Grafts Limited to the Groin

The management of aorto-femoral bypass graft infection limited to the groin is more controversial. Treatment depends upon the extent of infection, patency status of the graft, status of the anastomosis and bacteriology. If both limbs are involved, it is likely that the entire graft is infected and treatment should proceed as for a graft with intra-abdominal involvement described above. If only one limb is involved the entire graft should be examined with CT, MRI, and/or radionucleotide scan to ensure that the rest of the graft does not have evidence of infection. If infection appears to be truly limited to the groin, then partial or complete graft preservation may be considered.

If complete graft preservation is to be performed, several criteria have been established by Calligaro and Veith, including that the affected portion of the graft must be extracavitary and patent, there must be no anastomotic disruption, there must be no systemic sepsis and *Pseudomonas* should not be present.[8] If these criteria are met, then total graft preservation can be attempted. Surgical treatment proceeds with exploration and wide debridement of the surrounding tissue followed by treatment of the open wound with dressing changes and repeated debridements with healing by secondary intention. The patient must be observed in an intensive care setting until a granulating bed has formed over the graft. If the patient develops signs of nonhealing, bleeding, or sepsis, graft preservation should be abandoned. Using this approach, Calligaro reported on the treatment of over 30 peripheral and aortic prosthetic graft infections limited to the groin. Total salvage of most grafts was accomplished and less than one third of cases ultimately required graft removal. This selective graft preservation approach resulted in low mortality and led to limb loss or higher amputation rate of less than 25%.[9]

When graft preservation is used, some reports have suggested a benefit of muscle flaps as an adjunct to successful preservation. This concept was examined in a series of 28 consecutive patients with infected peripheral grafts treated by complete graft preservation. Calligaro and associates compared patients treated with healing by secondary intention to those treated with rotational muscle flaps and found no significant difference in wound healing, cost or hospital or intensive care stay.[10] Patients with autogenous grafts or vein patches in infected fields may benefit from a vascularized flap to help prevent anastomotic disruption.

Partial graft preservation may also be used in the setting of infection confined to one groin. In this case the distal segment of the affected limb may be removed and an extra-anatomic bypass performed in uninfected fields, or the limb may be replaced in situ. In the former operation, bypass is first performed by a retroperitoneal approach from the uninfected proximal limb of the aortic graft. Exploration should confirm that the graft in this location is incorporated, free of surrounding fluid and has a negative gram stain. The uninvolved portion of the affected limb is divided, and an end to end anastomosis between the proximal graft and the new graft performed. The distal segment of the original graft is oversewn and covered with soft tissue. The new graft is then tunneled laterally to the infected groin, and then anastomosed to the superficial femoral, profunda or popliteal artery. Obturator bypass is an alternative route. Following completion of the new bypass, the wounds are closed and covered and the infected graft in the groin is removed.

An alternate approach is removal of the infected portion of the graft in the groin and in situ replacement with autogenous or prosthetic graft. A variety of autogenous tissues may be used including saphenous vein, endarterectomized superficial femoral artery or superficial femoral vein. The advantage of this approach is immediate reestablishment of arterial flow, but the anastomoses will be constructed in an infected field, and may be associated with anastomotic disruption. It is essential that the distal anastomosis be constructed to an uninvolved segment of patent artery. Bandyk has reported experience with replacement of an infected limb of aortobifemoral grafts using in situ replacement with prosthetic material.[11] If this is to be considered, the infection must be low grade. Cultures should be sterile or clinical and operative findings should suggest infection with *Staphylococcus epidermidis*. Bandik used this method to treat 20 patients presenting with groin false aneurysms, inflammatory masses or groin sinus tracts and found there were no deaths or early graft failures. All grafts remained patent without evidence of infection, but two patients later presented with proximal infection which required graft removal. When this method is practiced patients should be closely followed for recurrent infection with serial CT scan or ultrasound.

When some form of graft excision is determined to be the treatment of choice, the portion of graft being removed is usually excised in its entirety, including the anastomosis with the native vessel. Treatment of the involved native vessel may then be either ligation, primary closure or patch angioplasty with autogenous tissue. This may involve a difficult dissection and may compromise collateral vessels. We have recently reviewed our experience with subtotal graft removal in the setting of prosthetic graft infection with an intact anastomosis.[12] Forty-two patients with 45 infected aortic and peripheral grafts and 53 involved wounds were treated with subtotal graft excision and oversewing of a residual 2-3 mm prosthetic graft remnant followed by wide debridement, dressing changes and intravenous antibiotics. This technique was used to maintain patency of small diameter arteries which were critical for foot salvage or amputation healing. Ninety two percent of cases treated in this fashion did well after long-term follow-up with no complications. Two infected pseudoaneurysms developed and two wounds failed to heal. Patch oversewing led to foot salvage without need for secondary revascularization in 26 cases, foot salvage with secondary bypass in 16 cases and successful healing of amputation in 10 cases.

Conclusions

Aortic graft infection represent a difficult management problem that continues to challenge the vascular surgeon, and unfortunately, still results in significant morbidity and mortality. Traditional methods of treatment remain the standard by which other methods must be measured. If the intracavitary portion of an aortic graft is infected, we continue to recommend removal of the entire graft, wide debridement and extra-anatomic revascularization as the treatment of choice. Graft preservation challenges this concept and is gaining wider acceptance. It should always be performed with caution and meticulous adherence to the principles of wide debridement and drainage and should be abandoned if evidence of bleeding, nonhealing or sepsis occur. The role of antibiotic impregnated grafts and allografts are not yet clear, but offer exciting possibilities for the future.

Selected Readings

1. Ouriel K, Ricotta JJ, Adams JT et al. Management of cholelithiasis in patients with abdominal aortic aneurysms. Ann Surg 1983; 198:717-9.

    The authors report an 18% incidence of postoperative acute cholecystitis when gallstones were present in patients who underwent abdominal aortic aneurysm repair without cholecystectomy.

2. Olofsson PA, Auffermann W, Higgins CB et al. Diagnosis of prosthetic aortic graft infection by magnetic resonance imaging. JVS 1988; 8:99-105.

    This is a report of 18 patients evaluated by magnetic resonance imaging for graft infection. Of 18 patients with suspicious history and physical findings, MRI correctly diagnosed 14 of 16 patients found to have infection at surgery and correctly found no evidence of infection in 2 of 2 patients who did not have surgical findings of graft infection. There were two false negatives. MRI findings suggestive of infection are discussed.

3. Calligaro KD, Veith FG, Schwartz ML et al. Recommendation for initial antibiotic treatment of extracavitary arterial graft infections. Am J Surg. 1995; 170:123-5.

    This retrospective review of gram stain, culture and sensitivity results from 113 purulent wounds involving extracavitary graft infections found that gram stain results correlated with final culture results in only 25% of cases. Recommendations for initial antibiotic coverage of infected grafts are suggested.

4. Trout HH III, Kozloff L, Giordano JM. Priority of revascularization in patients with graft enteric fistulas, infected arteries, or infected arterial prostheses. Ann Surg 1984; 199:669-83.

    This review article addresses bacteriology, diagnosis and treatment of infected grafts or fistulas. It includes a report of nine patients treated with a staged approach utilizing extra-anatomic bypass followed by resection of the infected graft. The authors state that when possible, remote bypass should precede removal of an infected graft, as this incurs a lower mortality than resection followed by bypass.

5. Reilly LM, Altman H, Lusby RJ et al. Late results following surgical management of vascular graft infection. JVS 1984; 1:36-44.

    Long-term follow-up of ninety-two patients who underwent surgical treatment for graft infection or aortoenteric fistula is reported in this paper. An overall 14% perioperative mortality and long term success of 88% in those surviving the perioperative period was found. Factors associated with good and poor prognosis are reviewed.

6. Clagett GP, Valentine RJ, Hagino RT. Autogenous aortoiliac/femoral reconstruction from superficial femoral-popliteal veins: Feasibility and durability. JVS 1997; 25:255-70.

    This is a prospective study of autogenous aortoiliac/femoral reconstruction with superficial femoral-popliteal veins in the treatment of prosthetic graft infection or failure. Forty-one patients underwent treatment with resulting 7.3% 30-day mortality, 100% secondary patency at five years, and 86% limb salvage at five years. Complications occurred in a significant number of patients and these are reviewed.

7. Kieffer E, Plissonnier D, Bahnini A et al. Abdominal aortic graft excision and in situ allograft replacement. In: Calligaro KD, Veith FJ, eds. Management of Infected Arterial Grafts. St. Louis: Quality Medical Publishing 1994; 114-123.

This is an update of a previously reported series of patients with aortic graft infection who were treated with in situ allograft replacement. Fifty-eight patients are included in this report.

8. Calligaro KD, Veith FJ, Schwartz ML et al. Selective preservation of infected pros-
    thetic arterial grafts. Analysis of a 20-year experience with 120 extracavitary-infected
    grafts. Ann Surg 1994; 220:461-9.

    The authors report their extensive experience with 120 infected extracavitary grafts utilizing a strategy of selective graft preservation. If there was evidence of arterial bleeding or systemic sepsis, total graft excision was performed. If the graft was occluded, subtotal graft excision with oversewing of a remnant of prosthetic graft was performed. When well-defined criteria were met, total graft preservation was attempted. This strategy resulted in an in-hospital mortality of 12% and an amputation rate in survivors of 13%.

9. Calligaro KD, Veith FJ. Diagnosis and management of infected prosthetic aortic
    grafts. Surgery 1991; 110:805-813.

    This article reviews bacteriology, risk factors, diagnosis and treatment of prosthetic aortic graft infections.

10. Calligaro KD, Veith FJ, Sales CM et al. Comparison of muscle flaps and delayed
    secondary intention wound healing for infected lower extremity arterial grafts.
    Ann Vasc Surg 1994; 8:31-7.

    This retrospective review compares the use of muscle flaps versus healing by secondary intention for infected grafts. No difference was demonstrated in wound healing, hospital or intensive care stay or cost for these two treatments.

11. Bandyk, DF. In situ prosthetic graft replacement for coagulase-negative staphylo-
    cocci infection. In: Calligaro KD, Veith FJ, eds. Management of Infected Arterial
    Grafts. St. Louis: Quality Medical Publishing 1994:185-201.

    This chapter reviews the rationale, patient selection criteria, culture technique, operative technique and follow up for patients undergoing in-situ replacement of infected prosthetic grafts. Appropriate patient selection including contraindications such as systemic sepsis and virulent bacteriology are emphasized.

12. Calligaro KD, Veith FJ, Valladares JA et al. Prosthetic patch remnants to treat
    infected arterial grafts. J Vasc Surg (submitted).

    This is a review of the authors' experience treating infected prosthetic grafts with subtotal removal and oversewing of a small patch of graft remnant. The authors suggest that this is a safe method which preserves the underlying native artery and minimizes the morbidity associated with a reoperative field.

27

CHAPTER 28

Peripheral Vascular Manifestations of Acute Aortic Dissection

James I. Fann and R. Scott Mitchell

Acute aortic dissection is an entity not uncommonly encountered by the cardiovascular surgeon.[1-3] As the dissection propagates along the aorta, flow to branch arteries may be compromised as a result of a dissection flap or compression by the false lumen at their origins or somewhere along their course leading to ischemia or necrosis of end organs or tissues (Fig. 28.1). The other possibility is that these arteries may be sheared off resulting in unimpeded or only partially compromised distal flow from the false lumen. Because of the dynamic and unpredictable nature of acute aortic dissection, it is not surprising that approximately 30-50% of affected patients sustain one or more peripheral vascular complications.[4-6] Major reported vascular complications of aortic dissection include stroke, paraplegia, peripheral pulse loss and impaired renal or visceral perfusion. From the diagnostic standpoint, abrupt peripheral arterial occlusion in conjunction with an acute generalized illness involving unrelated organ systems should prompt strong suspicion of acute aortic dissection.

In acute type A dissection (i.e., involving the ascending aorta and presenting within 14 days of onset of symptoms) complicated by peripheral vascular manifestations, primary treatment is surgical graft replacement of the ascending aorta. This, in turn, is likely to relieve the peripheral ischemia.[4] In those with acute type B dissection (i.e., not involving the ascending aorta) and peripheral vascular compromise, optimal therapy is individualized. For certain patients, surgical management alone may be adequate, whereas for others, novel endovascular methods may be employed primarily thereby obviating surgery or secondarily in cases where peripheral ischemia persists after the surgical procedure.[7-12] This chapter focuses on the pathophysiology and treatment of those patients who develop peripheral vascular manifestations of aortic dissection.

Clinical Diagnosis

Acute aortic dissection remains a diagnostic challenge mainly because of its protean manifestations.[1-3] Most commonly, the patient complains of severe, lancinating chest or interscapular pain, which may or may migrate. Important, but less common, symptoms reflecting acute peripheral vascular compromise may occur either due to extrinsic luminal compression by the dissecting hematoma in the false lumen or an intimal flap compromising the orifice of a branch artery. Major reported peripheral vascular complications include stroke, paraplegia, pulse loss, or impaired renal or visceral perfusion.[1-6] A complete neurologic examination and assessment of

---

Aortic Surgery, edited by Jeffrey L. Ballard. ©2000 Landes Bioscience.

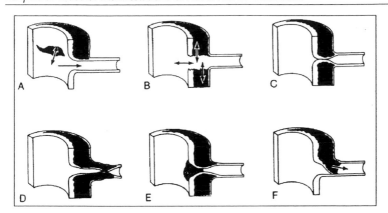

Fig. 28.1. Examples of pathoanatomic complications of aortic dissections. Perfusion of the aortic branch vessel is illustrated in A, B, and F. Perfusion takes place through the true lumen in A and B and through the false lumen in F. Obstruction of the aortic tributary from extrinsic compression is shown in C and D, and compromise of the true lumen and consequent thrombosis is shown in E. In F, re-entry of the dissection at a tributary has created an intimal flap; in chronic dissections, this may become a permanent situation if the flap heals to the opposite wall of the vessel, thus rendering this branch solely dependent upon perfusion from the false lumen. (Reproduced with permission from Miller DC. Surgical management of aortic dissections: Indications, perioperative management and long-term results. In: Doroghazi RM, Slater EE, eds. Aortic Dissection. New York: McGraw-Hill, 1983: 198.)

28

all peripheral pulses are thus critical, and blood pressure measurements in both arms and legs should be performed. Serial examinations are of paramount importance, since new vascular and neurologic deficits may appear over time. Initial laboratory tests should include chest X-ray, electrocardiogram, hematologic studies, hepatic and renal function tests.

Ascending aortic involvement can be determined reasonably accurately using transesophageal echocardiography (TEE), contrast-enhanced computer tomographic scan (CT), magnetic resonance imaging (MRI), or aortography.[3,13] TEE in many centers has become the preferred initial diagnostic procedure. CT is also highly accurate in establishing the diagnosis of aortic dissection. MRI is accurate in the diagnosis of aortic dissection and provides excellent anatomic delineation of the aorta; however, it cannot be performed in acutely ill patients who are hemodynamically unstable and are on ventilatory support. Aortography, the historic gold standard in the diagnosis of aortic dissection, has been largely superseded by TEE and MRI. Biplane aortography, however, can provide accurate information concerning perfusion status of important aortic branches.

Peripheral Vascular Complications

General

In order to further evaluate the impact of peripheral vascular complications in patients with aortic dissection (upwards of 50% of these patients), we reviewed our experience of 272 patients who underwent operation for spontaneous aortic dissection between 1963 and 1987.[4] In our series, 31% sustained one or more peripheral vascular complications; in fact, 21% suffered two complications, 7% had three complications, and one patient had four complications. A total of 3% presented with a stroke, 3% with paraplegia, and 24% with loss of one or more peripheral pulses. Eight percent had compromised renal perfusion by angiography and 5% had compromised visceral perfusion by angiography. The distribution of individual peripheral vascular complications according to dissection type is shown in Table 28.1. The frequency of specific complications subdivided by acuity and type of dissection is illustrated in Figure 28.2. The overall operative mortality rate for patients with aortic dissection complicated by peripheral vascular manifestation was 28%, which was not significantly higher than that for patients without peripheral vascular complications (24%).[4] In the acute type B dissection subgroup, patients with peripheral vascular complications had a significantly higher operative mortality rate than did those without vascular complications (64% vs. 31%). The mortality rates for patients with each individual peripheral vascular complication according to acuity and type of dissection is shown in Table 28.2.

28

Cerebrovascular Accident

Depending on the specific pathoanatomy, syndromes related to central nervous system involvement may vary from syncope to focal neurological signs to frank coma; peripheral nervous system involvement may be manifested as ischemic peripheral neuropathy or paraplegia. Stroke occurs infrequently, with an incidence of 3-7% of all patients with aortic dissection.[4-6] Because anticoagulation and sudden restoration of cerebral perfusion may precipitate hemorrhage and extension of cerebral infarction, stroke has been considered to be a contraindication to emergency surgery in patients with acute aortic dissection. In our experience, an aggressive surgical approach (replacing the ascending aorta for acute type A dissection) was associated with an operative survival rate of 86%.[4] Of the 7 patients with aortic dissection complicated by stroke who underwent surgical intervention, one patient with a profound neurologic deficit died early postoperatively as a result of brain death. The neurologic impairment persisted in another patient who underwent bypass grafting to the right common carotid artery at the time of ascending aortic replacement. One patient had extension of stroke and required a decompression craniotomy. Because of the irreversibility of the stroke, two patients with residual neurological deficits died within four months of discharge. The long-term survival, therefore, is severely limited by the residua of cerebral injury. Nonetheless, as reflected by a relatively favorable outcome in four (57%) patients in our experience, stroke should probably constitute only a relative contraindication to central aortic repair.[4]

Table 28.1. Location of absent peripheral pulses in 66 patients*

	AcA	ChA	AcB	ChB	Total
Right carotid	6	0	0	1	7
Left carotid	6	0	0	0	6
Right arm	25	2	0	0	27
Left arm	10	1	2	0	13
Right leg	21	4	4	1	30
Left leg	14	0	3	1	18
Total	82	7	9	3	101

*24 patients had two or more pulse deficits
LEGEND: AcA= acute type A; ChA= chronic type A; AcB= acute type B; ChB= chronic type B.
(Reproduced with permission from Fann JI, Sarris GE, Mitchell RS et al. Treatment of patients with aortic dissection presenting with peripheral vascular complications. Ann Surg 1990; 212:705-713.)

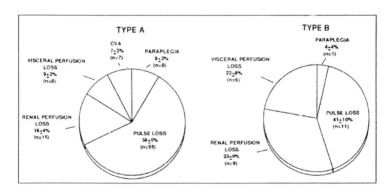

Fig. 28.2. Frequency of specific individual peripheral vascular complications subdivided according to type of aortic dissection. LEGEND: AcA= acute type A; ChA= chronic type A; AcB= acute type B; ChB= chronic type B. (Reproduced with permission from Fann JI, Sarris GE, Mitchell RS et al. Treatment of patients with aortic dissection presenting with peripheral vascular complications. Ann Surg 1990; 212: 705-713.)

Paraplegia

Spinal cord injury is a devastating complication in patients with acute aortic dissection. The incidence of paraplegia complicating aortic dissection is 3-6%; most affected patients have sustained extensive acute type A dissection.[4,5] In our surgical experience of patients with aortic dissection, nine (3%) presented with paraplegia, four (44%) of whom died in the hospital.[4] Two patients died from myocardial infarction and two due to respiratory insufficiency. Among the five operative survivors, one patient with a chronic type A dissection developed paraparesis preoperatively as a result of aortic rupture; he underwent replacement of the entire thoracoabdominal

Table 28.2. Operative mortality rates for patients with various peripheral vascular complications according to acuity and type of dissection

	AcA		ChA		AcB		ChB	
	N	OM	N	OM	N	OM	N	OM
Stroke	7	1(14±14%)	0	–	0	–	0	–
Paraplegia	7	3(43±19%)	1	0	1	1(100%)	0	–
Pulse Loss	48	12(25±6%)	7	1(14±14%)	8	4(50±18%)	4	1(25±22%)
Impaired Renal Perfusion	15	8(53±13%)	0	–	3	2(67±28%)	4	1(25±22%)
Compromised Visceral Perfusion	8	4(50±18%)	0	–	2	1(50±37%)	4	1(25±22%)

LEGEND: AcA= acute type A; ChA= chronic type A; AcB= acute type B; ChB= chronic type B.
OM = operative deaths (percent).
(Reproduced with permission from Fann JI, Sarris GE, Mitchell RS et al. Treatment of patients with aortic dissection presenting with peripheral vascular complications. Ann Surg 1990; 212:705-713.)

aorta and thereafter had substantial resolution of his spinal cord injury. In another patient with acute type A dissection, replacement of the ascending aorta resulted in gradual neurologic improvement postoperatively, and he was able to ambulate with a cane after lengthy rehabilitation. Our surgical approach in these cases has not been modified by the presence of paraplegia and has been primarily directed at the severity of the aortic dissection in order to prevent other lethal complications.[4] In general, there is only a small possibility of neurologic improvement postoperatively, a fact which must be understood by the patient, the patient's family and all involved health care personnel.

Peripheral Pulse Loss

Although the usual differential diagnosis of spontaneous acute limb ischemia includes arterial embolization and thrombosis due to pre-existing atherosclerosis, acute aortic dissection should also be considered. Sudden pulse loss occurs in upward of one-half of patients with type A dissection and one-quarter of all patients with aortic dissection.[4,5] In our experience, the majority of peripheral pulse deficits occurred in patients with acute type A dissection, probably because of the frequency and extensive nature of this lesion; 38% of patients with acute type A dissection and 24% of all patients had peripheral pulse deficits.[4] These peripheral pulse deficits may be dynamic and may resolve spontaneously in up to one-third of patients, presumably due to redirection of flow into the true lumen or spontaneous fenestration of the aortic false lumen.[5] A surgical approach, directed at the central aortic pathology, was associated with an operative mortality rate of 27%, which was not different from that of all patients undergoing surgery for aortic dissection.[4] After thoracic aortic repair in patients with aortic dissection and peripheral pulse deficit, only 8% of the patients required additional revascularization procedures to relieve peripheral ischemia. Thus, our policy is that in patients with leg ischemia, factors related to the proximal aorta (i.e., type and acuity of dissection and general operative risk) should dictate the mode of treatment.[4,5] In recent years, endovascular techniques have been developed to treat peripheral vascular complications of aortic dissection (see below).[8-12] We have considered endovascular techniques as part of the initial therapy in selected patients with peripheral arterial compromise complicating aortic dissection. Specifically, those with acute type B dissection who are not good candidates for graft replacement of the descending thoracic aorta are considered candidates as are those with type A dissection who have persistent distal malperfusion after ascending aortic graft replacement.

Impaired Renal Perfusion

Because dissection and/or occlusion of the renal arteries can result in renal ischemia or infarction, the presence of renal symptoms, such as oliguria, flank pain, and hematuria are of diagnostic and prognostic importance.[4,5] The incidence of renal artery involvement ranges from 5-60% in patients with aortic dissection; these differences probably reflect the method of detection (angiography vs. autopsy) rather than true population differences.[1,4,5] Both impaired renal perfusion and renal dysfunction in patients with aortic dissection have been associated with higher operative risk.[4] Although local surgical renal artery revascularization procedures during the acute phase of aortic dissection have been performed, this approach is rarely successful (in the presence of deteriorating renal function, the mortality rate approaches 50%).[4,5] Our previous approach to these patients has been to surgically replace the diseased thoracic aorta since this eliminates the most common causes of death and can potentially restore renal perfusion.[4] Nevertheless, the operative mortality rate in this subset of patients remains high in our experience, perhaps due to their moribund preoperative status and/or long delays in making the correct diagnosis after repair of the thoracic aorta. Increased experience with endovascular techniques for renal artery revascularization in acute aortic dissection has demonstrated that this is an important primary modality or adjunct to patients with acute aortic dissection and renal artery compromise (see below).[8-12]

Compromised Visceral Perfusion

Acute dissection leading to mesenteric ischemia or infarction fortunately is uncommon in the range of 3-5%.[4,5] The operative mortality rate for patients with this complication has been reported to be as high as 88%; notwithstanding successful visceral vascular reconstruction procedures, death often resulted from the sequelae of mesenteric infarction.[5] This experience prompted some to advocate local surgical treatment of visceral ischemia initially followed by medical treatment in patients with type B dissection or interval (within days) ascending aortic repair in patients with type A dissection.[5] In our experience with the initial operative approach focused on the thoracic aorta, the operative mortality rate for 14 patients with compromised visceral perfusion was 43%.[4] For patients who required abdominal exploration, the operative mortality rate was even higher approximating 80%.[7] Therefore, an early, aggressive surgical treatment focused primarily on the thoracic aorta may be a prudent option for these extremely ill patients, since it is clear that once bowel infarction

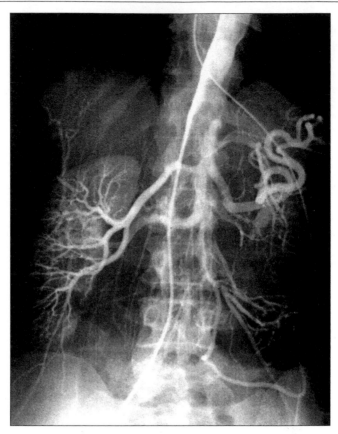

Fig. 28.3. Selective visceral angiogram of a patient who presented with an acute type A dissection. The flow to the right kidney is from the true lumen. The left renal artery and mesenteric artery are supplied by the false lumen.

occurs, the overall salvage rate will be disappointingly low no matter which tactic is employed. With the continued development of endovascular techniques for aortic fenestration and arterial stenting, these methods appear to be preferable in the initial treatment of selected patients with acute type B dissection complicated by visceral artery compromise (see below).[8-12]

Endovascular Treatment

Peripheral vascular complications of aortic dissection can be categorized into two groups based on pathophysiology.[8] The first includes patients whose peripheral ischemia is due to extension of the dissection flap into a branch artery with compression or obstruction (by a flap) of the true lumen. Endovascular techniques directed at stenting the true lumen open restore distal blood flow to the end-organ by compressing the false lumen. In the second category of patients, peripheral ischemia is the result of a generalized hemodynamic problem within the central aorta: severe compression of the true lumen (or "true lumen collapse") by flow in the false lumen can impede blood flow to any aortic branch vessel. The endovascular approach in these cases is to create a fenestration through the intimal flap to redirect blood flow from the false to the true lumen of the aorta, which in turn relieves the ischemia. Experimentally, Morales et al[14] have confirmed that aortic fenestration restores blood pressure and flow to hypoperfused organs in acute descending aortic dissection. In six dogs, descending thoracic aortic dissection was created, followed by fenestration of the infrarenal abdominal aorta, which resulted in restoration of femoral, mesenteric, and renal flows.

Endovascular approaches focused on the peripheral vascular complications of acute aortic dissection have been successfully employed by a number of groups.[8-12] At Stanford University, endovascular techniques have been employed as primary therapy in selected patients with peripheral arterial compromise complicating aortic dissection—namely, those with acute type B dissection who are not good candidates for surgical graft replacement and those with type A dissection who have persistent distal malperfusion after ascending aortic replacement.[8,9] Depending on findings of spiral CT scan, which is used to determine the potentially complex pathological anatomy, angiography with intravascular ultrasound in certain patients is performed as a prelude to flap fenestration or stenting. Using bilateral femoral access, balloon-expandable or self-expanding stents are deployed to support open the aortic true lumen, or the true lumen in an important arterial branch. Balloon fenestration of the dissection flap is another endovascular technique that has proved to be effective in relieving peripheral ischemia due to compression of the aortic true lumen.[8,9] Performed using fluoroscopic guidance (with or without intravascular ultrasound), aortic fenestration requires clear-cut definition of the pathoanatomy of aortic dissection. Once the fenestration is created with the needle, a guidewire is passed into the opposite lumen. A balloon catheter then is advanced over the guidewire and positioned across the fenestration; the balloon is dilated creating a fenestration relieving the pressure gradient between the false and true lumens.

Between 1991 and 1995, 22 selected patients with severe peripheral ischemic complications of aortic dissection underwent endovascular treatment at Stanford University.[8] Twelve patients had type A (5 acute, 7 chronic) and 10 had type B (9 acute, one chronic) aortic dissection. Ten patients presented with leg ischemia, 13 had renal ischemia and 6 had advanced visceral ischemia. A total of 16 patients underwent stent deployment in the true lumen. Eleven required renal artery stenting, 6 had lower extremity arterial stenting, 2 had superior mesenteric artery stenting and 2 had aortic stenting. Aortic flap fenestration was utilized in 3 patients, and 3 required combined fenestration and stenting. All 22 patients were successfully revascularized; however, 2 patients died at 3 days and 13 months after the procedure. One patient sustained a guidewire-induced perinephric hematoma. After a mean follow-up interval of 14 months, 19 patients had continued symptomatic relief, and one patient had been lost to follow-up.

28

Aortic dissection with aortic true lumen obliteration or "collapse" and compromised renal, mesenteric and/or lower extremity arterial flow can also be treated successfully using endovascular techniques.[9] Between 1992 and 1995, 11 patients required endovascular intervention for complicated aortic true lumen aortic collapse at Stanford University; two patients had chronic type A dissection and 9 had type B dissection (6 acute and 3 chronic). Seven patients had involvement of the renal artery, 6 had compromised mesenteric arteries and 6 had lower extremity arterial ischemia. Aortic stenting was performed in 2 patients, 4 underwent aortic flap fenestration and 3 had combined procedures. Nine patients were successfully revascularized using this approach. Two patients could not be revascularized; one underwent surgical revascularization of the superior mesenteric artery, and the other was treated medically for severe hypertension. The early mortality rate was 9%, but one patient developed thrombosis of the stented renal artery.

Williams et al[10] reported their experience at the University of Michigan in 24 patients who underwent endovascular treatment of peripheral vascular complications of aortic dissection. Twelve patients were treated with stenting combined with flap fenestration, 8 with fenestration alone and 4 with stenting alone. Flow was reestablished in 71 of 77 arteries (92%). The early mortality rate was relatively high (25%), as one might expect in such patients who have life threatening peripheral vascular ischemic complications of aortic dissection. Not surprisingly, patient outcome appeared to correlate with the degree of ischemic injury prior to endovascular intervention. Follow-up revealed that 2 patients died from complications of an expanding aortic false lumen.

Also from the University of Michigan, Deeb et al[12] reported their experience with a subset of patients (n = 20) who presented with acute type A aortic dissection complicated by preoperative malperfusion.[12] Initial treatment in these patients included percutaneous reperfusion, with aortic fenestration and branch stenting where appropriate. After reperfusion, all patients were stabilized in the intensive care unit. Once patients completely recovered from the consequences of malperfusion, surgical repair was performed. The mean delay to surgical repair was 20 days (range 2-67 days). Three (15%) of these patients died preoperatively—one of retrograde dissection and rupture and 2 of reperfusion injury. Seventeen patients underwent surgical repair with two deaths (operative mortality of 12%). They concluded that patients with an acute type A dissection and malperfusion should undergo percutaneous reperfusion, and that surgical repair should be delayed until the reperfusion injury resolves.[12]

Summary

Approximately 30-50% of patients develop one or more major peripheral vascular complications including stroke, paraplegia, peripheral pulse loss, and impaired renal or visceral perfusion. Aortic dissection should be considered early in the differential diagnosis of individuals with acute pulse loss and renal, visceral or cerebral ischemia. In patients with aortic dissection complicated by peripheral vascular manifestations, the overall operative mortality rate is no higher than that for patients without peripheral vascular complications. In general, surgical repair of the thoracic aorta results in satisfactory outcomes in patients with stroke and peripheral pulse deficits, but less favorably in those with paraplegia, impaired visceral perfusion or compromised renal blood flow. Endovascular techniques have been successfully employed to treat patients with aortic dissection and peripheral vascular complications either primarily (particularly in patients with acute type B dissection) or secondary to surgical repair of the ascending aorta in patients with acute type A dissection and persistent end-organ ischemia. Especially important is the continued need for earlier diagnosis and prompt surgical and/or endovascular intervention in patients with compromised renal and/or visceral perfusion in order to minimize the morbidity and mortality associated with these devastating complications.

Selected Readings

1. Hirst AE, John VL, Kime SW. Dissecting aneurysm of the aorta: A review of 505 cases. Medicine 1958; 37: 217-279.
    This article, perhaps the most historically significant work on the subject of aortic dissection in this past century, provides a comprehensive compilation of the presentation and pathology of over 500 patients.
2. Miller DC. Surgical management of aortic dissections: Indications, perioperative management, and long-term results. In: Doroghazi RM, Slater EE, eds. Aortic Dissection. New York: McGraw-Hill, 1983: 193-243.
    This chapter provides a thorough discussion of aortic dissection from the surgical prospective. Particularly important are the sections on preoperative evaluation and surgical technique, the principles of which have remained largely unchanged over the years; modifications since this publication include newer techniques of cardiopulmonary bypass and hypothermic circulatory arrest and various means of spinal cord protection.
3. DeSanctis RW, Eagle KA. Aortic dissection. Curr Probl Cardiol 1989; 14:227-278.
    This review is all-inclusive and provides an excellent basis for the understanding of aortic dissection—its etiology, diagnosis and treatment.
4. Fann JI, Sarris GE, Mitchell RS et al. Treatment of patients with aortic dissection presenting with peripheral vascular complications. Ann Surg 1990; 212:705-713.
    This article is focused on the peripheral vascular complications of a total of 272 patients who underwent surgical management of aortic dissection at Stanford University. In this early series, 85 patients developed one or more peripheral vascular complications, most of which improved with surgical aortic repair. As reflected in references 8 and 9, endovascular techniques have since been successfully employed to treat vascular complications of aortic dissection in certain patients and may represent the treatment of choice for some patients with these devastating complications.
5. Cambria RP, Brewster DC, Gertler J et al. Vascular complications associated with spontaneous aortic dissection. J Vasc Surg 1988; 7:199-209.
    This paper represents the combined Yale and Massachusetts General Hospital experience of 325 patients who presented with aortic dissection. Peripheral vascular complications occurred in 33% of the patients with an associated mortality rate of 51%. Particularly worrisome were cases of aortic dissection that involved the carotid, mesenteric and renal circulations. An approach directed at surgical revascularization of the affected ischemic organs was adopted. Since this important study, endovascular techniques have been utilized with greater success and have become a preferred initial therapeutic modality in selected patients.

28

6. Leonard JC, Hasleton PS. Dissecting aortic aneurysms: A clinicopathological study. I. Clinical and gross pathological findings. Quart J Med 1979; 189:55-63.

    This comprehensive paper from Manchester presents the clinical and pathologic experience in 171 patients with aortic dissection.

7. Glower DD, Fann JI, Speier RH et al. Comparison of medical and surgical therapy for uncomplicated descending aortic dissection. Circulation 1990; 82 (supple IV):39-46.

    This retrospective report based on the combined Stanford and Duke series addresses the issue of the optimal therapy of patients with uncomplicated type B aortic dissection. Recognizing the limitations of such an analysis, the data suggest that medical or early surgical therapy is associated with equivalent outcomes.

8. Slonim SM, Nyman U, Semba CP et al. Aortic dissection: percutaneous management of ischemic complications with endovascular stents and balloon fenestration. J Vasc Surg 1996; 23:241-253.

    This paper, along with reference 9, describes the Stanford experience with endovascular treatment of ischemic complications of aortic dissections. Endovascular stenting and balloon fenestration have become relatively safe and effective means of addressing the problem of peripheral vascular complications of aortic dissection and is the therapy of choice for some patients.

9. Slonim SM, Nyman UR, Semba CP et al. True lumen obliteration in complicated aortic dissection: endovascular treatment. Radiology 1996; 201:161-166.

10. Williams DM, Lee DY, Hamilton BH et al. The dissected aorta: Percutaneous treatment of ischemic complications—principles and results. J Vasc Interv Radiol 1997; 8:605-625.

    This is an important publication from the University of Michigan describing their experience with endovascular techniques in the diagnosis and treatment of patients with aortic dissection and peripheral vascular complications.

11. Dake MD, Kato N, Mitchell RS et al. Endovascular stent-graft placement for the treatment of acute aortic dissection. N Engl J Med 1999; 340 (20):1546-1552.

    This article evaluated the novel concept of endovascular stent-grafting to treat acute aortic dissection originating in the descending thoracic aorta in 19 patients. In selected patients, this approach may become an important therapeutic modality.

12. Deeb GM, Williams DM, Bolling SF et al. Surgical delay for acute type A dissection with malperfusion. Ann Thorac Surg 1997; 64:1669-1675.

    This article discusses an alternative approach to patients with peripheral vascular complications of aortic dissection—namely, the malperfusion is treated with endovascular techniques, delaying surgical repair until the reperfusion injury resolves. The potential difficulty with this approach is avoiding aortic rupture during the resolution phase of the malperfusion.

13. Cigarroa JE, Isselbacher EM, DeSanctis RW et al. Diagnostic imaging in the evaluation of suspected aortic dissection: Old standards and new directions. N Eng J Med 1993; 328:35-43.

    This is a comprehensive review of the available modalities in the diagnosis of aortic dissection from noted authorities in this field.

14. Morales DL, Quin JA, Braxton JH et al. Experimental confirmation of effectiveness of fenestration in acute aortic dissection. Ann Thorac Surg 1998; 66:1679-1683.

    In spite of previous use of aortic fenestration in the treatment of peripheral vascular complications of aortic dissection in the clinical setting, this paper provides experimental evidence that aortic fenestration is effective in increasing flow to the compromised organs.

28

Surgical Treatment of Acute and Chronic Aortic Dissection Distal to the Subclavian Artery

Joseph S. Coselli, Cüneyt Köksoy, Zachary C. Schmittling, and Scott A. LeMaire

Aortic dissection—a tear in the intima and inner media with subsequent progressive separation of the aortic wall layers—is the most common catastrophic event involving the aorta. Acute aortic dissection occurs in approximately 5-10 patients per million of population per year. The aorta distal to the left subclavian artery is involved in the vast majority of cases. Without treatment, 60% of patients with acute distal aortic dissection die within one month.

A simplified, descriptive classification of aortic dissection, advocated by Borst and associates,[1] is gaining favor over the traditional DeBakey and Stanford classifications (Fig. 29.1). Since their management differs substantially, it is useful to consider the proximal (ascending and transverse arch) and distal (descending thoracic and thoracoabdominal) aortic segments independently. Patients with isolated proximal aortic dissection (DeBakey type II) require emergent operation. In contrast, when only the distal aorta is involved (DeBakey type III or Stanford type B), initial treatment is medical; surgery is reserved for patients who develop complications. Patients with dissection that involves both the proximal and distal segments (DeBakey type I) require emergent surgical repair of the proximal segment followed by medical treatment for the remaining distal dissection.

Aortic dissection is also categorized based on the time elapsed since the initial event. Within the first 14 days following the initial tear in the aortic wall, the dissection is considered acute. After 14 days, the dissection is described as chronic. Although arbitrary, the distinction between acute and chronic distal aortic dissection has important implications in perioperative management strategies, operative techniques and surgical results.

Propagation of the separation within the layers of the media results in the formation of two or more channels (Fig. 29.1). The original lumen, which remains lined by the intima, is called the true lumen. The newly formed channel within the layers of the media is termed the false lumen. The true and false lumina are separated by the dissecting membrane. Additional tears in the dissecting membrane, located distal to the initial tear, allow communication between the two channels and are called reentry sites.

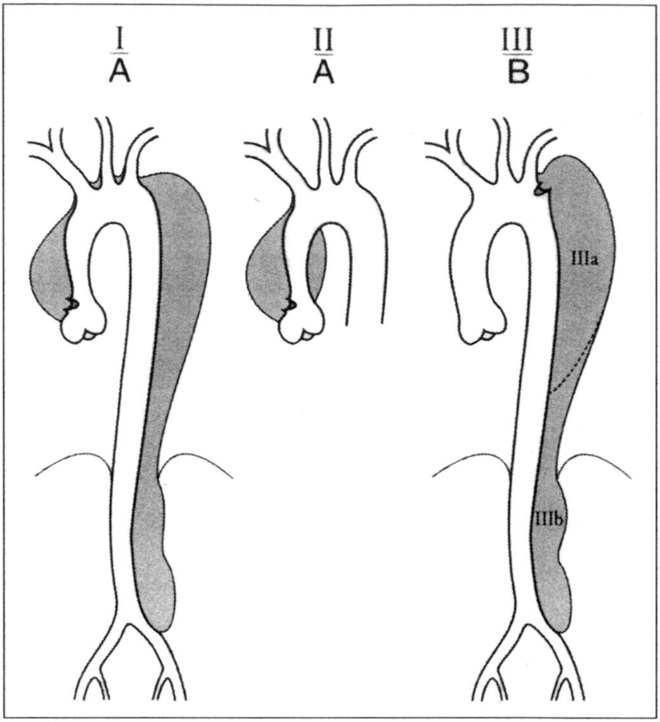

Fig. 29.1. Comparison of the traditional classifications for aortic dissection. The DeBakey classification (types I, II, IIIa, and IIIb) varies based on the extent of aortic involvement. The Stanford classification is based solely on the presence (type A) or absence (type B) of proximal aortic involvement; whether the distal aorta is involved is not specified. Using the simplified, descriptive classification system, patients are categorized as having proximal aortic dissection (as in the middle drawing), distal aortic dissection (the drawing on the right), or both proximal and distal dissections (the drawing on the left). In all three drawings, the false lumen is shaded and the true lumen is white. From Borst, Heinemann, and Stone[1] with permission.

Two rare but important variants of aortic dissection are penetrating aortic ulcers and intramural hematomas. Penetrating aortic ulcers are essentially disrupted atherosclerotic plaques. Eventually the ulcer can penetrate through the aortic wall leading to dissection or rupture. An intramural hematoma is a collection of blood within the aortic wall without an intimal tear; accumulation of the hematoma ultimately results in dissection. When located distal to the left subclavian artery, both variants indicate an impending dissection or rupture. Therefore, their treatment is identical to that for acute distal aortic dissection and that is aggressive medical management followed by surgery for complications.

Clinical Manifestations of Distal Aortic Dissection

Patients with acute distal aortic dissection may present with symptoms and findings that suggest many other acute medical or surgical diseases. This nonspecific presentation is the main reason that rapid diagnosis of acute dissection remains such a vexing clinical challenge. A high level of suspicion is the most important factor in establishing the diagnosis of aortic dissection.

Acute distal aortic dissection most commonly affects middle-aged to elderly men. The acute event is frequently associated with severe, lancing pain in the interscapular area, which subsequently migrates distally. The constellation of other symptoms and signs largely relates to the primary associated complications: rupture and malperfusion.

Rupture related to aortic dissection can occur during both the acute and chronic stages.[2] Being comprised of only the outer media and adventitia, the outer wall of the false lumen is usually only about one-fourth as thick as the normal intact wall and, therefore, is quite prone to dilation and rupture. Expansion of the weakened aortic wall may be even more rapid in patients with Marfan syndrome or other connective tissue disorder that results in severe medial degeneration. Signs of rupture with bleeding into the thoracic cavity or retroperitoneum include hypotension and profound shock, respiratory distress, flank hematoma and abdominal distention.

Although imaging studies often demonstrate a left pleural effusion, diagnostic thoracentesis is not recommended. Patients with acute distal aortic dissection characteristically have a bloody left pleural effusion related to the acutely injured tissues. Because bloody pleural fluid is ubiquitous in this setting, it is not considered a sign of rupture nor an indication for emergency surgery.

Malperfusion and ischemic damage of the viscera or extremities occur in one-fourth of patients with distal aortic dissection. Extrinsic compression of the true lumen by the enlarging false lumen causes distal ischemia and is called pseudocoarctation. Although the false lumen usually occupies the left perimeter of the aorta, any arterial branch can be compromised. Disruption of intercostal arteries causes spinal cord ischemia in 2-6% of patients; neurologic findings can vary from minor sensory deficits to frank paraplegia. The origin of the left renal artery is disrupted in 5-25% of patients, whereas the visceral and right renal arteries usually arise from the true aortic lumen. Abdominal pain and tenderness suggest mesenteric ischemia. Compromise of renal arterial blood flow may cause flank pain and hematuria, mimicking the signs usually associated with ureteral colic. Beyond the aortic bifurcation, the false lumen can expand and compromise the true lumen of the iliac artery, thereby obstructing blood flow to the corresponding leg. This phenomenon occurs predominantly on the left side. In the setting of distal aortic dissection, a diminished left upper extremity pulse generally denotes retrograde propagation.

Similar to thoracic aortic aneurysms of other causes, aneurysms related to chronic aortic dissection are often asymptomatic until they rupture. The compression of adjacent structures may cause chest pain, hoarseness, stridor, dysphagia or the superior vena cava syndrome.

29

Imaging Studies

Although chest radiographs are not diagnostic, they may provide some early clues suggesting the presence of distal aortic dissection, including mediastinal widening, left pleural effusion and displacement of mediastinal structures. Once the suspicion of distal aortic dissection is raised, additional imaging studies are obtained to (1) confirm the diagnosis and (2) determine whether or not the ascending aorta is also involved. The later objective is critical because the presence of proximal dissection mandates emergency operation. Contrast enhanced computed tomography (CT) scanning is well suited for stable patients with suspected acute dissection because it allows rapid diagnosis and accurately identifies the extent of aortic involvement. In patients who are too unstable for transport to the radiology suite, echocardiography can be performed in the intensive care unit or operating room. While transesophageal echocardiography (TEE) is an excellent means of diagnosing distal aortic dissection, transthoracic echocardiography (TTE) is superior for evaluating whether or not the proximal aorta is involved. When TTE and TEE are both used in the setting of suspected aortic dissection, the combination yields sensitivity and specificity that approach 100%. In addition to revealing the presence of aortic dissection usually by demonstrating the dissecting membrane separating the true and false lumina, echocardiography also allows assessment of valvular and myocardial function. Like CT, magnetic resonance imaging (MRI) is very accurate in diagnosing aortic dissection and determining its extent. Although often impractical for critically ill patients with acute dissection, MRI is a useful alternative to contrast enhanced CT in stable patients with compromised renal function. Aortography, once considered the imaging modality of choice, is generally reserved for patients in whom the other studies are equivocal and the diagnosis remains unclear. Aortography is also useful in patients presenting with visceral malperfusion. In addition to providing detailed information on branch vessel anatomy and perfusion, aortography facilitates percutaneous fenestration or stenting for the treatment of malperfusion.

Initial Management of Acute Distal Aortic Dissection

Because of the potential for rupture before the diagnosis of aortic dissection is confirmed, aggressive medical management is started immediately upon the initial clinical suspicion and is continued through all phases of the diagnostic evaluation. The goals of medical therapy in acute dissection are to
1. stabilize the dissection and
2. prevent rupture and other complications, such as malperfusion.[3]

Optimal management mandates careful monitoring in an intensive care unit. A dependable arterial catheter is required to monitor blood pressure and titrate antihypertensive agents. The radial artery is the preferred site since the lower extremities are commonly malperfused. Although central venous catheters are often inserted to assure reliable intravenous access, pulmonary artery catheters are reserved for critically ill patients or those with severe cardiopulmonary dysfunction. A urinary catheter is used monitor renal function and to judge the adequacy of fluid replacement. Frequent neurologic exams are extremely important. Baseline laboratory

29

investigations should include a complete blood cell count, arterial blood gases, prothrombin and partial thromboplastin times, serum electrolytes, creatinine, blood urea nitrogen and liver enzymes. Although laboratory studies are generally not helpful in diagnosis, findings such as elevated creatinine or hepatic enzyme levels provide information about the presence of organ ischemia. Blood work is repeated according to the patient's clinical course.

An increase in aortic wall stress is the main factor responsible for the propagation and rupture of the dissection. Therefore, the cornerstone of medical treatment is the reduction of aortic wall stress by minimizing the force of left ventricular ejection (dP/dT). Reductions in blood pressure must be balanced with the maintenance of adequate cerebral, coronary and renal perfusion. Experimental and clinical studies have demonstrated that the pharmacologic reduction of blood pressure and cardiac contractility reduces morbidity and mortality. Therefore, medical treatment should be initiated in all patients suspected of having aortic dissection and continued until the diagnosis has been ruled out. Drugs commonly used in dissection include direct vasodilators, beta-adrenergic blockers, calcium channel blockers and angiotensin-converting enzyme inhibitors (Table 29.1). Intravenous agents are used initially to achieve and maintain hemodynamic targets. Systolic and mean arterial blood pressures are maintained between 100-110 mm Hg and 60-75 mm Hg, respectively, provided that urine output is adequate and neurological function is not impaired.

Recent literature supports the administration of beta-blockers (e.g., esmolol, propanolol and labetalol) to all patients with acute aortic dissection, unless contraindications exist. General contraindications include heart failure, bradyarrhythmias, atrioventricular conduction blocks and bronchospastic disease. Esmolol, a cardioselective ultra-fast acting agent with a short half-life, may be useful in patients with bronchospastic disease. Labetalol, both a nonselective beta-blocker and postsynaptic alpha-1 blocker, reduces systemic vascular resistance without impairing cardiac output. The dose of beta-blockers should be titrated to achieve a heart rate of 60-80 beats per minute. Once adequate beta-blockade is obtained, nitroprusside, a direct vasodilator, may be added. When used alone, however, nitroprusside can increase dP/dT and cause progression of the dissection.

When beta-blockers cannot be used, calcium channel blockers such as diltiazem can be an effective alternative. The angiotensin-converting enzyme inhibitors, like enalaprilat, are ideal in patients with renal malperfusion; the reduction in renin release may lead to improved kidney blood flow. Ganglionic blockers, such as trimethephan, are no longer front line agents.

Once the patient has been stabilized and a decision made that surgery will not be necessary, a plan must be made for shifting from intravenous to oral medications. Oral therapy should be initiated when systolic pressure is in the 100-110 mm Hg range and the neurologic, renal and cardiovascular systems are stable. Oral therapy often begins with a beta-blocker. The dose is then increased until adequate blood pressure control is obtained or side effects develop. The dose of one drug should be maximized before starting another. Many patients can be discharged home after the blood pressure is well controlled on oral agents.

29

Table 29.1. Recommended agents for initial medical management of acute aortic dissection

Agent	Class	Dose
Propranolol	Beta-blocker	Give 1 mg IV every 3-5 minutes until heart rate and blood pressure are controlled (up to 0.15 mg/kg), then administer 2-6 mg IV every 4-6 hours.
Labetalol	Beta-blocker	Give 10 mg IV over 2 minutes initially with additional doses of 20-80 mg every 10-15 minutes until heart rate and blood pressure are controlled (up to 300 mg total), then begin an infusion at 2 mg/min and titrate up to 20 mg/min.
Esmolol	Beta-blocker	Give 30 mg IV and begin an infusion at 3 mg/min – titrate up to 12 mg/min.
Nitroprusside	Vasodilator	Begin only after beta-blockers given. Administer 20 mcg/min IV initially and titrate up to 800 mcg/min.
Nifedipine	Calcium channel antagonist	Give 10-20 mg PO while other medications are prepared.
Diltiazem	Calcium channel antagonist	Give 0.25 mg/kg IV over 2 minutes followed by an infusion of 5-15 mg/hr.
Enalaprilat	Angiotensin-converting enzyme inhibitor	Give 0.625 mg IV every 4-6 hours.

29

The most common causes of death during medical treatment are aortic rupture and end-organ malperfusion. Therefore, during initial medical management patients are continually reassessed for the development of complications. Pain despite adequate pressure control, changes in neurological findings, loss of peripheral pulses and hemodynamic instability indicate progression of the disease and mandate surgical treatment.

Surgical Treatment

Indications for Operation

Medical management of acute distal aortic dissection results in lower morbidity and mortality rates than achieved with surgical treatment. Therefore, acute distal aortic dissections are primarily managed medically, and surgery is reserved for patients who experience complications.[4] In simple terms, operative intervention for acute distal aortic dissection is directed towards prevention or repair of rupture and relief of ischemic manifestations. The specific indications for operative intervention include:

1. aortic rupture,
2. increasing periaortic or intrapleural fluid,
3. rapidly expanding aortic diameter,
4. uncontrolled hypertension,
5. persistent pain despite adequate medical therapy and

6. ischemia of limbs, spinal cord or abdominal viscera. Acute dissection superimposed on a pre-existing aneurysm is considered a life-threatening condition and is also an indication for operation.

Finally, patients who have a history of noncompliance with medical therapy present a problematic situation; surgical treatment should be considered if these patients are otherwise reasonable operative candidates.

Indication for operative intervention in chronic dissection is similar to that of degenerative aortic aneurysms. Rapid expansion of the aneurysm and factors that increase the likelihood of rupture are indications for surgery. When the affected segment has reached 5.5-6 cm or when an aneurysm has enlarged more than 1 cm during a 6-month period, elective operative intervention is recommended. A lower threshold, 5-5.5 cm, is often used for patients with Marfan syndrome. In the majority of patients treated for acute proximal dissection, the dissection persists distal to the site of the operative repair; subsequent extensive dilatation of the distal aortic segment develops in 16% of the survivors (Fig. 29.2).[1,2] Rupture of the dilated distal aorta is the most common cause of late death after surgical repair of proximal aortic dissections.

Extent of Repair

In patients with acute distal aortic dissection, the primary goal of surgery is to prevent rupture. Therefore, graft repair of the symptomatic segment is the mainstay of surgical treatment. Since the most common site of rupture in distal aortic dissection is in the proximal third of the descending thoracic aorta, at least the upper half of the descending thoracic aorta is repaired. In addition, any distal segment that is dilated more than 4 cm needs to be replaced. Graft replacement of the entire thoracoabdominal aorta is not attempted in the setting of acute dissection unless a coexisting aneurysm mandates this radical approach.

Because long-term survival is not improved by resecting the primary tear, the extent of surgical repair is based on aortic size and symptoms rather than the anatomic location of the intimal tear.[5] For example, if the intimal tear is located in the transverse aortic arch and the life-threatening portion of the dissection involves the descending thoracic aorta, only the descending segment is repaired. The transverse arch is only replaced if it is also aneurysmal.

In the setting of chronic dissection, a more aggressive replacement is usually performed. Although the entire descending aorta may be dissected and aneurysmal, typically a relatively localized segment is the cause of the symptoms. In high-risk patients, a limited repair focusing on the symptomatic portion may be warranted. Although this practice is successful in minimizing early postoperative morbidity, its principle disadvantage is that it leaves the patient with a larger segment of dissected aorta, which can potentially expand and rupture in the future. Therefore, in appropriate surgical candidates, we advocate replacing the entire descending thoracic aorta, and often extend the repair to include the thoracoabdominal aorta.

29

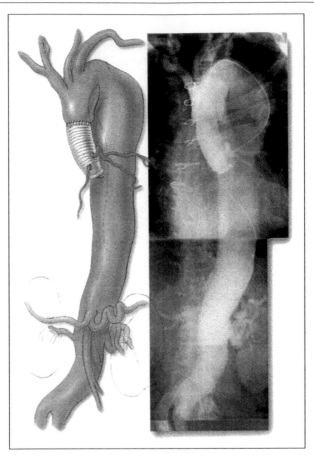

Fig. 29.2. Preoperative drawing and aortogram of a patient with an extent II thoracoabdominal aortic aneurysm secondary to chronic distal aortic dissection following composite valve graft replacement of the aortic root for proximal aortic dissection.

Adjuncts for Spinal Cord, Renal, and Visceral Protection

Patients undergoing the more extensive aortic repairs (Fig. 29.3) are at an increased risk of developing postoperative paraplegia or paraparesis from spinal cord ischemia. In addition to the inherent physical disability, patients with spinal cord complications have a decreased long-term survival.

In brief, our current routine strategy for preventing ischemic spinal cord injury during aortic surgery involves liberal reattachment of critical intercostal arteries (T8 to L1), mild permissive hypothermia, moderate heparinization (1 mg/kg) and avoidance of postoperative hypotension. Additionally, cerebrospinal fluid drainage and

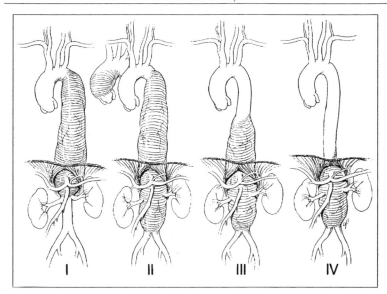

Fig. 29.3. The Crawford classification of thoracoabdominal aortic aneurysms based on the extent of aortic involvement and replacement. Extent I and II aneurysm repairs carry the highest paraplegia rates, and are therefore considered "extensive repairs."

29

left heart bypass are used as adjuncts during extensive (extents I and II, Fig. 29.3) thoracoabdominal aortic aneurysm repair.

Hypothermia provides effective protection for the spinal cord and brain. Therefore, mild permissive hypothermia is routinely used during distal aortic surgery. During the operation, the patient's rectal temperature is allowed to drift down to near 32°C. Temperatures below 32°C are carefully avoided to minimize the risks of cardiac dysrhythmias and coagulopathy. After completion of the aortic repair, warm water irrigation of the operative field is employed to arrest the hypothermic trend.

A recent prospective randomized trial has demonstrated the efficacy of using cerebrospinal fluid drainage in patients undergoing extensive repairs. Drainage is initiated after induction of anesthesia and continued for approximately 48 hours postoperatively. Fluid is drained as needed to maintain cerebrospinal fluid pressures at 10 mm Hg.

Left heart bypass is used to perfuse the distal aorta during proximal portion of the repair. Distal aortic perfusion provides circulation to the abdominal viscera, kidneys, lower extremities and the lower intercostal and lumbar arteries. Left heart bypass also enables control of proximal arterial pressure and left heart filling, reducing the amount of pharmacological intervention needed. When the pericardium has been previously entered for coronary artery bypass grafting or valve replacement, access to the left atrium should be obtained by cannulation of the superior or inferior pulmonary vein. Distal aortic perfusion is provided by either left atrium-to-femoral artery bypass or left atrium-to-distal aorta bypass. Cannulation of the distal descending aorta is the preferred approach due to the lack of complications and the avoidance of femoral artery exposure and repair. Careful review of preoperative CT scans and aortograms assists selection of an appropriate site for aortic cannulation; areas with obvious intraluminal thrombus and plaques are avoided, reducing the risk of embolic events. The perfusion flow should be manipulated to keep distal aortic pressure around 70 mmHg while maintaining normal proximal arterial and venous filling pressures. Generally, flows between 1500 and 2500 ml/min are adequate.

During extent I thoracoabdominal aortic repairs, intermittent perfusion of the kidneys with cold saline is used to provide renal protection. In extent II repairs, a side-arm off of the left heart bypass circuit is employed to provide selective perfusion of the celiac, superior mesenteric, and renal arteries after distal aortic perfusion has been stopped. Consequently, the total ischemic time of these organs can be reduced to a few minutes for even the most complex aortic reconstructions.

Graft Selection and Anastomotic Techniques

Dacron grafts are selected so that the diameter is slightly smaller than that of the proximal aortic cuff. These smaller grafts, usually 22 mm or 24 mm, will reduce propagation of the systolic pressure wave and thus may decrease the risk of subsequent aneurysm formation in the dissected aorta that remains distal to the repair.

Compared to degenerative aneurysms, the fragile tissue in aortic dissection mandates that suture lines consist of a larger number of smaller suture bites. This reduces tearing and subsequent bleeding along the anastomoses. In acute aortic dissection, the proximal and distal suture lines obliterate the false lumen and reestablish blood flow within the true lumen; 4-0 suture is preferred because of the extreme fragility of the acutely injured aortic wall. In chronic aortic dissection, a wedge of dissecting membrane is excised distally and proximally from within the aortic cuffs, allowing blood to flow through both true and false channels (Fig. 29.4). The anastomoses are created between the graft and the outer wall of the aortic cuffs using running 3-0 polypropylene suture.

Placement of a clamp across the distal aorta can cause damage to the fragile dissected tissue. By performing an open distal anastomosis without a distal aortic clamp this problem is eliminated. If profuse back-bleeding from the distal aorta makes sewing difficult, a balloon catheter can be placed in the lumen and inflated.

Surgical Technique–Descending Thoracic Aortic Repair

The patient is placed in the right lateral decubitus position. A left thoracotomy incision is made and the chest is entered through the 5th or 6th intercostal space (Fig. 29.5A). Proximal control is obtained near the left subclavian artery. In the setting of acute dissection, mediastinal hematoma near the proximal descending thoracic aorta should be avoided until proximal control is established. Intravenous heparin is administered and, whenever possible, the aorta is clamped distal to the left subclavian artery. When the aneurysm involves the aorta immediately adjacent to the left subclavian artery, the clamp must be placed between the left common carotid artery and the left subclavian artery; a bulldog clamp is used to occlude the

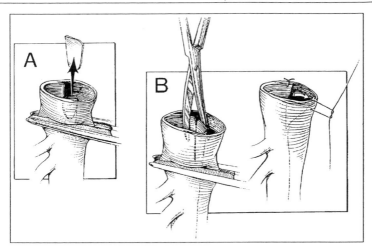

Fig. 29.4. Management of the distal aorta using fenestration in patients with chronic aortic dissection. This procedure is done just before performing the distal anastomosis during repair of a chronic dissection. In addition, fenestration can be done as an independent procedure for distal malperfusion. (A) A wedge of dissecting membrane is excised to ensure that both the true lumen and the false lumen are perfused. (B) After the septum is excised, if there is concern as to whether both lumina will be perfused, the septum is tacked open.

29

subclavian artery (Fig. 29.5B). The aorta should be completely transected approximately 2 cm distal to the clamp and carefully separated from the underlying esophagus. This reduces the risk of esophageal injury and ensures that all lumens are identified. After the dissecting membrane is excised, back-bleeding upper intercostal arteries are ligated with 2-0 silk sutures, and the proximal anastomosis is performed (Fig. 29.5C). In cases of chronic dissection, patent lower intercostal arteries are reattached to an opening in the graft. In acute dissection, however, the intercostal arteries are not reattached to the graft because the tissues are extremely friable and an anastomosis here can to lead catastrophic bleeding. After cutting the graft to proper length, an end-to-end distal anastomosis is performed (Fig. 29.5D).

Surgical Technique–Thoracoabdominal Aortic Repair

In the setting of aortic dissection, most thoracoabdominal aortic repairs are extent I or II. In extent I repairs, the distal anastomosis is performed above the renal arteries, often in a beveled fashion. In extent II repairs, as described below in detail, the entire distal aorta is replaced with the graft. The patient is placed in a right lateral oblique decubitus position with the hips rotated to allow access to both groins. A left thoracoabdominal incision is made at the 6th intercostal space. The diaphragm is divided in a circumferential fashion, leaving a 2 cm rim of diaphragmatic tissue on the chest wall to allow closure after the completion of the aortic repair. The abdominal aortic segment is exposed using the transperitoneal approach and the

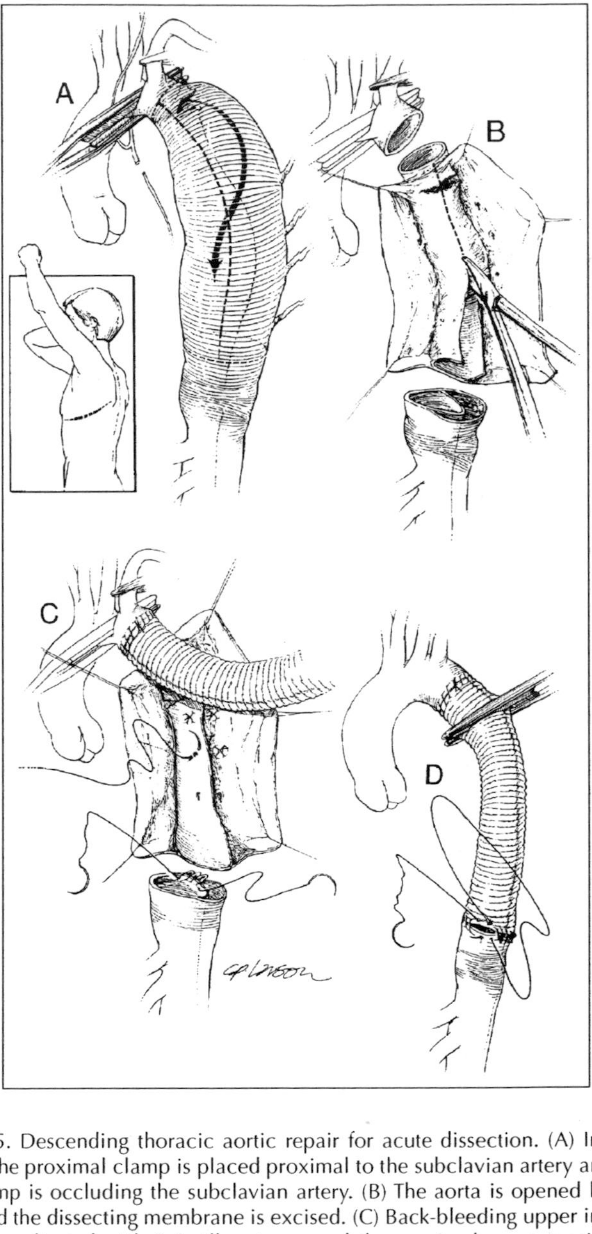

Fig. 29.5. Descending thoracic aortic repair for acute dissection. (A) In this example, the proximal clamp is placed proximal to the subclavian artery and a bulldog clamp is occluding the subclavian artery. (B) The aorta is opened longitudinally and the dissecting membrane is excised. (C) Back-bleeding upper intercostal arteries are ligated with 2-0 silk sutures, and the proximal anastomosis is completed. In preparation for the distal anastomosis, the false lumen is obliterated with running suture. (D) After moving the proximal clamp, the graft is cut to proper length and the distal anastomosis is performed.

retroperitoneum is entered lateral to the left colon. An open abdominal approach with medial visceral rotation allows for direct inspection of the abdominal viscera. An entirely retroperitoneal approach is used in patients with multiple prior abdominal procedures, a history of severe adhesions or peritonitis. The left crus of the diaphragm is divided and the left renal artery is exposed.

The distal aortic arch is gently exposed only enough to allow placement of a clamp. The vagus and recurrent laryngeal nerves are identified and preserved. It is particularly important to preserve and the recurrent laryngeal nerve in patients with chronic obstructive pulmonary disease and reduced pulmonary function. Intravenous heparin is administered (1 mg/kg). In patients who will require left heart bypass, the inferior pulmonary vein and mid-thoracoabdominal aorta are cannulated. The proximal aortic clamp is positioned either distal to the left subclavian artery or between the left carotid and subclavian arteries. In the later situation, the left subclavian artery is clamped separately. After starting left heart bypass, the distal aorta is clamped between T4 and T7 (Fig. 29.6A) and the aorta is opened along its posterolateral aspect (Fig. 29.6B). Electrocautery is used to open the outer false lumen; the inner true lumen is opened with scissors (Fig. 29.6C). After identifying both aortic channels, back-bleeding upper intercostal arteries are suture-ligated. The proximal aorta should be completely transected in order to allow for full thickness suturing of the aortic wall with minimal risk of esophageal injury. A collagen-impregnated woven Dacron graft, usually 22–24 mm in diameter, is anastomosed to the proximal aorta using 3-0 polypropylene suture (Fig. 29.6D). In patients with Marfan syndrome and acute dissection, 4-0 polypropylene suture is used. If the left subclavian artery is involved, the false channel is closed within the proximal anastomosis. Full-thickness bites incorporate the left margin of the origin of the left subclavian artery within the suture line.

As replacement of the aorta proceeds distally, the distal aortic clamp may be sequentially moved to lower positions on the aorta. This maintains distal aortic perfusion and restores blood flow to proximal tissues. Alternatively, left heart bypass may be discontinued following completion of the proximal anastomosis. The aneurysm is then opened longitudinally, staying posterior to left renal artery, to its distal termination (Fig. 29.6E). The distal aorta is not clamped in order to allow an open distal anastomosis and to prevent clamp injury to the aorta. All blood is removed from the operative field using a cell saving device. The remainder of the dissecting membrane is completely excised (Fig. 29.6F); this is important in facilitating the exposure of branches arising from the aorta.

In order to reduce visceral ischemic time, the abdominal viscera and kidneys are perfused using balloon catheters attached to the arterial perfusion line. These catheters are positioned within the origins of the celiac, superior mesenteric and renal arteries (Fig. 29.6G). The rate of flow to the visceral arteries ranges from 200-800 ml/min depending on the proximal aortic pressure. With regard to the intercostal arteries, patent intercostal arteries between T7 and L2 are reattached to an opening made in the graft while others are over-sewn to limit back-bleeding. The clamp is then moved down on the graft to a position below the reattached intercostal arteries.

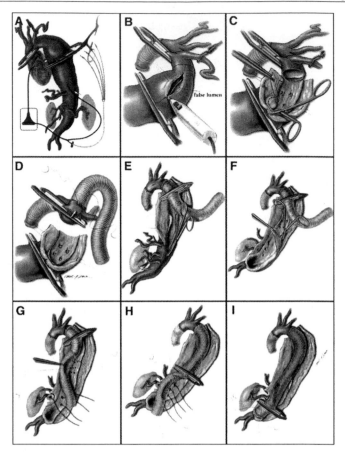

The celiac, superior mesenteric along with the right and left renal artery origins are reattached to one or more openings in the graft (Fig. 29.6H). Occasionally, the distance between the renal arteries is excessive. In this case, the left renal artery must be reanastomosed either directly (Fig. 29.6I) or by graft interposition. If visceral or renal arteries are involved in the dissection, they must be repaired to allow perfusion of the true lumen; this can be achieved by taking deep suture bites of the vessel orifice which simultaneously reapproximates the dissecting membrane to the outer aortic coat and connects the arterial branch to the graft. When the intima of a visceral artery is disrupted, the true lumen is reconstructed with fine running polypropylene sutures before the anastomosis to the graft. After completion of the last visceral anastomosis, all air and clot is flushed from the graft and a clamp is placed on the graft below the renal arteries. The proximal clamp is removed to resume perfusion of the viscera and kidneys. Next, an end-to-end anastomosis is performed immediately proximal to the aortic bifurcation. For chronic dissections, the aorta is

Fig. 29.6. (opposite page) Extent II graft repair of a thoracoabdominal aortic aneurysm due to chronic distal aortic dissection (same patient as in Fig. 29.2). (A) The bypass circuit from the left atrium to the lower descending thoracic aorta employs a centrifugal pump. Note that the proximal aorta is clamped between the left common carotid and left subclavian arteries. The proximal portion of the aneurysm is isolated between clamps and (B) opened with cautery. (C) The aorta is completely transected immediately distal to the left subclavian artery. The dissecting membrane separating the true and false lumens is opened and completely excised. Proximal intercostal arteries are oversewn. (D) The proximal anastomosis is carried out running polypropylene suture. (E) The proximal clamp is moved to the graft, restoring perfusion to the left subclavian artery, and left heart bypass is discontinued. The aneurysm is opened along its full length and (F) the remaining membrane between the true and the false lumina is completely excised. (G) Balloon perfusion catheters are placed in the celiac, superior mesenteric and both renal arteries for perfusion via the bypass circuit. An oval opening is used to reattach patent intercostal arteries. (H) The cross-clamp is sequentially moved down the graft, restoring flow to the intercostal arteries while visceral vessels are reattached. The left renal artery reattached with a separate aortic button and the aortic clamp is moved down the graft to restore flow to visceral and renal vessels (I) while the distal anastomosis is completed.

fenestrated as described previously to allow adequate blood flow to both lumina (Fig. 29.4). Some cases require a bifurcated graft with anastomoses made to the distal common iliac, external iliac or femoral arteries.

When a distal dissection has progressed retrograde into the transverse aortic arch and placement of the proximal clamp is not technically feasible, hypothermic circulatory arrest can be used to allow the proximal portion of the repair. Similarly, if the aneurysm extends to the chest wall or if extensive scarring is present, then deep hypothermic circulatory arrest may be the safest option. The use of circulatory arrest should also be considered in patients expected to have a friable aorta that is prone to tear during proximal clamping.

Alternative Options

When ischemic complications are the primary indication for emergency surgery, aortic fenestration is an effective option.[6] Fenestration involves partial resection of the dissecting membrane, which results in decompression of the false lumen proximally and restoration of blood flow in the true lumen (Fig. 29.4). The fenestration can be created in the descending thoracic aortic, infrarenal abdominal aorta, or iliac artery. It can be performed as the primary procedure or combined with concomitant aortic repair. Membrane fenestration of branch vessels, such as the renal arteries, is also occasionally required. A modification of the open technique targets the thoracoabdominal aorta (Fig. 29.7A-C). Fenestration can also be performed under fluoroscopic guidance using percutaneous catheters. Because no prosthetic material is used, fenestration procedures are extremely valuable for situations that are associated with a high risk for graft infection, such as colonic perforation due to mesenteric ischemia and concomitant intraabdominal sepsis. They are also well suited for those patients with malperfusion who are critically ill and unable to tolerate a more extensive operation.

29

Thromboexclusion is performed through a midline thoracoabdominal incision from the suprasternal notch to the pubis. After a Dacron graft is attached end-to-side to the ascending aorta, the graft is routed through the pericardium into the right hemithorax and through the diaphragm into the abdominal cavity. The graft is then placed behind the transverse mesocolon, into the retroperitoneum, and anastomosed end-to-side to the infrarenal aorta. The rationale for this procedure is that thrombosis of the excluded descending aorta will occur gradually and allow progressive formation of collateral blood vessels. This gradual conversion to collateral circulation may lead to decreased complication rates. Data regarding the efficacy of this operation, however, is limited.[6]

Postoperative Management

Aortic dissection is a progressive and chronic disease that requires lifelong surveillance. Repair usually eliminates only a portion of the false lumen; therefore patients remain at risk for complications of dissection following surgical repair. Rupture and ischemic events related to the chronic dissection are responsible for 15-30% of late deaths.

The importance of the adequate follow-up was emphasized by Glover et al in a study on the long-term outcomes of patients with all types of aortic dissections.[7] The authors reported that 18% of late deaths were caused by aortic rupture. In addition, 38% of deaths were secondary to cardiovascular events and 24% to undetermined "sudden events" which may have included additional aortic ruptures. Onefourth of patients required surgical repair during the follow-up period. Therefore, a dedicated program of follow-up with imaging studies is required in these patients. Contrast-enhanced CT scanning is the most available technique and is extremely reliable. The use of MRI, which provides excellent images of the aorta, is an alternative that is advocated by several authors. Both modalities are capable of detecting:

1. expansion of the aorta and its branches,
2. chronic visceral perfusion defects and
3. late complications of surgery, such as pseudoaneurysms.

In patients being managed medically for acute dissection, the first surveillance CT scan of the chest and abdomen is obtained within 6-12 weeks. Subsequent evaluation of the aorta is obtained at least every 6 months in the early period. After one or two years, follow-up imaging studies can be obtained once each year as long as the patient has remained asymptomatic and the aortic size has not changed substantially. More frequent studies are indicated in high-risk patients such as those with Marfan syndrome. Patients who have undergone graft repair are also evaluated with annual CT scans of the chest and abdomen. The purpose of such rigorous surveillance is to detect dilation or false aneurysm formation in the aorta before rupture or other complications develop. Early detection allows the patient to have timely elective intervention.

Long-term pharmacological therapy is important for patients with chronic aortic dissection following either medical or surgical therapy for the acute event. In a twenty-year follow-up study, DeBakey and associates demonstrated that blood pressure control was critical in predicting late aneurysm formation. Of those with "good"

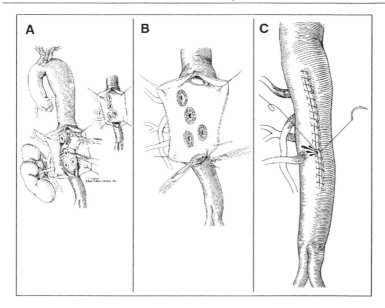

Fig. 29.7. The thoracoabdominal fenestration procedure: (A) thoracoabdominal aortotomy with excision of the intimal flap, (B) reattachment of the visceral vessels, obliteration of the distal false lumen, and (C) primary closure of the aortotomy. From Howell JF, LeMaire SA, Kirby RP. Ann Thorac Surg 1997;64:242-4. Used with permission.

29

blood pressure control only 17% developed aneurysmal degeneration compared to 45% of those labeled as having "poor" control.[2] Therefore, strict blood pressure control is the mainstay of outpatient management. Beta-blockers remain the drugs of choice.

Results

In last decade, the mortality rate for patients with acute distal aortic dissection has significantly decreased. This is true for both surgically and medically treated patients. Approximately 10-17.6% of medically treated patients die during the initial treatment phase.[3,4,8] The main causes of death during medical management include rupture, malperfusion, and cardiac failure.[3] Risk factors associated with an unfavorable outcome (death or need for surgery) during medical therapy include an enlarged aorta, persistent hypertension despite maximal treatment, oliguria, and peripheral ischemia.

Patients undergoing surgery for acute distal aortic dissection are a high-risk group. This group includes patients with rupture, neurological dysfunction, renal failure, or peripheral ischemia. Therefore, it is not surprising that results following surgery for acute aortic dissection are equal or slightly worse to those of medical therapy. Surgical mortality rates for acute dissection range from 8.7-21%, which represents an improvement over results that were obtained 15 years ago.[3,4,7-10] This progress can be attributed to advances in diagnostic methods, better surgical technique and improved perioperative care. Variables that increase operative risk include:

1. renal or visceral ischemia,
2. rupture and
3. advancing age.[4]

Acute dissection secondary to an intimal tear in the transverse arch is rare but a highly lethal variant. In these patients, mortality rate is high regardless of whether early surgery is performed or only medical treatment is used.

The operative risk for chronic distal aortic dissection is significantly lower than that for acute dissection. Early mortality rate for chronic distal aortic dissection ranges from 7-10%.[3,9,10] Predictors for mortality in patients with chronic distal dissection include:

1. advancing age,
2. history of congestive heart failure,
3. aortic rupture (contained or free) and
4. preoperative renal failure.

The 5-year survival for chronic distal aortic dissection varies between 70-78% and then declines to 25-55% at 10 years.[4,6,8] The survival curves in both the medical and surgical groups reflect the high early mortality seen in patients with acute dissection. The early mortality is even greater in the surgical group, due to the number of unstable patients that are taken to the operating room as a last-chance effort to save them. However, in the long term, survival curves become very similar. Factors that influence long-term survival following operative repair include:

1. postoperative renal failure,
2. postoperative cardiac dysfunction and
3. the extent of aorta replaced.[4]

Late mortality in patients treated either medically or surgically is usually due to residual aortic disease, myocardial infarction, sudden cardiac death or heart failure.

Surgery for acute distal aortic dissection carries an increased risk for the development of paraplegia or paraparesis. The rate of neurologic dysfunction after surgical repair ranges from 13-32%.[3,9,10] In contrast, the risk of paraplegia or paraparesis in chronic aortic dissection does not differ from that encountered during degenerative thoracoabdominal aortic aneurysm resection: approximately 7-9%.[3,9,10] Independent risk factors for spinal cord injury include aortic rupture and extent II thoracoabdominal aortic repair.

Summary

The management of distal aortic dissection remains challenging. A high level of suspicion is critical for the timely diagnosis of this fatal disease. Once the diagnosis of aortic dissection is considered, aggressive medical therapy must be started. The patient can be managed medically if the following do not develop:

1. rupture or impending rupture,
2. progression of symptoms and
3. ischemic complications due to malperfusion.

When operative treatment is indicated for a patient with acute distal aortic dissection, graft repair is limited to the symptomatic and enlarged segments of the dissected aorta. In the setting of chronic dissection, more extensive graft repair is often warranted. Regardless of the treatment, careful long-term follow-up with imaging surveillance is mandated in these patients.

Selected Readings

1. Borst HG, Heinemann MK, Stone CD. Surgical treatment of aortic dissection. New York: Churchill Livingstone 1996.

   This well-illustrated comprehensive review of aortic dissection includes chapters regarding pathophysiology, clinical presentation, surgical techniques, results and recommendations for follow-up. The operative tactics and techniques for dealing with the dissected aorta and its branches are presented in great detail.

2. DeBakey ME, McCollum CH, Crawford ES et al. Dissection and dissecting aneurysms of the aorta: Twenty year follow-up of five hundred twenty-seven patients treated surgically. Surgery 1982; 92(6):1118-1134.

   This landmark paper reports the authors' experience with surgical treatment of aortic dissection in 527 patients. Although nearly 20 years old, the data regarding patient characteristics, presenting symptoms, complications and mortality remain pertinent. The most common cause of operative death was rupture and the most frequent cause of late mortality was associated cardiovascular disease, the same results found in the current era. The authors confirm the validity of the DeBakey classification with regard to indicating the appropriate surgical treatment and long-term prognosis.

3. Gysi J, Schaffner T, Mohacsi P et al. Early and late outcome of operated and nonoperated acute dissection of the descending aorta. Eur J Cardiothorac Surg 1997; 11:1163-70.

   This paper summarizes the outcome of 205 patients with acute distal aortic dissection treated between 1980 and 1995. Of these patients, 38 (16.8%) underwent surgery for malperfusion, rupture, expanding aorta or uncontrolled hypertension. The rest were treated medically. Early mortality in the surgical and medical groups was 21% and 17.6% respectively. The main causes of death in each group were rupture and abdominal malperfusion. Forty-seven (31%) of the medically treated patients eventually required surgery. Membrane fenestration is advocated as the procedure of choice for treating abdominal malperfusion. The authors state that although medical therapy remains the treatment of choice in distal aortic dissection, a more aggressive surgical approach can be considered, especially in younger patients.

4. Svensson LG, Crawford ES, Hess KR et al. Dissection of the aorta and dissecting aortic aneurysms: improving early and long-term surgical results. Circulation 1990; 82 (Suppl IV): 24-48.

   This retrospective review of Crawford's experience with 690 patients who underwent operation between 1956 to 1989 demonstrated improvement in survival over time. The 30-day survival during the last five years of the study, for both acute and chronic DeBakey type III aortic dissections, was 95%. Early diagnosis, administration of beta-blockers for blood pressure control and diligent postoperative follow up are emphasized.

5. Fann JI, Smith JA, Miller DC et al. Surgical management of aortic dissection during a 30-year period. Circulation 1995; (92)9 (suppl) II:113-21.

   This retrospective review summarizes the management techniques and results in 360 patients with aortic dissection (174 acute type A, 46 acute type B, 106 chronic type A

29

and 34 chronic type B) treated at Stanford from 1963 to 1992. As in other reports, survival did improve over time, especially in those patients who presented acutely. For the past ten years of the study, operative mortality was 20% for those with acute distal dissection and 6% for those with chronic distal dissection. Chronic dissections underwent surgery for symptoms for an enlarged false lumen. Risks for early death included renal dysfunction, advancing age, hypertension and cardiac tamponade. Ten-year survival remained disappointing, 11% following repair of acute distal dissection and 27% following surgery for chronic distal dissection. The authors stress that close follow-up is mandatory and may help to improve long term survival.

6. Elefteriades JA, Hartlerroad J, Gusberg RJ et al. Long-term experience with descending aortic dissection: the complication specific approach. Ann Thorac Surg 1992; 53:11-21.

   In this retrospective review of 71 patients treated for distal aortic dissection, 31% underwent surgery for complications, while the rest were managed medically. Ten-year survival was 28% for the surgically treated group and 25% for the medically treated group. Long-term follow up in the medically treated patients did reveal thrombosis of the false lumen in the majority of patients. The authors stress a complication specific approach, where only patients with complicated distal aortic dissection undergo surgery. Those with rupture are treated with aortic grafting, those with limb or organ ischemia undergo fenestration and those with aortic enlargement are treated with thromboexclusion.

7. Glover DD, Speier RF, White WD et al. Management and long-term outcome of aortic dissection. Ann Surg 1991; (214)1:31-41.

   This review of 163 patients with aortic dissection treated at Duke University Medical Center reported that long-term mortality following repair of ascending aortic dissection was increased in those patients with thoracoabdominal extension of the dissection or an aortic arch tear. For patients with acute distal aortic dissection, 24% required operation for rupture or aortic expansion; their 30-day mortality was 28%. The rest were managed medically with an 18% 30-day mortality and a 29% 10-year survival. Twelve percent of the patients needed subsequent operation related to their dissection.

8. Schor JS, Yerlioglu ME, Galla JD et al. Selective management of acute type B aortic dissection: Long-term follow-up. Ann Thorac Surg 1996; 61:1339-1341.

   This review of 68 patients with acute distal aortic dissection treated at the Mount Sinai Hospital over a 10-year period covers the authors' diagnostic and treatment plans in detail. All patients were initially treated with aggressive antihypertensive therapy (beta-blockade and nitroprusside). Seventeen patients required surgery for increasing symptoms or malperfusion. There was no mortality or paraplegia in this group. Of the patients treated medically, one patient died of a rupture and the rest were discharged. However, 25% of patients treated medically eventually required aorta-related interventions. Five-year survival was similar in both groups. The authors suggest that selective surgical management of acute distal aortic dissection results in acceptable short- and long-term survival.

9. Coselli JS, LeMaire SA, Poli de Figueirdo L et al. Paraplegia after thoracoabdominal aortic aneurysm repair: is dissection a risk factor? Ann Thorac Surg 1997; 63:28-36.

   In this review of 660 patients who underwent thoracoabdominal aortic aneurysm repair, dissection was present in 25% of patients. Early mortality was no different in patients with degenerative aneurysms, acute dissections, or chronic dissection. However, acute dissection markedly increased the risk of a neurologic deficit; 19% of patients with acute dissection developed paraplegia or paraparesis. Rupture and extent II aneurysms also increased the risk of deficits. Patients with chronic dissection did not have higher rates of neurological deficits than those without a dissection.

10.   Safi HJ, Miller CC, Reardon MJ et al. Operation for acute and chronic aortic dissection: Recent outcome with regard to neurologic deficit and early death. Ann Thorac Surg 1998; 66:402-11.

This review of 195 patients with aortic dissection treated from 1991 to 1996 includes 114 patients with distal aortic dissection; 22 presented acutely and 92 presented chronically. Although mortality rates were similar, postoperative neurologic complication rates were significantly higher in patients operated on for complications of acute dissection. The mortality and paraplegia rates for chronic dissection were similar to those of routine thoracoabdominal repair.

CHAPTER 30

Endovascular Management of Aortic Dissection

Suzanne M. Slonim, Michael D. Dake, Charles P. Semba

A secondary complication of acute aortic dissection is life-threatening ischemia of distal end-organs. With the development of percutaneous endovascular techniques, minimally invasive options are emerging to aid in the management of complicated aortic dissection. With a Stanford Type A dissection standard therapy consists of surgical replacement of the ascending aorta with an interposition graft and aortic valve replacement when valvular insufficiency is present. In Type B dissections, conventional therapy involves aggressive medical management of hypertension with surgical replacement of the descending thoracic aorta reserved for aneurysmal dilatation of the false lumen. Peripheral ischemic complications occur in approximately 30% of patients with acute aortic dissection resulting in significantly higher mortality rates compared to patients without ischemia. This distal organ ischemia is caused by obstruction from the dissected flap and traditional surgical strategies are often inadequate in reperfusing the compromised vascular bed. The purpose of this chapter is to describe the various endovascular techniques used to restore perfusion of ischemic regions using endoluminal stents, percutaneous fenestration, and/or stent-grafts in patients with complicated aortic dissection

Patients and Methods

Patients considered candidates for percutaneous intervention have evidence of extremity, renal or mesenteric ischemia associated with acute (< 14 days) aortic dissection. The diagnosis of Stanford Type A or B dissection is usually well established by transesophageal echocardiography or computed tomography before angiography and endovascular intervention is considered. Ischemic complications of acute Type A dissection are managed only following surgical repair of the ascending aorta and after further evaluation to determine whether the presenting ischemic complications persist. Ischemia is determined by clinical suspicion based on signs, symptoms, and laboratory data in conjunction with imaging of the arterial supply to the affected region based upon computed tomography, magnetic resonance imaging, intravascular ultrasound, and/or digital subtraction angiography. If any anatomic arterial abnormality related to the aortic dissection involves the arterial supply to the region suspected of being ischemic, the anatomic abnormality is considered responsible for the ischemia, and the lesion is treated. Anatomic abnormalities discovered incidentally to an asymptomatic region are not treated.

Aortic Surgery, edited by Jeffrey L. Ballard. ©2000 Landes Bioscience.

All procedures are performed in a state-of-the-art angiography suite (Multi-Star TOP; Siemens Medical Imaging Systems, Erlangen, Germany) equipped with a 16-inch diameter image intensifier, high resolution 1024 x 1024 pixel digital subtraction imaging matrix with the ability to link with real-time intravascular ultrasound (CVIS/ Boston Scientific Vascular, Inc., Natick, MA). When renal failure is present, portions of the diagnostic angiogram are performed using hand injection of carbon dioxide as the contrast agent. Intravascular ultrasound (IVUS) using a 7 Fr, 12 MHz catheter is used to define anatomic details such as vessel diameter and qualitatively assess luminal compromise by the dissected flap. Transcatheter hemodynamic pressure measurements in both true and false lumens are obtained to further evaluate the significance of branch vessel involvement before and after interventions.

Stent Placement

Endovascular stents are useful in treating many of the complex dissection flap configurations that can cause ischemia (Fig. 30.1). Williams described a classification system for branch vessel obstruction related to aortic dissection. According to this classification system, "static obstruction" occurs if the dissection flap extends into the branch and narrows the lumen. Static obstruction can have many configurations, all of which can be treated with stents. If a branch vessel is occluded proximally by a flap, a stent can be placed across the occluded segment to restore patency and antegrade flow. Flow within the true lumen of a branch vessel may be compromised by a cuff of false lumen extending into the branch without a re-entry tear. In this situation, a stent can be used to expand the true lumen and compress or obliterate the false lumen. Even if a re-entry tear within the branch relieves the compressing force of the false lumen, the presence of a flap in the bloodstream may disturb flow enough to cause ischemia. A stent can hold a flap against the vessel wall, restoring normal flow. "Dynamic obstruction" occurs when the dissection flap narrows the aortic true lumen and falls like a curtain over the orifice of the branch vessel to decrease flow. In this situation, stents can be placed along the course of the compressed true lumen of the aorta to hold it open.

Stents are deployed through angiographic sheaths ranging in size from 7 French to 14 French. Stent size is chosen based on measurements from intravascular ultrasound, arteriography or a high quality spiral CT scan. A stent with high radial strength is necessary to buttress the true lumen against the compressive force of the false lumen. This is particularly true in the aorta. A variety of stents are available, however, in our practice the most commonly used stents are the balloon expandable stainless steel Palmaz (Cordis/ Johnson and Johnson Endovascular Systems, Warren, NJ) and the self-expanding Wallstent (Boston Scientific Vascular, Inc.).

Balloon Fenestration

Creation of a fenestration between the true and false lumens has been an accepted surgical method of attempting revascularization of ischemic vascular beds. The ability to create a fenestration using endovascular techniques can significantly decrease

Fig. 30.1. Endovascular stent placement for persistent hypertension and compromised blood flow to the left kidney in a 45-year old with Marfan's syndrome and acute Stanford Type B dissection. (A) True lumen injection demonstrates prompt opacification of the right renal artery (arrowhead) but poor flow in left renal artery (arrow). (B) Following selective catheterization of the left renal artery from the true lumen and intravascular ultrasound, an 8 mm Palmaz stent was deployed in the left renal artery to tack down the obstructing intimal flap. (C) Completion angiography of the true lumen shows restored flow to the left kidney after stent deployment.

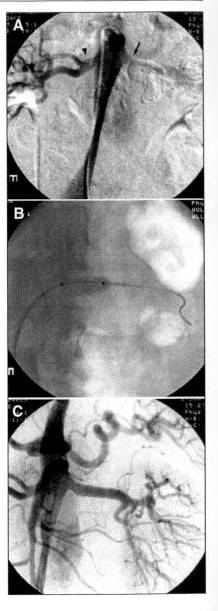

30

the morbidity and mortality in patients who may be undesirable surgical candidates (Fig. 30.2).

Dynamic obstruction of visceral vessels is most severe in cases where there is an inadequate distal re-entry tear. The high pressure in the false lumen contributes to

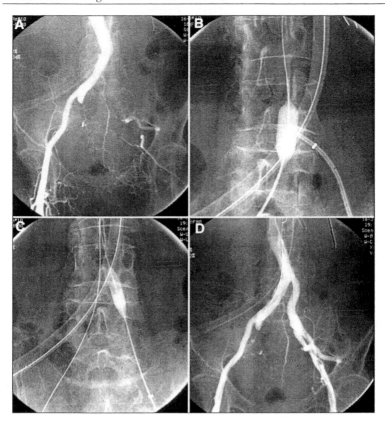

Fig. 30.2. Balloon fenestration of the intimal flap used to treat an 80-year old woman with left lower extremity ischemia immediately after surgical repair of Type A dissection. (A) Angiogram of the aortic false lumen demonstrates flow into the right lower extremity but no flow into the left lower extremity. (B) A large angioplasty balloon was inflated in the false lumen to use as a target. A curved metallic cannula is placed in the true lumen and pointed toward the inflated balloon in the opposite lumen. (C) After a small needle is passed through the cannula into the opposite lumen, a 5 Fr angiographic catheter is advanced over the needle, and the needle is exchanged for a guide wire. An angioplasty balloon is advanced over the guide wire and inflated to dilate the fenestration in the intimal flap. (D) Completion angiography after creation of the fenestration demonstrates good flow from the false lumen through the fenestration to the left lower extremity.

the collapse of the true lumen. As the true lumen collapses, the aortic intimal flap is pushed to a position overlying the orifices of aortic branch vessels. Balloon fenestration of the intimal flap essentially creates a re-entry tear and allows decompression of the high-pressure false lumen. After the fenestration is created, the aortic flap often moves away from the vessel ostia, reperfusing the ischemic vascular bed.

30

Fenestration at the level of the aortic bifurcation is particularly useful when the absence of a re-entry tear causes ischemia of one of the lower extremities. The fenestration allows the false lumen to reperfuse the ischemic leg.

Fenestration is performed using either intravascular ultrasound or fluoroscopic guidance. Intravascular ultrasound guidance is the preferred method when the transducer in one lumen can be positioned parallel to the long axis of the opposite lumen at the level of the planned fenestration. When the fenestration is being performed just above the aortic bifurcation, the oblique angle of the intravascular ultrasound probe placed in one iliac artery makes it difficult to visualize instruments approaching from the opposite iliac artery. Therefore, fluoroscopic guidance is more useful at this level.

Fenestration of the intimal flap is usually performed using a Rosch-Uchida set (Cook, Inc., Bloomington, IN), which requires a 10 French sheath. This set contains a long curved metallic cannula covered by a 7 French Teflon sheath. It also contains a small needle (0.038 in) covered by a 5 French catheter that passes coaxially through the cannula. After the fenestration is made, the needle can be removed, leaving the 5 French catheter across the fenestration. A guidewire can then be passed through this catheter.

When using intravascular ultrasound guidance, an IVUS probe is placed into the larger (usually false) lumen while the Rosch-Uchida cannula is placed into the smaller (usually true) lumen. The cannula is positioned at the same level as the IVUS probe to allow real-time guidance during creation of the fenestration. The needle-5F catheter combination is passed through the cannula, through the intimal flap, into the opposite lumen. The IVUS is continuously monitored to assure that the puncture is made through the middle of the intimal flap and not toward a free wall of the aorta. The needle is then removed and a balloon catheter is advanced over a guidewire to dilate the fenestration in the intimal flap.

When using fluoroscopic guidance, the Rosch-Uchida cannula is placed into the smaller lumen and a balloon catheter is placed in the larger lumen. The inflated balloon acts as a target for the needle puncture from the opposite lumen through the intimal flap. A balloon is chosen which can easily be punctured. The alignment of the tip of the needle with the inflated balloon is confirmed with multiple fluoroscopic obliquities to assure that the throw of the needle will pass through the intimal flap toward or into the balloon rather than toward a free wall of the aorta. Otherwise, the technique is the same as with intravascular ultrasound guidance. In our experience, no puncture of an aortic free wall has occurred.

Once the fenestration in the flap has been dilated with the balloon, an arteriogram is performed to assess flow through the fenestration. The fenestration created by the balloon tends to have the configuration of a transverse slit. Especially in chronic dissections, in which the flap is thickened and fibrotic, flow through this slit may be limited. When the fenestration has been created at the level of the aortic bifurcation and has limited flow through it, a stent may need to be placed bridging the fenestration and extending into the iliac artery.

Results of Endovascular Stenting and Balloon Fenestration

Peripheral ischemic complications of aortic dissection have been treated with endovascular stenting or balloon fenestration of the intimal flap in 77 patients at Stanford University. The 59 men and 18 women had a mean age of 53 years (range 16-86 years). Twenty-five patients had a Type A dissection (13 acute and 12 chronic) and 52 patients had Type B dissection (34 acute and 18 chronic). Twenty-one of the 25 patients with Type A dissection had surgical repair of the ascending aorta prior to endovascular treatment. Six of the 52 patients with Type B dissection had surgical repair of the thoracic aorta prior to endovascular treatment.

Many patients had ischemia involving multiple vascular beds. Fifty-six patients had renal, 41 had lower extremity, 28 had mesenteric and 2 had upper extremity ischemia. Forty-seven patients were treated with stent placement into an ischemic branch vessel or into the aortic true lumen. Twenty-five patients were treated with a combination of stent placement and balloon fenestration of the intimal flap. Four patients were treated only with fenestration of the intimal flap.

Endovascular treatments were successful in revascularizing ischemic regions in 73 of the 77 patients (95%). There have been complications related to the procedure in 6 patients. One patient had a posterior tibial artery embolus that eventually resulted in a transmetatarsal amputation. One patient in whom no other source of infection could be identified developed sepsis with blood cultures positive for *S. aureus* after placement of a renal artery stent. Another renal artery stent thrombosed acutely in one patient and resulted in atrophy of the kidney despite immediate attempts at thrombolysis. One patient with a heparin induced antibody, in whom brachiocephalic artery stent placement was being performed without anticoagulation (but with low dose urokinase infusion), had a transient ischemic attack. Two patients developed groin pseudoaneurysms. One of these was treated with ultrasound-guided compression and one was treated with surgical repair.

Thirteen of the 77 patients (17%) died within 30 days of treatment. Nine died of multi-organ ischemia despite successful re-establishment of flow to the ischemic region. Two died of rupture of the false lumen shortly after endovascular treatment. Autopsy in both of these patients demonstrated the region of rupture to be unrelated to the region of endovascular treatment. One patient (who was not a surgical candidate because he had a heparin induced antibody) died of right heart failure due to retrograde dissection into the right coronary artery. The last patient with Type A dissection died of complications of surgery.

Five patients have died after 30 days. One died at 2.5 months of rupture of the thoracic false lumen. Two died suddenly at 13.4 and 23.8 months and did not have an autopsy. One died at 19.8 months of cancer, and one died at 20.6 months of congestive heart failure. Two patients are lost to follow up. The remaining 57 patients are alive and well at a mean follow-up time of 22 months (range 1 month to 8 years).

Stent-Graft Repair of the Primary Tear

Although percutaneous revascularization of ischemic vascular beds after aortic dissection can be achieved, the procedures are often technically complex and time consuming. An additional drawback of endovascular stenting and fenestration is that they do not address the primary tear and the potential for aneurysmal dilatation of the false lumen over time. Attention has now turned to placement of a stent graft over the primary tear as an alternative percutaneous treatment technique for aortic dissection. It is hoped that this approach will be effective in rapidly treating acute peripheral ischemic complications of aortic dissection as well as preventing chronic dilatation of the false lumen.

In patients with an acute dissection, indications for treatment with a stent graft include ischemia of multiple vascular beds, persistent back pain despite medical therapy, an entry tear in an atypical location or acute aortic rupture. The patients included 15 men and 4 women, with a mean age of 53.2 years (range 16-75 years). Fifteen patients had Type B dissection and 4 had Type A dissection. The primary tear was distal to the left subclavian artery in all patients, however in the 4 patients with Type A dissection there was retrograde extension to involve the ascending aorta. A distance of at least 1 cm between the left subclavian artery and the primary tear was necessary to be considered a candidate for stent graft treatment.

The primary tear was covered with a custom fabricated stent graft composed of a Z-stent endoskeleton covered with either woven polyester or balloon expanded polytetrafluoroethylene graft material. The device was delivered into the true lumen bridging the primary tear through a 22 French sheath (Keller-Timmerman sheath, Cook) which had been placed through the femoral artery. The stent grafts ranged in diameter from 20-38 mm (mean 29 mm) and ranged in length from 4.5-10 cm (mean 7.0 cm).

Device deployment was technically successful in all patients. The mean interval from the initial onset of symptoms to the stent graft procedure was 3.8 days (range 1-13 days). Restoration of flow to ischemic vessels was achieved with the stent-graft alone in 76% of the previously obstructed branches. The remaining vessels were revascularized after stent graft placement using bare endovascular stents. Thrombosis of the false lumen was complete in 15 patients (79%) and partial in 4 patients (21%). Three patients (16%) died within 30 days because of aortic rupture (1), sepsis (1) and pneumonia (1). There have been no late deaths, and no patient has had aneurysmal dilatation or rupture of the false lumen at a mean follow-up time of 10.5 months (range 1-26 months).

Treatment of patients with a sub-acute or chronic Type B dissection using a stent graft has been compared to surgical treatment of a similar group of patients. Although all patients were required to have at least one indication for elective surgical repair of the dissection, these indications were not specified. The 12 endovascular patients were treated with placement of a Talent endoprosthesis (World Medical/AVE, Sunrise, FL) over the primary tear. A minimum distance of 5 mm between the primary tear and left subclavian artery was necessary to be considered a candidate for stent

30

graft treatment. The 12 surgical patients were treated with Dacron graft replacement of the dissected descending thoracic aorta.

At 3 months, all patients treated with stent grafts had complete thrombosis of the false lumen. There were statistically significant differences in the duration of the procedure (1.6 hours for stent graft versus 8 hours for surgery), time in the intensive care unit (36 hours for stent graft versus 92 hours for surgery), and length of hospital stay (7 days for stent graft versus 40 days for surgery). While there were no statistically significant differences in mortality rate, surgery was associated with higher morbidity and a lower rate of physical recovery.

Conclusion

The challenge of finding an effective treatment for the multiple complex problems that occur in patients with aortic dissection fosters enthusiasm for new treatment options. Peripheral ischemic complications of aortic dissection can be managed with endovascular stenting and balloon fenestration of the intimal flap. However, these maneuvers are often time consuming and technically challenging. Stent graft placement over the primary tear is a technique still in its infancy. It may provide a rapid alternative treatment for patients who are not candidates for open surgery or who are at high risk for operative management due to peripheral ischemic complications. Thrombosis of the false lumen seen in the majority of patients treated thus far raises the possibility that this new, less invasive therapy may have a role in the prophylactic prevention of subsequent aneurysmal dilatation of the false lumen and aortic rupture. More experience with longer follow-up, however, is needed before final conclusions can be drawn.

Selected Readings

30

1. Cambria RP, Brewster DC, Gertler J et al. Vascular complications associated with spontaneous aortic dissection. J Vasc Surg 1988; 7(2):199-209.
    Three hundred and twenty-five spontaneous aortic dissections were evaluated over a 21-year period to assess the incidence, morbid sequelae, and specific management of aortic branch compromise. Noncardiac complications occurred in 33% and in these patients the overall mortality (51%) was significantly higher than in those (29%) without such complications. Peripheral operative management of ischemic complications was ineffective in reducing the mortality rate in the setting of mesenteric (87%) and renal (50%) ischemia.
2. Fann JI, Sarris GE, Mitchell RS et al. Treatment of patients with aortic dissection presenting with peripheral vascular complications. Ann Surg 1990; 212(6):705-13.
    This study reviews a 25-year surgical experience (272 patients) with aortic dissection at Stanford University consisting of 128 (47%) patients with acute type A, 70 (26%) with chronic type A, 40 (15%) with acute type B, and 34 (12%) with chronic type B dissections. Peripheral vascular complications were present in 31%. Overall operative mortality was 25%. For the subset with paraplegia, renal or visceral ischemia, the operative mortality was 44%, 50%, and 43%, respectively.
3. Slonim SM, Nyman U, Semba CP et al. Aortic dissection: Percutaneous management of ischemic complications with endovascular stents and balloon fenestration. J Vasc Surg 1996; 23(2):241-51; discussion 251-3.

*A frequent and catastrophic complication of acute aortic dissection is complete oblitera-
tion of the true lumen in which critical branch vessels arise from the compromised
lumen. Endovascular methods are described in treating 11 patients with true lumen
collapse and renal, mesenteric, and/or limb ischemia. Technical and clinical success was
achieved in 82% with a 30-day mortality of 9% and mean follow-up of 10.1 months.*

4. Williams DM, Lee DY, Hamilton BH et al. The dissected aorta: percutaneous
    treatment of ischemic complications— principles and results. J Vasc Interv Radiol
    1997; 8(4):605-25.

    *This clinical study outlines the endovascular experience at the University of Michigan
    and recommends percutaneous fenestration and endoluminal stent placement for com-
    promised blood flow in branch vessels from the dissected intimal flap. The prognosis of
    patients in their series was related to the ischemic injury prior to percutaneous interven-
    tion. In patients with acute type I dissection who had not undergone surgery prognosis
    was also related to the preoperative stability of the false lumen.*

5. Slonim SM, Miller DC, Mitchell RS et al. Percutaneous balloon fenestration and
    stenting for life-threatening ischemic complications in patients with acute aortic
    dissection. J Thorac Cardiovasc Surg 1999; 117(6):1118-26.

    *This is a summary of the six-year cumulative experience at Stanford University in the
    percutaneous management of complicated aortic dissections in the patients with acute,
    profound and life-threatening ischemia. Successful reperfusion was achieved in 93%.
    Mortality was related to the extent of pre-existing irreversible ischemia at the time of
    intervention.*

6. Williams DM, Lee DY, Hamilton BH et al. The dissected aorta: part III. Anatomy
    and radiologic diagnosis of branch-vessel compromise. Radiology 1997;
    203(1):37-44.

    *An outstanding paper (one of three in a series) characterizing the anatomic, hemody-
    namic and radiologic findings in branch vessel compromise from the dissected aorta.
    The authors highlight the utility of intravascular ultrasound in the diagnostic assess-
    ment of branch vessel ischemia.*

7. Elefteriades JA, Hammond GL, Gusberg RJ et al. Fenestration revisited. A safe
    and effective procedure for descending aortic dissection. Arch Surg 1990;
    125(6):786-90.

    *A small series describing results of surgical fenestration in the management of peripheral
    ischemic complications of aortic dissection. Fenestration was recommended for acute
    dissection in the descending aorta with organ ischemia; fenestration was not advised for
    acute dissection with aortic rupture or chronic dissection flaps.*

8. Williams DM, Brothers TE, Messina LM. Relief of mesenteric ischemia in type III
    aortic dissection with percutaneous fenestration of the aortic septum. Radiology
    1990; 174(2):450-2.

    *A case report which represents the pioneering and pivotal concepts in the percutaneous
    approach towards creating fenestrations in the aortic flap.*

9. Williams DM, Andrews JC, Marx MV et al. Creation of reentry tears in aortic
    dissection by means of percutaneous balloon fenestration: Gross anatomic and
    histologic considerations. J Vasc Interv Radiol 1993; 4(1):75-83.

    *A detailed and nicely described paper evaluating the gross and histological features of
    aortic dissection treated by percutaneous fenestration in clinical patients, human cadaver
    models and canines. Percutaneous fenestration, when performed in areas free of athero-
    sclerosis, results in a transverse tear.*

30

10. Dake MD, Kato N, Mitchell RS et al. Endovascular stent-graft placement for the treatment of acute aortic dissection. N Engl J Med 1999; 340(20):1546-52.
The preliminary Stanford University experience in treating the primary entry tear using endoluminal stent-grafts. The initial results suggest that stent-graft coverage of the primary tear may be a promising treatment for selected patients with acute dissection.

11. Nienaber CA, Fattori R, Lund G et al. Nonsurgical reconstruction of thoracic aortic dissection by stent-graft placement. N Engl J Med 1999; 340(20):1539-45.
A parallel study by a German group evaluating the safety, efficacy and feasibility of stent-graft placement in repairing the primary entry tear with similar conclusions. That is, endoluminal repair may be useful for reconstruction of thoracic aortic dissections.

30

Index